BIOZONE

Biology **Modular Workbook**

CELL BIOLOGY & BIOCHEMISTRY

CELL BIOLOGY & BIOCHEMISTRY

Biology **Modular Workbook**

First Edition 2006
Second Edition 2013
ISBN: 978-1-927173-73-2

Published by: **BIOZONE International Ltd**

Printed by REPLIKA PRESS PVT LTD using paper produced from renewable and waste materials

Distribution Offices:

United Kingdom & Europe
Biozone Learning Media (UK) Ltd, UK
Telephone: +44 1283 530 366
Fax: +44 1283 530 961
Email: sales@biozone.co.uk
Website: www.biozone.co.uk

Australia
Biozone Learning Media Australia, Australia
Telephone: +61 7-5535-4896
Fax: +61 7-5508-2432
Email: sales@biozone.com.au
Website: www.biozone.com.au

USA, Canada, and ROW
Biozone International Ltd, New Zealand
Telephone: +64 7-856 8104
Fax: +64 7-856 9243
FREE phone: 1-855-246-4555 (USA-Canada only)
FREE fax: 1-855-935-3555 (USA-Canada only)
Email: sales@biozone.co.nz
Website: www.thebiozone.com

Front cover photographs

Diatoms.
Image ©2005 JupiterImages Corporation www.clipart.com

Space filling model of a globular protein
Rendered by MacPyMOL
©2006 DeLano Scientific LLC http://wwwpymol.org

Meet the writing team

Tracey Greenwood
I have been writing resources for students since 1993. I have a Ph.D in biology, specialising in lake ecology and I have taught both graduate and undergraduate biology.

Tracey
Senior Author

Lissa Bainbridge-Smith
I worked in industry in a research and development capacity for eight years before joining BIOZONE in 2006. I have an M.Sc from Waikato University.

Lissa
Author

Kent Pryor
I have a BSc from Massey University majoring in zoology and ecology and taught secondary school biology and chemistry for 9 years before joining BIOZONE as an author in 2009.

Kent
Author

Richard Allan
I have had 11 years experience teaching senior secondary school biology. I have a Masters degree in biology and founded BIOZONE in the 1980s after developing resources for my own students.

Richard
Founder & CEO

Biology **Modular Workbook Series**

The BIOZONE *Biology Modular Workbook Series* has been developed to meet the demands of customers with the requirement for a flexible modular resource. Each workbook provides a collection of visually interesting and accessible activities, catering for students with a wide range of abilities and background. The workbooks are divided into a series of chapters, each comprising an introductory section and a series of write-on worksheets ranging from paper practicals and data handling exercises, to activities requiring critical thinking and analysis. Page tabs identifying "**Related activities**" and "**Weblinks**" help students to find related material within the workbook and locate online support that will enhance their understanding of the topic. During the development of this series, we have taken the opportunity to develop new content, while retaining the basic philosophy of a student-friendly resource, which spans the gulf between textbook and study guide. Its highly visual presentation engages students, increasing their motivation and empowering them to take control of their learning.

CELL BIOLOGY & BIOCHEMISTRY

This title in the *Biology Modular Workbook Series* provides students with a set of comprehensive guidelines and highly visual worksheets through which to explore aspects of cell biology and biochemistry. *Cell Biology & Biochemistry* is the ideal companion for students of the life sciences, encompassing basic biochemistry, the structure and function of cells and their organelles, and an introduction to cell division and differentiation. This workbook comprises five chapters, each covering a different aspect of cell biology. These areas are explained through a series of one and two page activities, each of which explores a specific concept (e.g. diffusion or mitosis). *Cell Biology & Biochemistry* is a student-centered resource. Students completing the activities, in concert with their other classroom and practical work, will consolidate existing knowledge and develop and practise skills that they will use throughout their course. This workbook may be used in the classroom or at home as a supplement to a standard textbook. Some activities are introductory in nature, while others may be used to consolidate and test concepts already covered by other means. Biozone has a commitment to produce a cost-effective, high quality resource, which acts as a student's companion throughout their biology study. Please do not photocopy from this workbook; we cannot afford to provide single copies of workbooks to schools and continue to develop, update, and improve the material they contain.

ACKNOWLEDGEMENTS & PHOTO CREDITS

Royalty free images, purchased by Biozone International Ltd, are used throughout this manual and have been obtained from the following sources: istockphotos (www.istockphoto.com) • Corel Corporation from various titles in their Professional Photos CD-ROM collection; ©Hemera Technologies Inc, 1997-2001; © 2005 JupiterImages Corporation www.clipart.com; PhotoDisc®, Inc. USA, www.photodisc.com. Biozone's authors also acknowledge the generosity of those who have kindly provided photographs for this edition. Contributors identified by way of coded credits: **BF**: Brian Finerran (University of Canterbury), **CDC**: Centers for Disease Control and Prevention, Atlanta, USA, **EII**: Education Interactive Imaging, **RCN**: Ralph Cocklin, **TG**: Tracey Greenwood, **WBS**: Warwick Silvester (University of Waikato), **WMU**: Waikato Microscope Unit, **VMRVCM**: VA Maryland Regional Veterinary College of Medicine, **JDG**: John Green, **GW**: Graham Walker.

The writing team would also like to thank: Dartmouth College for their electron micrographs, Alison Roberts for the image of the plasmodesmata, Wadsworth Center (NYSDH) for the photo of the cell undergoing cytokinesis, Alan Sheldon, Sheldon's Nature Photography, Wisconsin for the photo of the lizard without its tail, Ed Uthman for the image of the nine week old human embryo, Louisa Howard Dartmouth College for the image of the mitochondrion.

Wikimedia Commons under Creative Commons Licence 3.0: Barfooz

Other titles

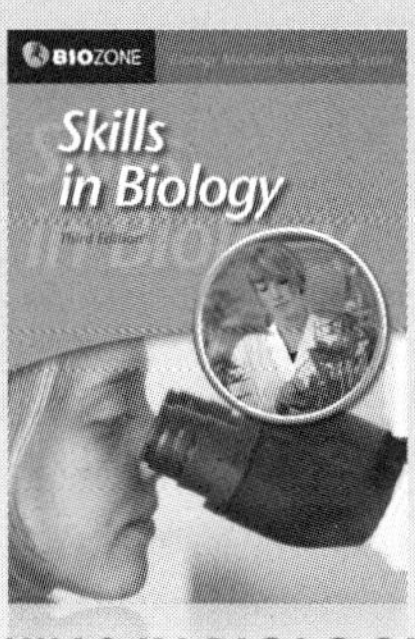
BIOZONE
Skills in Biology

SKILLS IN BIOLOGY

BIOZONE
Biology Modular Workbook Series
Health & Disease

HEALTH & DISEASE

BIOZONE
Genes & Inheritance

GENES & INHERITANCE

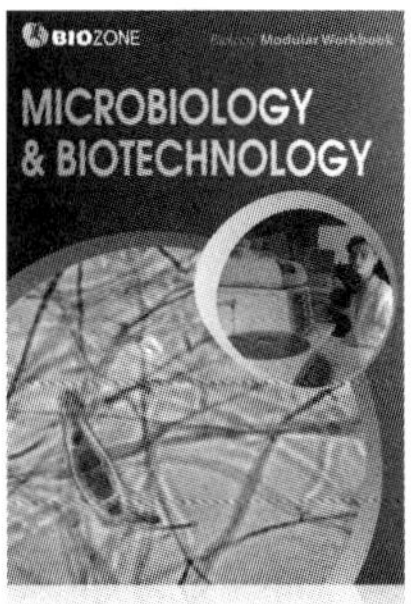
BIOZONE
MICROBIOLOGY & BIOTECHNOLOGY

MICROBIOLOGY & BIOTECHNOLOGY

See the whole series at:
www.**theBIOZONE**.com

Contents

CODES: △ **Upgraded** this edition ★ **New** this edition

Activity is marked: ❑ to be done; ☑ when completed

Features of the Chapter Topic Page

An understanding of the structure and function of cells and their biochemistry in modern biology is important in many biology curricula. *Cell Biology and Biochemistry* aims to provide material in a way that will help you to acquire the knowledge and skills needed for this course of study. This workbook is suitable for biology students grades 10-12 and will reinforce and extend material covered by your teacher. Its aim is to complement the main text for your course.

Key terms

A list of important key terms used throughout the chapter. These will help you focus on important ideas.

Key concepts

The important key ideas in this chapter. You should have a thorough understanding of the concepts summarized here.

Page references

The page numbers for the activities covering the material in this subsection of objectives.

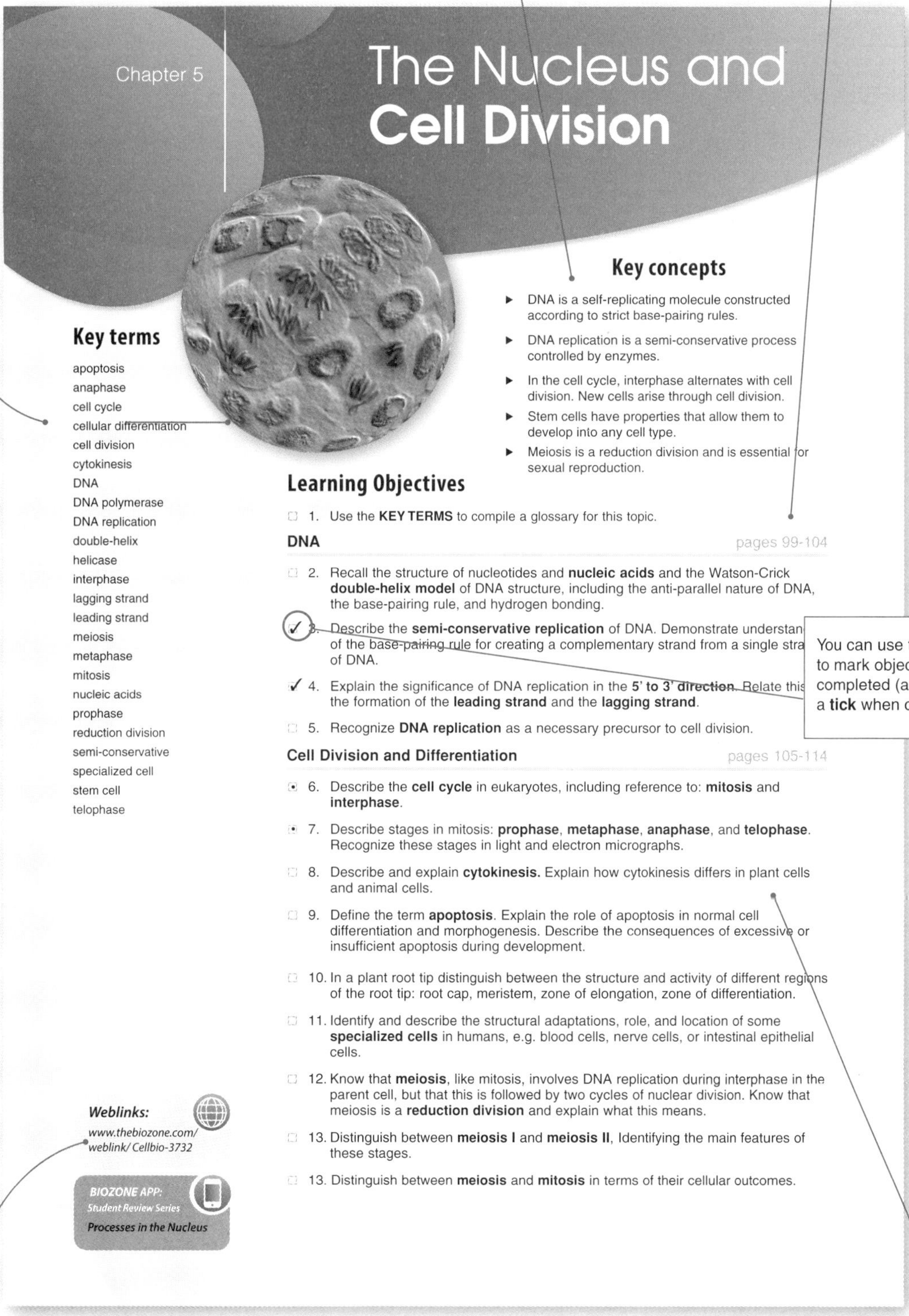

Chapter 5

The Nucleus and **Cell Division**

Key concepts

- DNA is a self-replicating molecule constructed according to strict base-pairing rules.
- DNA replication is a semi-conservative process controlled by enzymes.
- In the cell cycle, interphase alternates with cell division. New cells arise through cell division.
- Stem cells have properties that allow them to develop into any cell type.
- Meiosis is a reduction division and is essential for sexual reproduction.

Key terms

apoptosis
anaphase
cell cycle
cellular differentiation
cell division
cytokinesis
DNA
DNA polymerase
DNA replication
double-helix
helicase
interphase
lagging strand
leading strand
meiosis
metaphase
mitosis
nucleic acids
prophase
reduction division
semi-conservative
specialized cell
stem cell
telophase

Learning Objectives

1. Use the **KEY TERMS** to compile a glossary for this topic.

DNA pages 99-104

2. Recall the structure of nucleotides and **nucleic acids** and the Watson-Crick **double-helix model** of DNA structure, including the anti-parallel nature of DNA, the base-pairing rule, and hydrogen bonding.
3. Describe the **semi-conservative replication** of DNA. Demonstrate understan of the base-pairing rule for creating a complementary strand from a single stra of DNA.
4. Explain the significance of DNA replication in the **5' to 3' direction**. Relate this the formation of the **leading strand** and the **lagging strand**.
5. Recognize **DNA replication** as a necessary precursor to cell division.

Cell Division and Differentiation pages 105-114

6. Describe the **cell cycle** in eukaryotes, including reference to: **mitosis** and **interphase**.
7. Describe stages in mitosis: **prophase**, **metaphase**, **anaphase**, and **telophase**. Recognize these stages in light and electron micrographs.
8. Describe and explain **cytokinesis.** Explain how cytokinesis differs in plant cells and animal cells.
9. Define the term **apoptosis**. Explain the role of apoptosis in normal cell differentiation and morphogenesis. Describe the consequences of excessive or insufficient apoptosis during development.
10. In a plant root tip distinguish between the structure and activity of different regions of the root tip: root cap, meristem, zone of elongation, zone of differentiation.
11. Identify and describe the structural adaptations, role, and location of some **specialized cells** in humans, e.g. blood cells, nerve cells, or intestinal epithelial cells.
12. Know that **meiosis**, like mitosis, involves DNA replication during interphase in the parent cell, but that this is followed by two cycles of nuclear division. Know that meiosis is a **reduction division** and explain what this means.
13. Distinguish between **meiosis I** and **meiosis II**, Identifying the main features of these stages.
13. Distinguish between **meiosis** and **mitosis** in terms of their cellular outcomes.

Weblinks: *www.thebiozone.com/weblink/Cellbio-3732*

BIOZONE APP: Student Review Series *Processes in the Nucleus*

You can use the check boxes to mark objectives to be completed (a **dot** to be done; a **tick** when completed).

The Weblinks on many of the activities can be accessed through the web links page at: *www.thebiozone.com/weblink/Cellbio-3732/* See page 3 for more details.

The objectives provide a point by point summary of what you should have achieved by the end of the chapter. They can also be used to derive **essential questions** for this chapter.

Features of the Activity Pages

The activities and exercises make up most of the content of this workbook. They are designed to reinforce concepts in the topic. Your teacher may use the activity pages to introduce a topic for the first time, or you may use them to revise ideas already covered. They are excellent for use in the classroom, and as homework exercises and revision. In most cases, the activities should not be attempted until you have carried out the necessary background reading from your textbook.

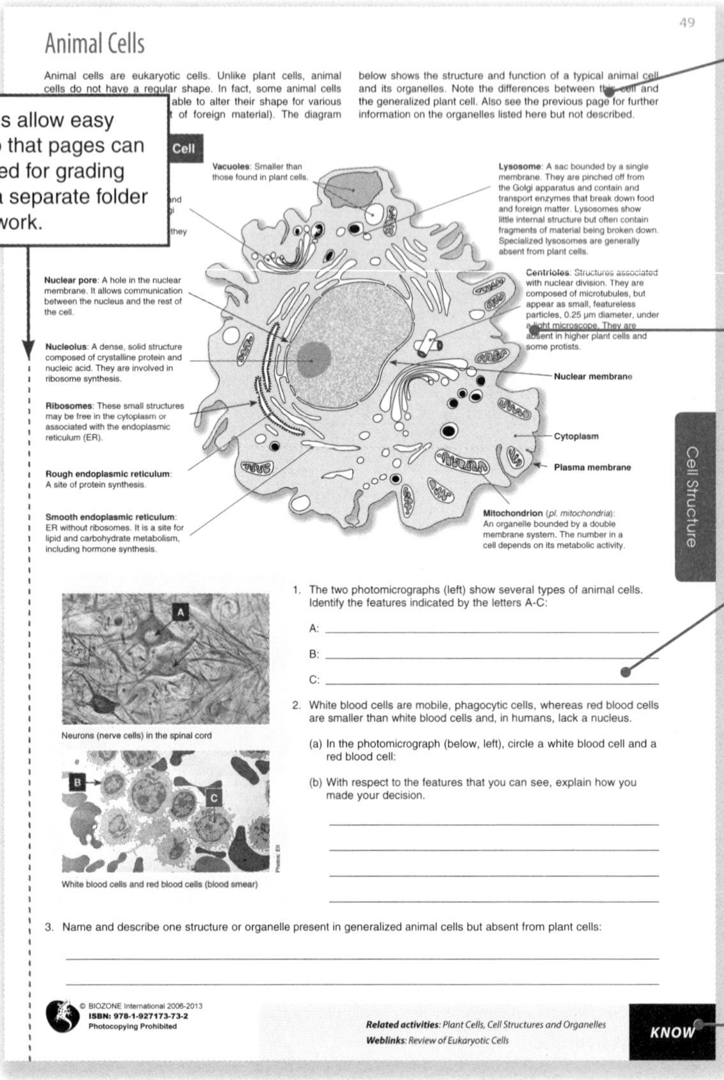
Animal Cells
49
Cell Structure
KNOW
Related activities: Plant Cells, Cell Structures and Organelles
Weblinks: Review of Eukaryotic Cells

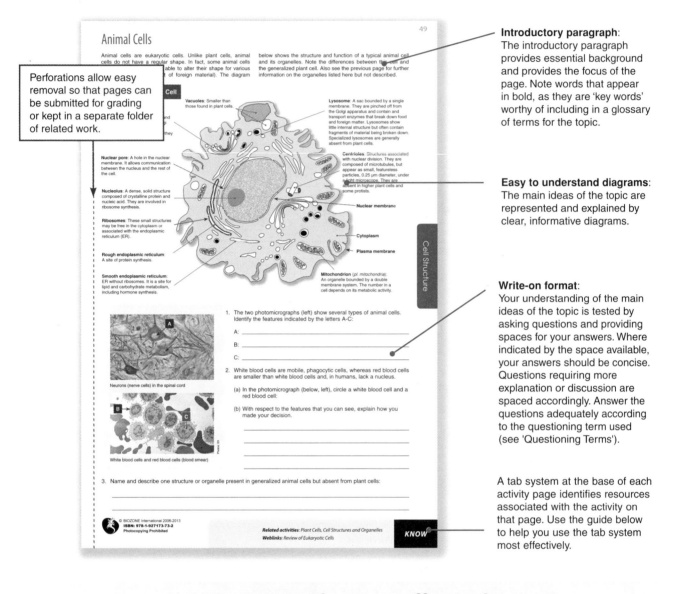

Perforations allow easy removal so that pages can be submitted for grading or kept in a separate folder of related work.

Introductory paragraph: The introductory paragraph provides essential background and provides the focus of the page. Note words that appear in bold, as they are 'key words' worthy of including in a glossary of terms for the topic.

Easy to understand diagrams: The main ideas of the topic are represented and explained by clear, informative diagrams.

Write-on format: Your understanding of the main ideas of the topic is tested by asking questions and providing spaces for your answers. Where indicated by the space available, your answers should be concise. Questions requiring more explanation or discussion are spaced accordingly. Answer the questions adequately according to the questioning term used (see 'Questioning Terms').

A tab system at the base of each activity page identifies resources associated with the activity on that page. Use the guide below to help you use the tab system most effectively.

Using page tabs more effectively

Related activities: *Plant Cells, Cell Structures and Organelles*
Weblinks: *Review of Eukaryotic Cells*
KNOW

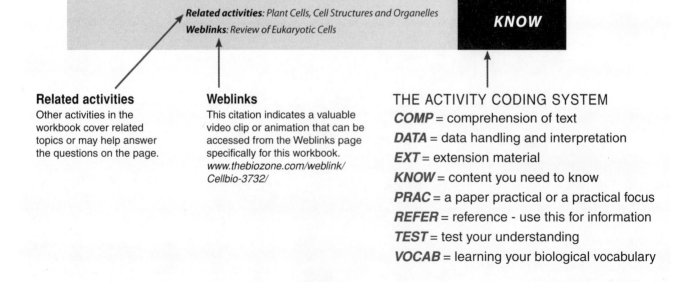

Related activities
Other activities in the workbook cover related topics or may help answer the questions on the page.

Weblinks
This citation indicates a valuable video clip or animation that can be accessed from the Weblinks page specifically for this workbook. *www.thebiozone.com/weblink/Cellbio-3732/*

THE ACTIVITY CODING SYSTEM

COMP = comprehension of text
DATA = data handling and interpretation
EXT = extension material
KNOW = content you need to know
PRAC = a paper practical or a practical focus
REFER = reference - use this for information
TEST = test your understanding
VOCAB = learning your biological vocabulary

Using BIOZONE's Website

Access the **BIOLINKS** database of web sites directly from the homepage of our new website. Biolinks is organized into easy-to-use sub-sections relating to general areas of interest. It's a great way to quickly find out more on topics of interest.

Contact us with questions, feedback, ideas, and critical commentary. We welcome your input.

Use Google to search for websites of interest. The more precise your search words are, the better the list of results. Be specific, e.g. "Proteins in plasma membranes", rather than "Proteins".

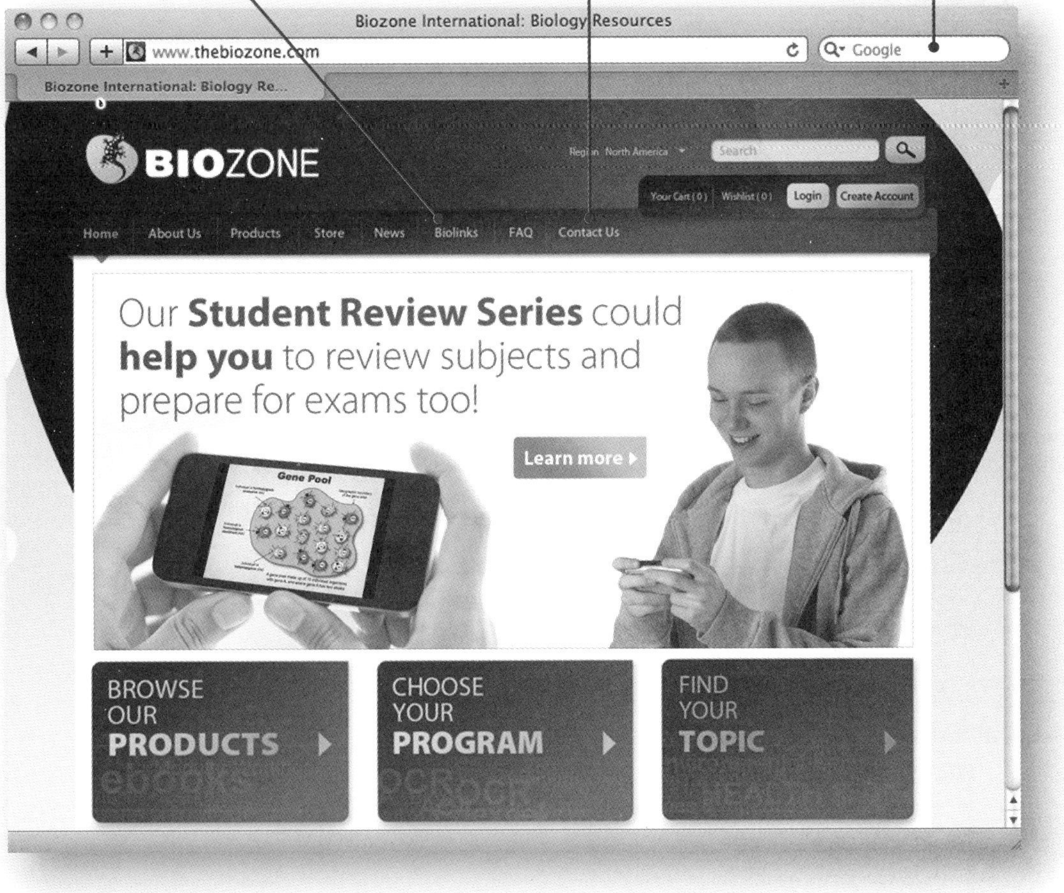

Biozone International: Biology Resources
www.thebiozone.com
Google
Biozone International: Biology Re...
BIOZONE
Region North America
Search
Your Cart (0)
Wishlist (0)
Login
Create Account
Home
About Us
Products
Store
News
Biolinks
FAQ
Contact Us
Our Student Review Series could help you to review subjects and prepare for exams too!
Learn more
Gene Pool
BROWSE OUR PRODUCTS
CHOOSE YOUR PROGRAM
FIND YOUR TOPIC

Weblinks: www.thebiozone.com/weblink/cellbio-3732/

BOOKMARK WEBLINKS BY TYPING IN THE ADDRESS: IT IS NOT ACCESSIBLE DIRECTLY FROM BIOZONE'S WEBSITE

Throughout this workbook, some pages make reference to websites that have particular relevance to the activity by providing an explanatory animation or video clip. They are easy to use and a very useful supplement to the activity.

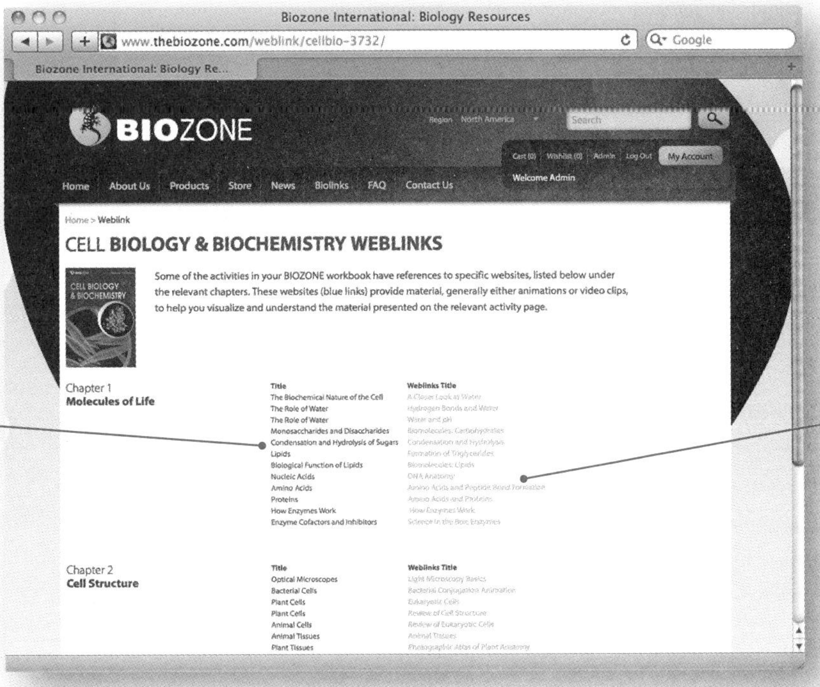

Biozone International: Biology Resources
www.thebiozone.com/weblink/cellbio-3732/
Google
Biozone International: Biology Re...
BIOZONE
Region North America
Search
Cart (0)
Wishlist (0)
Admin
Log Out
My Account
Welcome Admin
Home
About Us
Products
Store
News
Biolinks
FAQ
Contact Us
Home > Weblink
CELL BIOLOGY & BIOCHEMISTRY WEBLINKS
CELL BIOLOGY & BIOCHEMISTRY
Some of the activities in your BIOZONE workbook have references to specific websites, listed below under the relevant chapters. These websites (blue links) provide material, generally either animations or video clips, to help you visualize and understand the material presented on the relevant activity page.
Chapter 1
Molecules of Life
Title
The Biochemical Nature of the Cell
The Role of Water
The Role of Water
Monosaccharides and Disaccharides
Condensation and Hydrolysis of Sugars
Lipids
Biological Function of Lipids
Nucleic Acids
Amino Acids
Proteins
How Enzymes Work
Enzyme Cofactors and Inhibitors
Weblinks Title
A Closer Look at Water
Hydrogen Bonds and Water
Water and pH
Biomolecules: Carbohydrates
Condensation and Hydrolysis
Formation of Triglycerides
Biomolecules: Lipids
DNA Anatomy
Amino Acids and Peptide Bond Formation
Amino Acids and Proteins
How Enzymes Work
Science in the Box: Enzymes
Chapter 2
Cell Structure
Title
Optical Microscopes
Bacterial Cells
Plant Cells
Plant Cells
Animal Cells
Animal Tissues
Plant Tissues
Weblinks Title
Light Microscopy Basics
Bacterial Conjugation Animation
Eukaryotic Cells
Review of Cell Structure
Review of Eukaryotic Cells
Animal Tissues
Photographic Atlas of Plant Anatomy

Activity reference
The activity on which the weblink is cited.

Weblink
Provides a link to an **external web site** with supporting information for the activity.

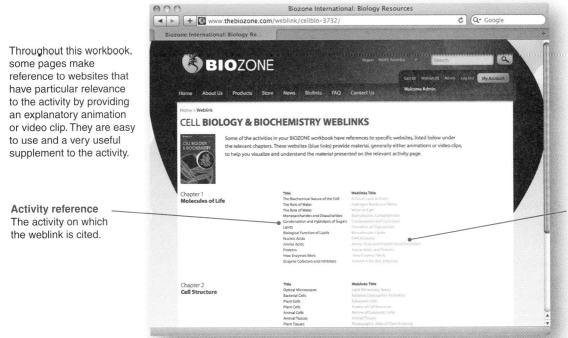

Concept Map for Cell Biology and Biochemistry

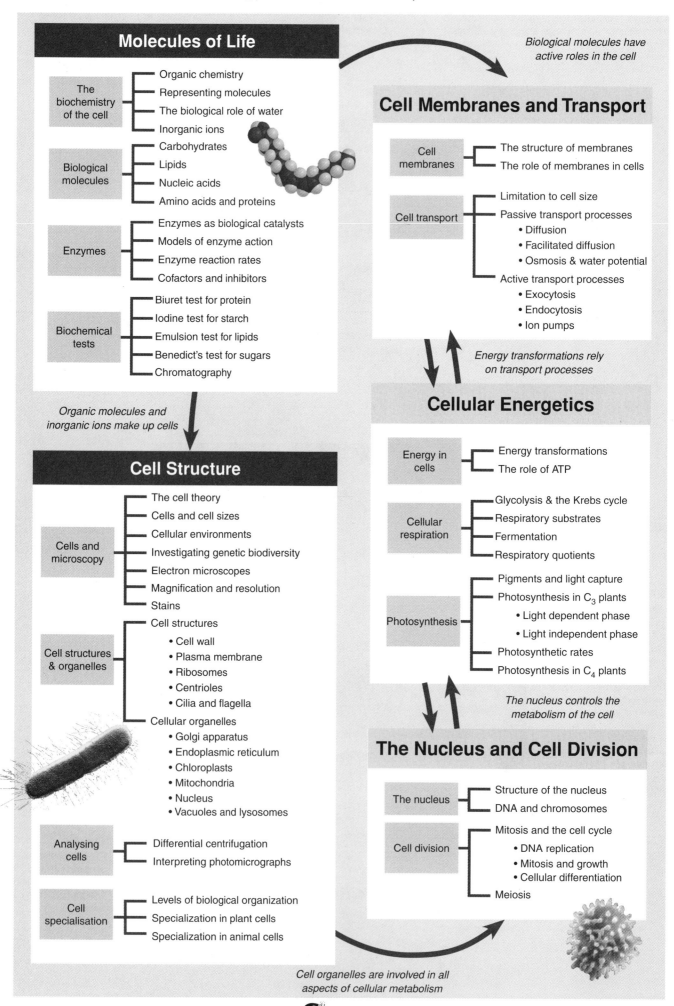

Molecules of Life

The biochemistry of the cell
- Organic chemistry
- Representing molecules
- The biological role of water
- Inorganic ions

Biological molecules
- Carbohydrates
- Lipids
- Nucleic acids
- Amino acids and proteins

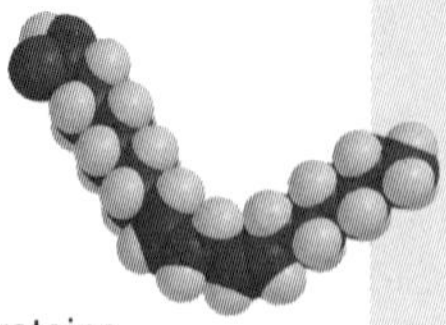

Enzymes
- Enzymes as biological catalysts
- Models of enzyme action
- Enzyme reaction rates
- Cofactors and inhibitors

Biochemical tests
- Biuret test for protein
- Iodine test for starch
- Emulsion test for lipids
- Benedict's test for sugars
- Chromatography

Biological molecules have active roles in the cell

Organic molecules and inorganic ions make up cells

Cell Structure

Cells and microscopy
- The cell theory
- Cells and cell sizes
- Cellular environments
- Investigating genetic biodiversity
- Electron microscopes
- Magnification and resolution
- Stains

Cell structures & organelles
- Cell structures
  - Cell wall
  - Plasma membrane
  - Ribosomes
  - Centrioles
  - Cilia and flagella
- Cellular organelles
  - Golgi apparatus
  - Endoplasmic reticulum
  - Chloroplasts
  - Mitochondria
  - Nucleus
  - Vacuoles and lysosomes

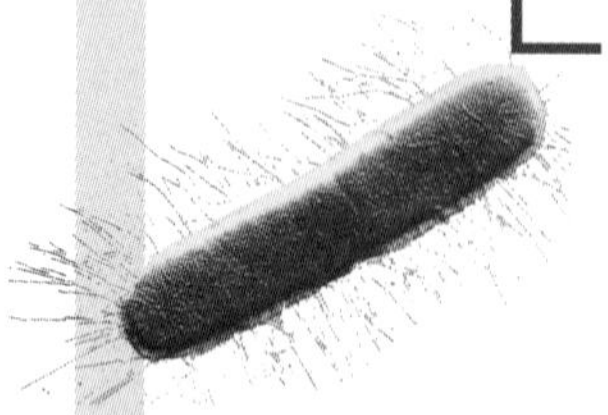

Analysing cells
- Differential centrifugation
- Interpreting photomicrographs

Cell specialisation
- Levels of biological organization
- Specialization in plant cells
- Specialization in animal cells

Cell Membranes and Transport

Cell membranes
- The structure of membranes
- The role of membranes in cells

Cell transport
- Limitation to cell size
- Passive transport processes
  - Diffusion
  - Facilitated diffusion
  - Osmosis & water potential
- Active transport processes
  - Exocytosis
  - Endocytosis
  - Ion pumps

Energy transformations rely on transport processes

Cellular Energetics

Energy in cells
- Energy transformations
- The role of ATP

Cellular respiration
- Glycolysis & the Krebs cycle
- Respiratory substrates
- Fermentation
- Respiratory quotients

Photosynthesis
- Pigments and light capture
- Photosynthesis in C_3 plants
  - Light dependent phase
  - Light independent phase
- Photosynthetic rates
- Photosynthesis in C_4 plants

The nucleus controls the metabolism of the cell

The Nucleus and Cell Division

The nucleus
- Structure of the nucleus
- DNA and chromosomes

Cell division
- Mitosis and the cell cycle
  - DNA replication
  - Mitosis and growth
  - Cellular differentiation
- Meiosis

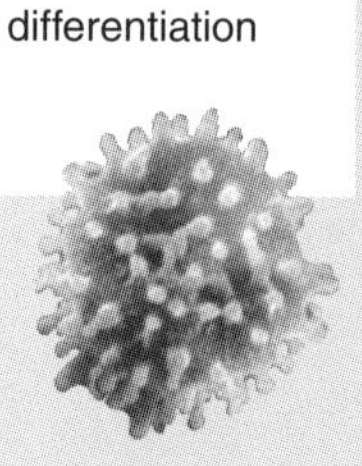

Cell organelles are involved in all aspects of cellular metabolism

Resources Information

Your set textbook should always be a starting point for information, but there are also many other resources available. A list of readily available resources is provided below. Access to the publishers of these resources can be made directly from BIOZONE's web site. Please note that our listing of any product in this workbook does not denote BIOZONE's endorsement of it.

Supplementary Texts

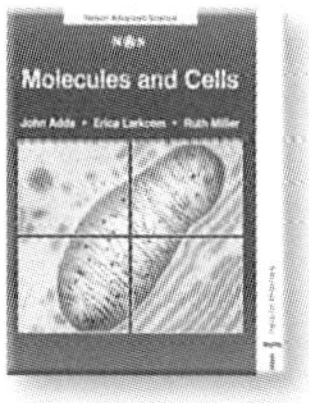
Molecules and Cells

Adds, J., E. Larkcom & R. Miller, 2003.
Molecules and Cells, revised ed., 112 pp.
ISBN: 0-7487-7484-X
Publisher: Nelson Thornes
Comments *Covers biological molecules, with detail on nucleic acids, enzymes, cellular organisation, and cell division. Practical activities are provided for most chapters.*

Tools, Techniques and Assessment in Biology

Adds, J., E. Larkcom, R. Miller, & R. Sutton, 1999.
Tools, Techniques and Assessment in Biology, 160 pp. **ISBN**: 0-17-448273-6
Publisher: Nelson Thornes
Comments *A course guide covering basic lab protocols, microscopy, quantitative techniques in the lab and field, advanced DNA techniques and tissue culture, data handling and statistical tests, and exam preparation.*

Biochemistry

Garrett, R.H. & C.M.Grisham, 2012.
Biochemistry, 5 ed., 1280 pp.
Publisher: Brooks Cole
ISBN: 1133106293
Comments *Covers all aspects of biochemistry using an innovative framework that reveals biochemistry in the everyday world.*

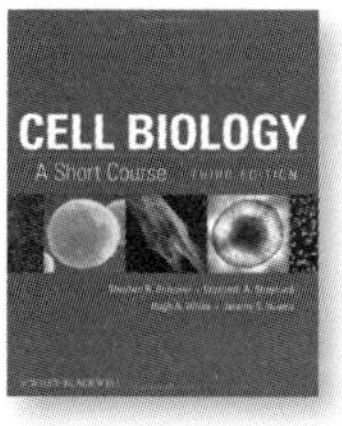
CELL BIOLOGY
A Short Course

Bolsover, S.R., E.A. Shepard, H.A. White, J.S. Hyams
Cell Biology: A Short Course 3 ed., 432 pp.
ISBN: 0470526998
Comments *The cell as the unit of life, with the "essentials only" approach. Concepts presented with clear diagrams and current research. Supported with its own website.*

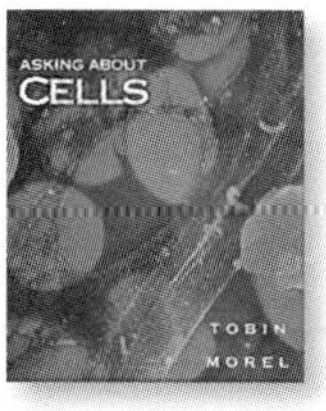
ASKING ABOUT
CELLS
TOBIN
MOREL

Tobin, A.J. and R.E Morel, 1997
Asking About Cells, 698 pp (paperback)
Publisher: Thomson Brooks/Cole
ISBN: 0-030-98018-6
Comments: *An introduction to cell biology, cellular processes and specialization, DNA and gene expression, and inheritance. The focus is on presenting material through inquiry.*

THE CELL
A Molecular Approach

Cooper, G.M. and R.E Hausman, 2013
The Cell, 6 ed. 832 pp (paperback)
Publisher: Sinauer Associates
ISBN: 1605351555
Comments: *A current, comprehensive molecular approach to cell biology. Includes classic experiments and up-to-date information on the latest discoveries.*

Biology Dictionaries

Access to a good biology dictionary is useful when dealing with biological terms. Some of the titles available are listed below. Link to the relevant publisher via BIOZONE's web site.

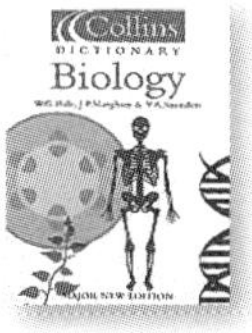
Collins
DICTIONARY
Biology

Hale, W.G., J.P. Margham, & V.A. Saunders.
Collins: Dictionary of Biology 3 ed. 2003, 672 pp. HarperCollins. **ISBN**: 0-00-714709-0.
Updated to take in the latest developments in biology from the Human Genome Project to advancements in cloning.

HENDERSON'S
Dictionary of
BIOLOGY

Henderson, E. Lawrence. **Henderson's Dictionary of Biological Terms**, 2008, 776 pp. Benjamin Cummings. **ISBN**: 978-0321505798 *This edition has been updated, rewritten for clarity, and reorganised for ease of use. An essential reference and the dictionary of choice for many.*

Periodicals, Magazines, & Journals

BIOLOGICAL
SCIENCES

Biological Sciences Review: *An informative quarterly publication for biology students.* Enquiries:
UK: Philip Allan Publishers **Tel**: 01869 338652
Fax: 01869 338803 **E-mail**: sales@philipallan.co.uk
Australasia: **Tel**: 08 8278 5916, **E-mail**: rjmorton@adelaide.on.net

NewScientist
THE FIRST
HUMAN
CLONES
GRAVITY

New Scientist: *Widely available weekly magazine with research summaries and features.* Enquiries: Reed Business Information Ltd, 51 Wardour St. London WIV 4BN **Tel**: (UK and intl):+44 (0) 1444 475636 **E-mail**: ns.subs@qss-uk.com *or subscribe from their web site.*

SCIENTIFIC
AMERICAN
THE FIRST
Human
Clone

Scientific American: *A monthly magazine containing specialist features. Articles range in level of reading difficulty and assumed knowledge.* Subscription enquiries: 415 Madison Ave. New York. NY10017-1111 **Tel**: (outside North America): 515-247-7631 **Tel**: (US& Canada): 800-333-1199

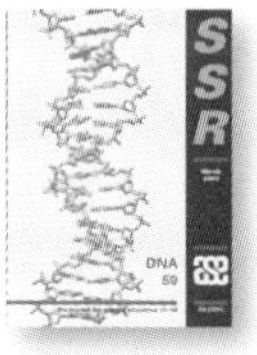
SSR

School Science Review: *A quarterly journal which includes articles, reviews, and news on current research and curriculum development. Free to Ordinary Members of the ASE or available on subscription.* Enquiries: **Tel**: 01707 28300
Email: info@ase.org.uk *or visit their web site.*

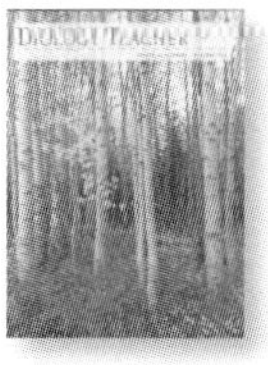

The American Biology Teacher: *The peer-reviewed journal of the NABT. Published nine times a year and containing information and activities relevant to biology teachers.* Contact: NABT, 12030 Sunrise Valley Drive, #110, Reston, VA 20191-3409
Web: www.nabt.org

Biozone's Student Review Series

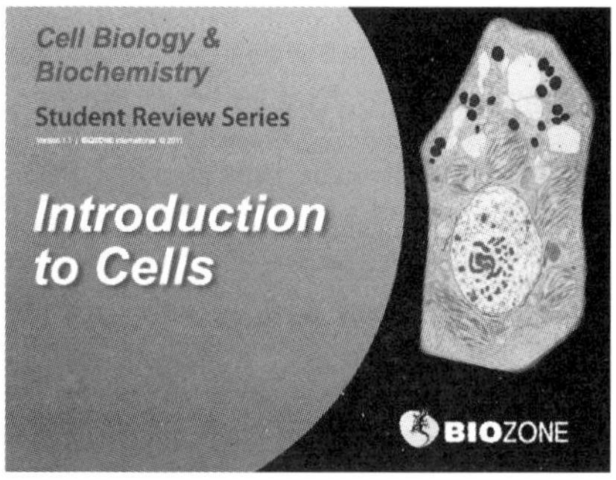
Cell Biology &
Biochemistry
Student Review Series
Introduction
to Cells
BIOZONE

Download titles in Biozone's **Student Review Series** via the free Biozone App. An easy and enjoyable way to review and consolidate the content requirement for a topic.

Questioning Terms

Questions come in a variety of forms. Whether you are studying for an exam or writing an essay, it is important to understand exactly what the question is asking. A question has two parts to it: one part of the question will provide you with information, the second part of the question will provide you with instructions as to how to answer the question. Following these instructions is most important. Often students in examinations know the material but fail to follow instructions and do not answer the question appropriately. Examiners often use certain key words to introduce questions. Look out for them and be clear as to what they mean. Below is a description of terms commonly used when asking questions in biology.

Commonly used Terms in Biology

The following terms are frequently used when asking questions in examinations and assessments. Students should have a clear understanding of each of the following terms and use this understanding to answer questions appropriately.

Account for: Provide a satisfactory explanation or reason for an observation.

Analyze: Interpret data to reach stated conclusions.

Annotate: Add **brief** notes to a diagram, drawing or graph.

Apply: Use an idea, equation, principle, theory, or law in a new situation.

Appreciate: To understand the meaning or relevance of a particular situation.

Calculate: Find an answer using mathematical methods. Show the working unless instructed not to.

Compare: Give an account of similarities and differences between two or more items, referring to both (or all) of them throughout. Comparisons can be given using a table. Comparisons generally ask for similarities more than differences (see contrast).

Construct: Represent or develop in graphical form.

Contrast: Show differences. Set in opposition.

Deduce: Reach a conclusion from information given.

Define: Give the precise meaning of a word or phrase as concisely as possible.

Derive: Manipulate a mathematical equation to give a new equation or result.

Describe: Give an account, including all the relevant information.

Design: Produce a plan, object, simulation or model.

Determine: Find the only possible answer.

Discuss: Give an account including, where possible, a range of arguments, assessments of the relative importance of various factors, or comparison of alternative hypotheses.

Distinguish: Give the difference(s) between two or more different items.

Draw: Represent by means of pencil lines. Add labels unless told not to do so.

Estimate: Find an approximate value for an unknown quantity, based on the information provided and application of scientific knowledge.

Evaluate: Assess the implications and limitations.

Explain: Give a clear account including causes, reasons, or mechanisms.

Identify: Find an answer from a number of possibilities.

Illustrate: Give concrete examples. Explain clearly by using comparisons or examples.

Interpret: Comment upon, give examples, describe relationships. Describe, then evaluate.

List: Give a sequence of names or other brief answers with no elaboration. Each one should be clearly distinguishable from the others.

Measure: Find a value for a quantity.

Outline: Give a brief account or summary. Include essential information only.

Predict: Give an expected result.

Solve: Obtain an answer using algebraic and/or numerical methods.

State: Give a specific name, value, or other answer. No supporting argument or calculation is necessary.

Suggest: Propose a hypothesis or other possible explanation.

Summarize: Give a brief, condensed account. Include conclusions and avoid unnecessary details.

In Conclusion

Students should familiarize themselves with this list of terms and, where necessary throughout the course, they should refer back to them when answering questions. The list of terms mentioned above is not exhaustive and students should compare this list with past examination papers and essays etc. and add any new terms (and their meaning) to the list above. The aim is to become familiar with interpreting the question and answering it appropriately.

Chapter 1

Molecules of **Life**

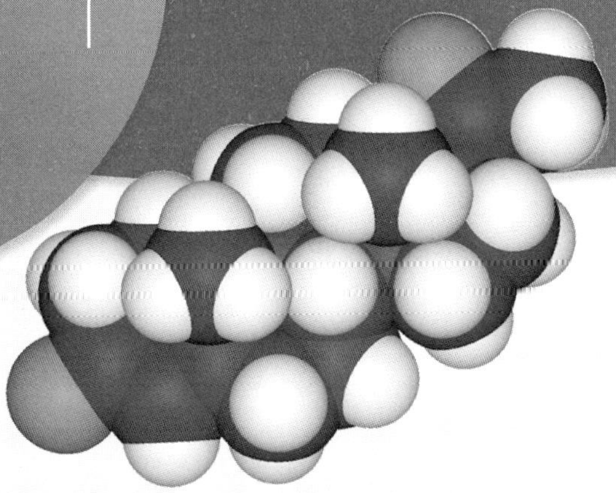

Key terms

activation energy
active site
amino acid
carbohydrate
chromatography
cofactor
condensation
disaccharide
enzyme
fibrous protein
globular protein
hydrolysis
induced fit
inhibition
inorganic ion
lipid
lock and key
monomer
monosaccharide
nucleic acid
organic molecule
polymer
primary structure
polysaccharides
proteins
Rf value
secondary structure
specificity
tertiary structure

Key concepts

- Organic molecules are carbon-containing molecules and are central to living systems.
- Water's properties make it essential to life.
- Proteins, carbohydrates, and lipids are three key groups of biological macromolecules.
- Condensation and hydrolysis reaction are important in building and breaking apart biological molecules.
- Enzymes are biological catalysts and regulate the metabolism of cells.

Learning Objectives

☐ 1. Use the **KEY TERMS** to compile a glossary for this topic.

The Structure and Function of Biological Molecules — pages 8-25

☐ 2. Identify the common elements found in organisms and give examples of where these elements occur in cells. Describe the importance of **organic molecules** and **inorganic ions** in biological systems.

☐ 3. Describe the structure of water, including reference to its polar nature and the physical and chemical properties that are important in biological systems.

☐ 4. Distinguish between **monomers** and **polymers**. Describe the range of **macromolecules** produced by cells.

☐ 5. Describe the molecular structure and biological roles of **monosaccharides** (e.g. **glucose, fructose**), **disaccharides** (e.g. **sucrose, lactose**), **and polysaccharides** (e.g. **cellulose**, **glycogen**).

☐ 6. Describe the synthesis of macromolecules by **condensation** and their breakdown by **hydrolysis**. Identify the bonds formed or broken in each case.

☐ 7. Using examples, describe the basic structure and roles of **carbohydrates**, **amino acids**, **proteins**, **lipids**, and **nucleic acids**.

☐ 8. Demonstrate an understanding of simple biochemcial tests for organic compounds, including the Benedict's test for reducing sugars, the I_2/KI test for starch, the emulsion test for lipids, and the biuret test for proteins.

☐ 9. Recognize **chromatography** as a technique for separating and identifying biological molecules. Describe the calculation and use of **Rf values**.

☐ 10. Describe where (in the cell) proteins are made. Describe the structure and functional diversity of proteins including their primary, secondary, and tertiary structure and their classification based on structure (e.g. **globular** or **fibrous)** or **function** (e.g. catalytic).

☐ 11. Describe how and why proteins are modified by the cell.

Enzymes — pages 26-30

☐ 12. Describe the properties and mode of action of **enzymes**, including the role of the **active site**, **specificity**, and **activation energy**.

☐ 13. Contrast the **lock and key** and **induced fit** models of enzyme function.

☐ 14. Describe the effect of substrate concentration, enzyme concentration, pH, and temperature on enzyme activity. Explain the term **optimum** with respect to enzyme activity. Recognize that enzymes (as proteins) can be denatured.

☐ 15. Using examples, explain the role of **cofactors** in enzyme activity.

☐ 16. Distinguish between reversible and irreversible **inhibition**, and competitive and non-competitive inhibition. Explain how inhibition affects enzyme activity.

Weblinks:
www.thebiozone.com/weblink/cellbio-3732/

BIOZONE APP: Student Review Series
Molecules of Life

The Biochemical Nature of the Cell

Water is the main component of organisms, and provides an equable environment in which metabolic reactions can occur. Apart from water, most other substances in cells are compounds of **carbon**, **hydrogen**, **oxygen**, and **nitrogen**. The combination of carbon atoms with the atoms of other elements provides a huge variety of molecular structures, collectively called **organic molecules**. The organic molecules that make up living things can be grouped into four broad classes: carbohydrates, lipids, proteins, and nucleic acids. These are discussed in more detail in subsequent activities. In addition, a small number of **elements** and **inorganic ions** are also essential for life as components of larger molecules or extracellular fluids.

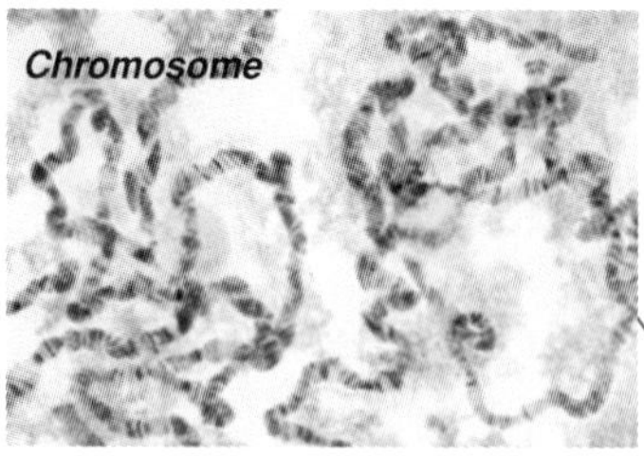
Chromosome

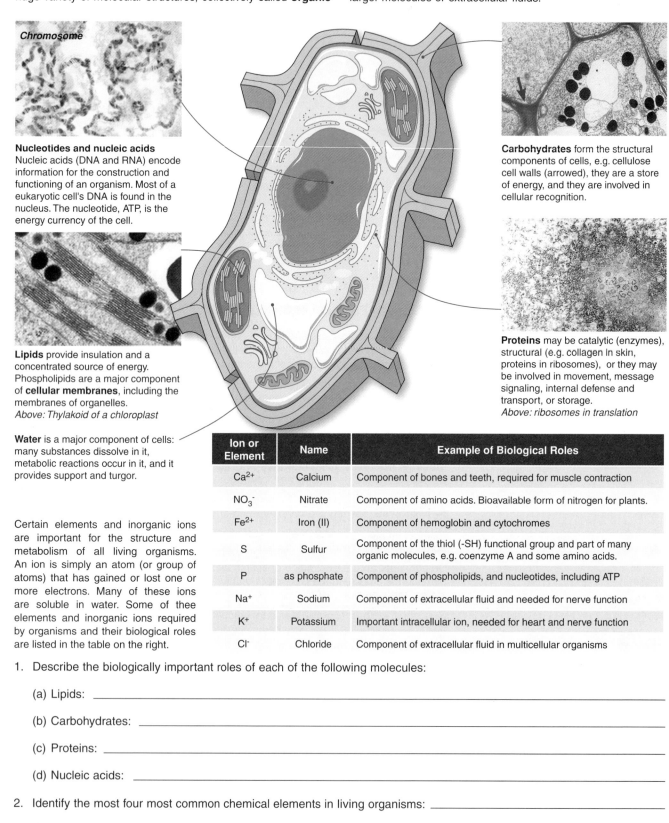

Nucleotides and nucleic acids
Nucleic acids (DNA and RNA) encode information for the construction and functioning of an organism. Most of a eukaryotic cell's DNA is found in the nucleus. The nucleotide, ATP, is the energy currency of the cell.

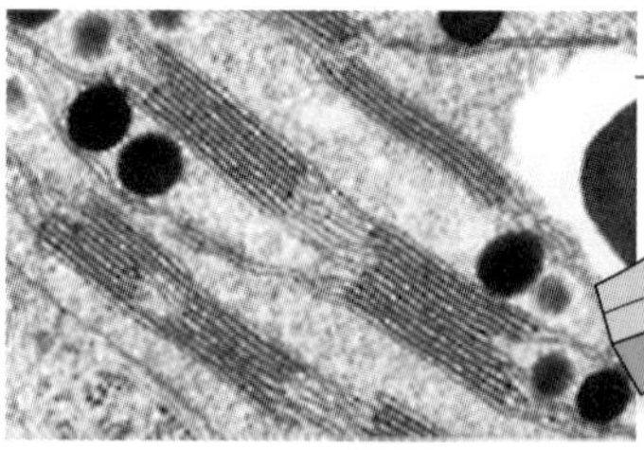

Lipids provide insulation and a concentrated source of energy. Phospholipids are a major component of **cellular membranes**, including the membranes of organelles.
Above: Thylakoid of a chloroplast

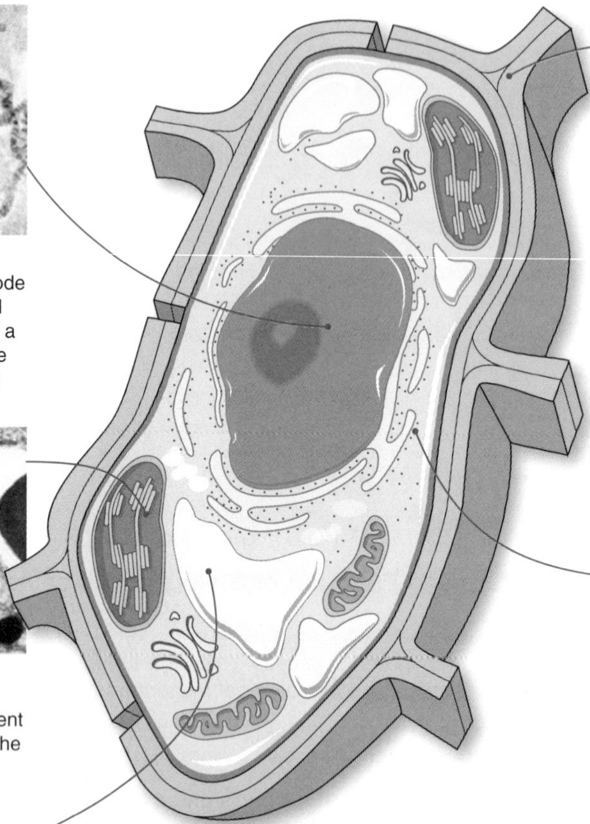

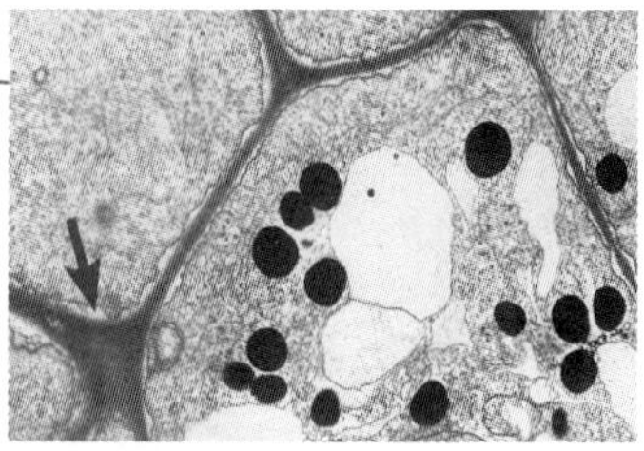

BF

Carbohydrates form the structural components of cells, e.g. cellulose cell walls (arrowed), they are a store of energy, and they are involved in cellular recognition.

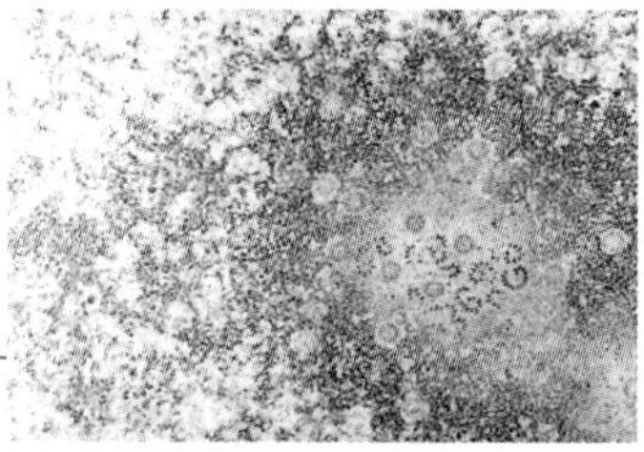

Proteins may be catalytic (enzymes), structural (e.g. collagen in skin, proteins in ribosomes), or they may be involved in movement, message signaling, internal defense and transport, or storage.
Above: ribosomes in translation

Water is a major component of cells: many substances dissolve in it, metabolic reactions occur in it, and it provides support and turgor.

Certain elements and inorganic ions are important for the structure and metabolism of all living organisms. An ion is simply an atom (or group of atoms) that has gained or lost one or more electrons. Many of these ions are soluble in water. Some of thee elements and inorganic ions required by organisms and their biological roles are listed in the table on the right.

Ion or Element	Name	Example of Biological Roles
Ca^{2+}	Calcium	Component of bones and teeth, required for muscle contraction
NO_3^-	Nitrate	Component of amino acids. Bioavailable form of nitrogen for plants.
Fe^{2+}	Iron (II)	Component of hemoglobin and cytochromes
S	Sulfur	Component of the thiol (-SH) functional group and part of many organic molecules, e.g. coenzyme A and some amino acids.
P	as phosphate	Component of phospholipids, and nucleotides, including ATP
Na^+	Sodium	Component of extracellular fluid and needed for nerve function
K^+	Potassium	Important intracellular ion, needed for heart and nerve function
Cl^-	Chloride	Component of extracellular fluid in multicellular organisms

1. Describe the biologically important roles of each of the following molecules:

   (a) Lipids: ______

   (b) Carbohydrates: ______

   (c) Proteins: ______

   (d) Nucleic acids: ______

2. Identify the most four most common chemical elements in living organisms: ______

3. Giving examples, describe the roles of some of the less common elements in living organisms: ______

______

______

ISBN: 978-1-927173-73-2

Organic Molecules

Organic molecules are those chemical compounds containing carbon that are found in living things. Specific groups of atoms, called **functional groups**, attach to a carbon-hydrogen core and confer specific chemical properties on the molecule. Some organic molecules in organisms are small and simple, containing only one or a few functional groups, while others are large complex assemblies called **macromolecules**. The macromolecules that make up living things can be grouped into four classes: carbohydrates, lipids, proteins, and nucleic acids. An understanding of the structure and function of these molecules is necessary to many branches of biology, especially biochemistry, physiology, and molecular genetics. The diagram below illustrates some of the common ways in which biological molecules are portrayed. Note that the **molecular formula** expresses the number of atoms in a molecule, but does not convey its structure; this is indicated by the **structural formula**. Molecules can also be represented as **models**. A ball and stick model shows the arrangement and type of bonds while a space filling model gives a more realistic appearance of a molecule, showing how close the atoms really are.

Portraying Biological Molecules

The numbers next to the carbon atoms are used for identification when the molecule changes shape

$C_6H_{12}O_6$

Glucose

Molecular formula

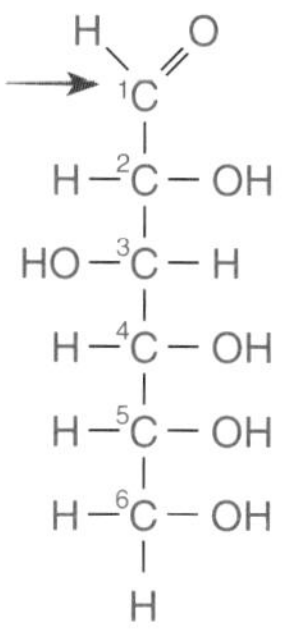

Structural formula
Glucose (straight form)

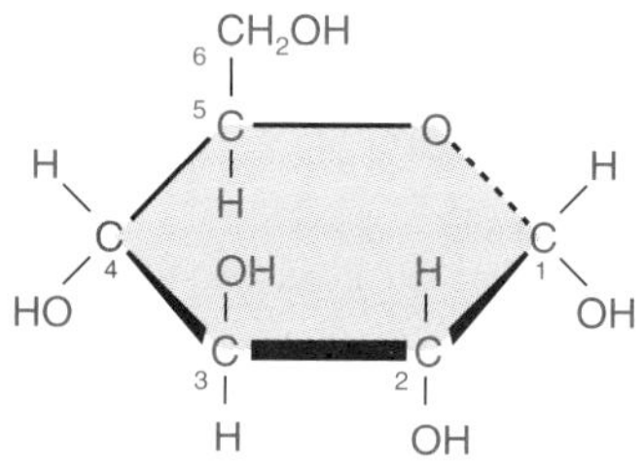

Structural formula
α-glucose (ring form)

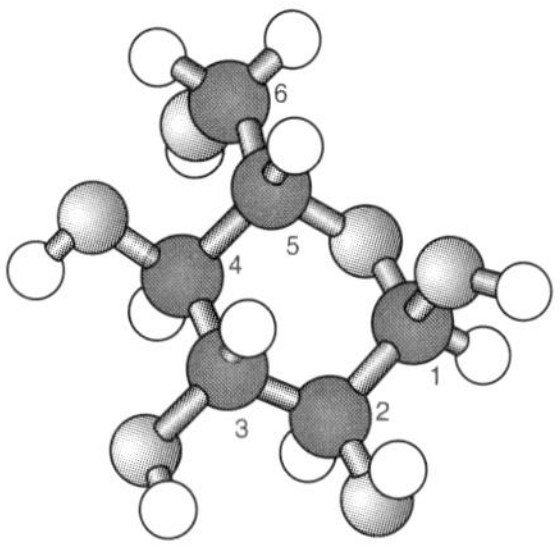

Ball and stick model
Glucose

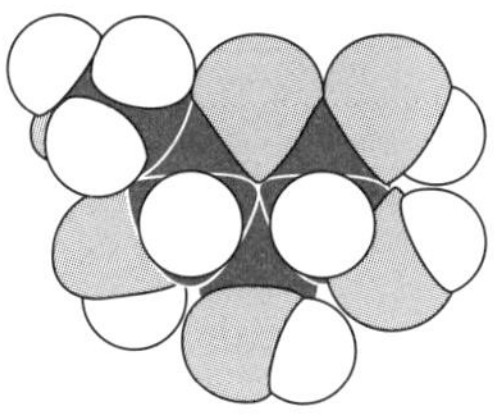

Space filling model
β-D-glucose

Example of Biological Molecules

Biological molecules may also include atoms other than carbon, oxygen, and hydrogen atoms. Nitrogen and sulfur are components of molecules such as amino acids and nucleotides. Some molecules contain the C=O (carbonyl) group. If this group is joined to at least one hydrogen atom it forms an aldehyde. If it is located between two carbon atoms, it forms a ketone.

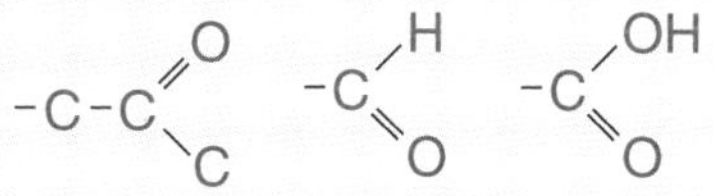

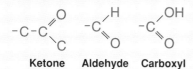

Ketone **Aldehyde** **Carboxyl**

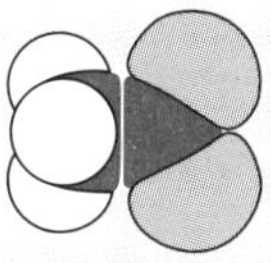

Acetate

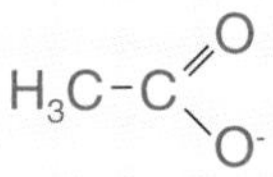

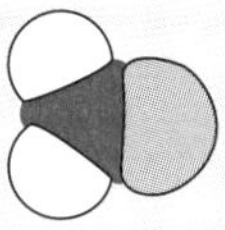

Methanal

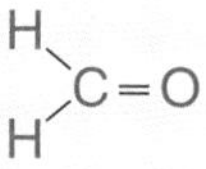

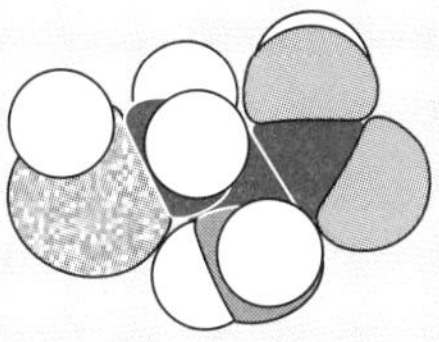

Cysteine

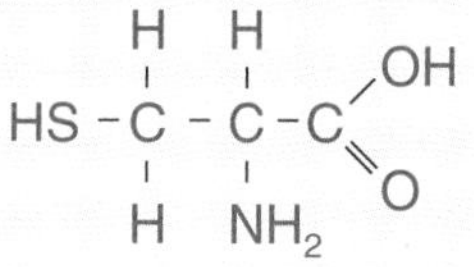

Key to Symbols

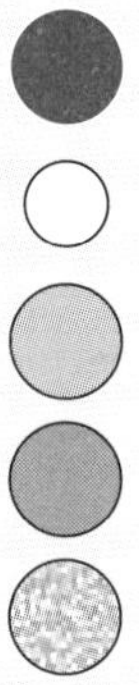
Carbon
Hydrogen
Oxygen
Nitrogen
Sulfur

1. Identify the three main elements comprising the structure of organic molecules: ______

2. Name two other elements that are also frequently part of organic molecules: ______

3. State how many covalent bonds a carbon atom can form with neighboring atoms: ______

4. Distinguish between molecular and structural formulae for a given molecule: ______

______

______

5. Describe what is meant by a functional group: ______

______

6. Classify methanal according to the position of the C=O group: ______

7. Identify a functional group always present in amino acids: ______

8. Identify the significance of cysteine in its formation of disulfide bonds: ______

______

ISBN: 978-1-927173-73-2

Related activities: *The Biochemical Nature of the Cell, Amino Acids, Proteins*

KNOW

The Role of Water

Water is the most abundant of the smaller molecules making up living things, and typically makes up about two-thirds of any organism. Water is a liquid at room temperature and many substances dissolve in it. It is a medium inside cells and for aquatic life. Water takes part in, and is a common product of, many reactions. Water molecules are **polar** and have a weak attraction for each other and inorganic ions, forming large numbers of weak hydrogen bonds. It is this feature that gives water many of its unique properties, including its low viscosity and its chemical behavior as a **universal solvent**.

Important Properties of Water

A lot of energy is required before water will change state so aquatic environments are thermally stable. In terrestrial organisms, sweating and transpiration cause cooling.

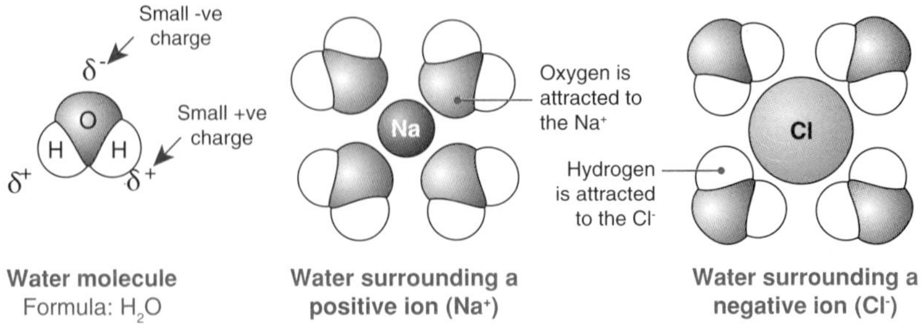

Small -ve charge
δ-
O
H
H
Small +ve charge
δ+
δ+
Water molecule
Formula: H2O
Na
Oxygen is attracted to the Na+
Water surrounding a positive ion (Na+)
Cl
Hydrogen is attracted to the Cl-
Water surrounding a negative ion (Cl-)

The most important feature of the chemical behavior of water is its dipole nature. It has a small positive charge on each of the two hydrogens and a small negative charge on the oxygen.

Water is colorless, with a high transmission of visible light, so light penetrates tissue and aquatic environments.

Ice is less dense than water. Consequently ice floats, insulating the underlying water and providing valuable habitat.

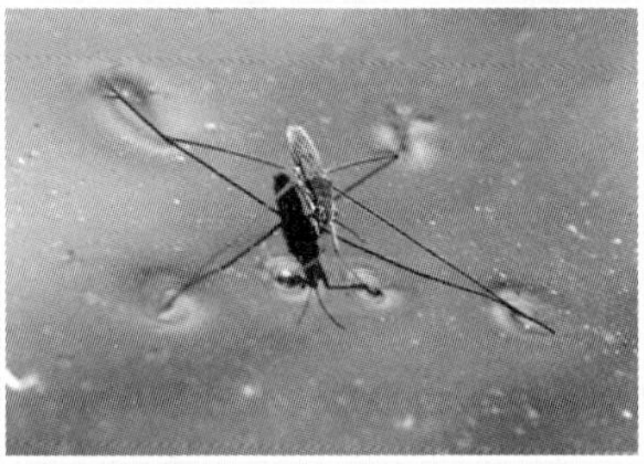

Water has low viscosity, strong cohesive properties, and high surface tension. It can flow freely through small spaces.

1. On the diagram above, showing a positive and a negative ion surrounded by water molecules, indicate the polarity of the water molecules (as shown in the example provided).

2. Explain the importance of the **dipole nature** of water molecules to the chemistry of life: ____________________

____

____

3. For (a)-(f), identify the important property of water, and describe an example of that property's biological significance:

(a) Property important in the clarity of seawater: ____________________

Biological significance: ____________________

(b) Property important in the transport of water in xylem: ____________________

Biological significance: ____________________

(c) Property important in the relatively stable temperature of water bodies: ____________________

Biological significance: ____________________

(d) Property important in the transport of glucose around the body: ____________________

Biological significance: ____________________

(e) Property important in the cooling effect of evaporation: ____________________

Biological significance: ____________________

(f) Property important in ice floating: ____________________

Biological significance: ____________________

ISBN: 978-1-927173-73-2

Monosaccharides and Disaccharides

Sugars (monosaccharides and disaccharides) are carbohydrates, which are a family of organic molecules with the general formula $C_m(H_2O)_n$. The most common arrangements found in sugars are hexose (6 sided) or pentose (5 sided) rings. Sugars play a central role in cells, providing energy and joining together to form carbohydrate macromolecules, such as starch and glycogen. Monosaccharide polymers form the major component of most plants (as cellulose). Monosaccharides are important as a primary energy source for cellular metabolism. Disaccharides (double-sugars) are important in human nutrition and are found in milk (lactose) table sugar (sucrose), and malt (maltose). They are formed from different combinations of monosaccharides.

Monosaccharides

Monosaccharides are used as a primary energy source for fuelling cell metabolism. They are single-sugar molecules and include glucose (grape sugar and blood sugar) and fructose (honey and fruit juices). The commonly occurring monosaccharides contain between three and seven carbon atoms in their carbon chains and, of these, the 6C hexose sugars occur most frequently. All monosaccharides are reducing sugars (i.e. they can participate in reduction reactions).

Single sugars (monosaccharides)

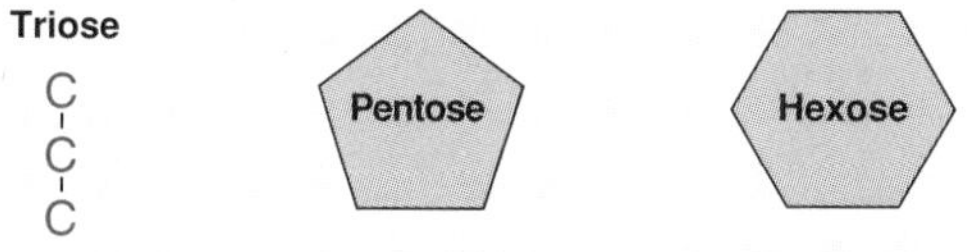
Triose
C
C
C
Pentose
Hexose

e.g. glyceraldehyde | e.g. ribose, deoxyribose | e.g. glucose, fructose, galactose

Disaccharides

Disaccharides are double-sugar molecules and are used as energy sources and as building blocks for larger molecules. The type of disaccharide formed depends on the monomers involved and whether they are in their α- or β- form. Only a few disaccharides (e.g. lactose) are classified as reducing sugars.

Sucrose = α-glucose + β-fructose (simple sugar in plant sap)
Maltose = α-glucose + α-glucose (a product of starch hydrolysis)
Lactose = β-glucose + β-galactose (milk sugar)
Cellobiose = β-glucose + β-glucose (from cellulose hydrolysis)

Double sugars (disaccharides)

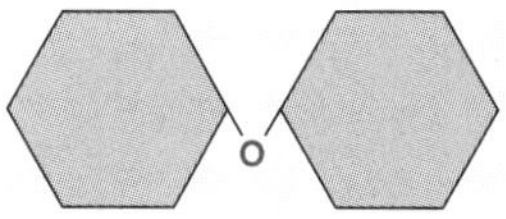
O

Examples sucrose, lactose, maltose, cellobiose

Lactose, a milk sugar, is made up of β-glucose + β-galactose. Milk contains 2-8% lactose by weight. It is the primary carbohydrate source for suckling mammalian infants.

Maltose is composed of two α-glucose molecules. These germinating wheat seeds contain maltose because the plant breaks down their starch stores to use it for food.

Sucrose (table sugar) is a simple sugar derived from plants such as sugar cane (above), sugar beet, or maple sap. It is composed of an α-glucose molecule and a β-fructose molecule.

1. Describe the two major functions of monosaccharides:

   (a) ______________________________

   (b) ______________________________

2. The breakdown of a disaccharide into its constituent monosaccharide units is catalyzed by enzymes. For each of the following disaccharides, identify the enzyme that catalyzes the reaction. HINT: The enzyme names end in the term -ase. Also identify the hydrolysis products, and give an example of where this enzyme might naturally occur:

   (a) Lactose: Enzyme: Lactase Products of hydrolysis: ______________

   Found: ______________________________

   (b) Maltose: Enzyme: ______________ Products of hydrolysis: ______________

   Found: ______________________________

   (c) Sucrose: Enzyme: ______________ Products of hydrolysis: ______________

   Found: ______________________________

3. Use your understanding of disaccharide chemistry to suggest how the digestive disorder lactose intolerance arises:

____

____

____

ISBN: 978-1-927173-73-2

Related activities: *Condensation and Hydrolysis of Sugars*
Weblinks: *Biomolecules: Carbohydrates*

Condensation and Hydrolysis of Sugars

Monomers are linked together by **condensation reactions**, so called because linking two units together results in the production of a water molecule. The reverse reaction, in which compound sugars are broken down into their constituent monosaccharides, is called **hydrolysis**. It splits polymers into smaller units by breaking the bond between two monomers. Hydrolysis literally means breaking with water, and so requires the addition of a water molecule to occur. Carbohydrates also exist as **isomers**. Isomers are compounds with the same molecular formula, but they have a different structural formula. Because of this they have different properties. For example, when α-glucose polymers are linked together they form starch, but β-glucose polymers form cellulose. In all carbohydrates, the structure is closely related to their functional properties.

Isomerism

Compounds with the same chemical formula (same types and numbers of atoms) may differ in the arrangement of their atoms. Such variations in the arrangement of atoms in molecules are called isomers. In structural isomers (such as fructose and glucose, and the α and β glucose, right), the atoms are linked in different sequences. Optical isomers are identical in every way but are mirror images of each other.

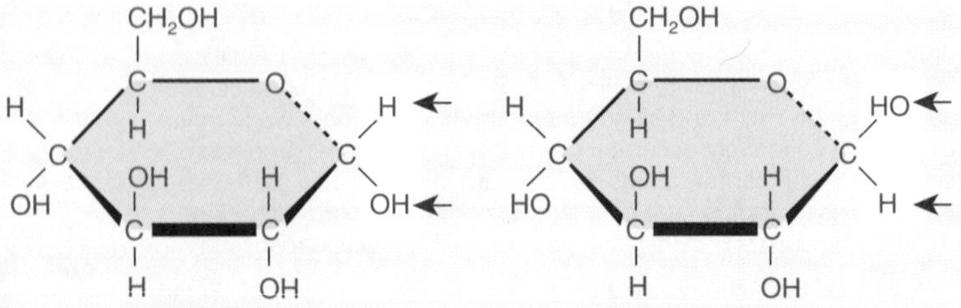

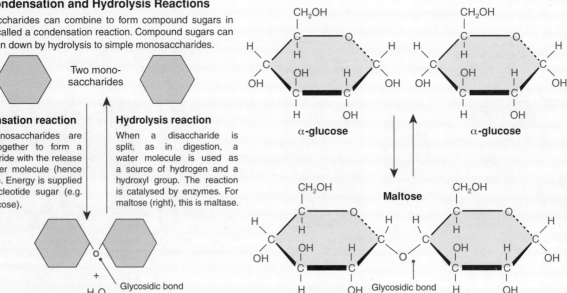

α-glucose **β-glucose**

Condensation and Hydrolysis Reactions

Monosaccharides can combine to form compound sugars in what is called a condensation reaction. Compound sugars can be broken down by hydrolysis to simple monosaccharides.

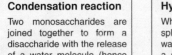

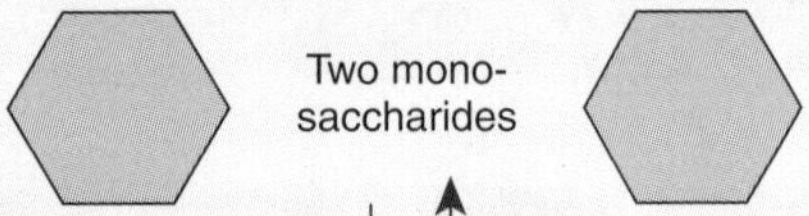
Two mono-
saccharides

Condensation reaction

Two monosaccharides are joined together to form a disaccharide with the release of a water molecule (hence its name). Energy is supplied by a nucleotide sugar (e.g. ADP-glucose).

Hydrolysis reaction

When a disaccharide is split, as in digestion, a water molecule is used as a source of hydrogen and a hydroxyl group. The reaction is catalysed by enzymes. For maltose (right), this is maltase.

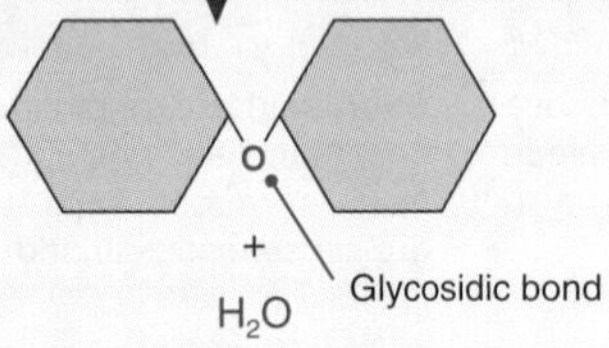
+
H_2O
Glycosidic bond

Disaccharide + water

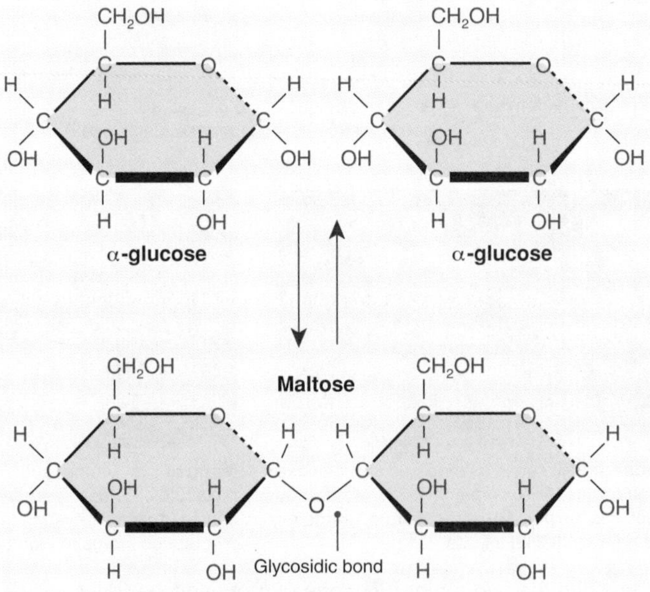
α-glucose
α-glucose
Maltose
Glycosidic bond

Disaccharide + water

1. Distinguish between structural and optical isomers in carbohydrates, describing examples of each:

2. Explain briefly how compound sugars are formed and broken down:

3. Using examples, explain how the isomeric structure of a carbohydrate may affect its chemical behavior:

Related activities: *Monosaccharides and Disaccharides, Polysaccharides*
Weblinks: *Condensation and Hydrolysis*

ISBN: 978-1-927173-73-2

Polysaccharides

Polysaccharides or complex carbohydrates are straight or branched chains of many monosaccharides (sometimes many thousands) of the same or different types. The most common polysaccharides, cellulose, starch, and glycogen, contain only glucose, but their properties are very different. These differences are a function of the glucose isomer involved and the types of glycosidic linkages joining the glucose monomers. Different polysaccharides, based on the same sugar monomer, can thus be highly soluble and a source of readily available energy or a strong structural material that resists being digested.

Cellulose

Cellulose is a structural material in plants and is made up of unbranched chains of β-glucose molecules held together by 1,4 glycosidic links. As many as 10,000 glucose molecules may be linked together to form a straight chain. Parallel chains become cross-linked with hydrogen bonds and form bundles of 60-70 molecules called **microfibrils**. Cellulose microfibrils are very strong and are a major component of the structural components of plants, such as the cell wall (photo, right).

Starch

Starch is also a polymer of glucose, but it is made up of long chains of α-glucose molecules linked together. It contains a mixture of 25-30% amylose (unbranched chains linked by α-1,4 glycosidic bonds) and 70-75% amylopectin (branched chains with α-1,6 glycosidic bonds every 24-30 glucose units). Starch is an energy storage molecule in plants and is found concentrated in insoluble starch granules within plant cells (see photo, right). Starch can be easily hydrolyzed by enzymes to soluble sugars when required.

Glycogen

Glycogen, like starch, is a branched polysaccharide. It is chemically similar to amylopectin, being composed of α-glucose molecules, but there are more α-1,6 glycosidic links mixed with α-1,4 links. This makes it more highly branched and water-soluble than starch. Glycogen is a storage compound in animal tissues and is found mainly in liver and muscle cells (photo, right). It is readily hydrolysed by enzymes to form glucose.

Chitin

Chitin is a tough modified polysaccharide made up of chains of β-glucose molecules. It is chemically similar to cellulose but each glucose has an amine group ($-NH_2$) attached. After cellulose, chitin is the second most abundant carbohydrate. It is found in the cell walls of fungi and is the main component of the exoskeleton of insects (right) and other arthropods.

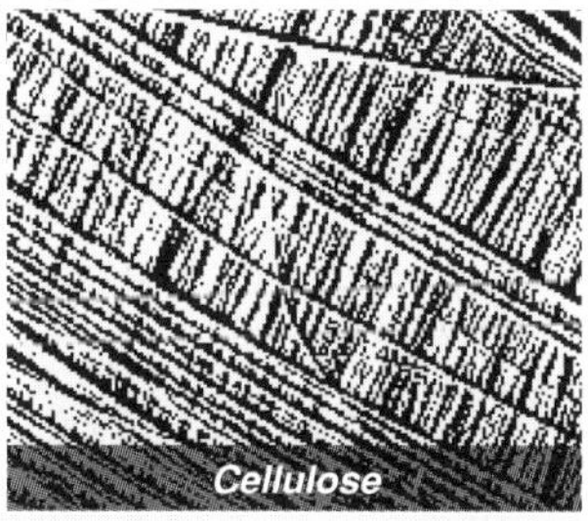

Cellulose

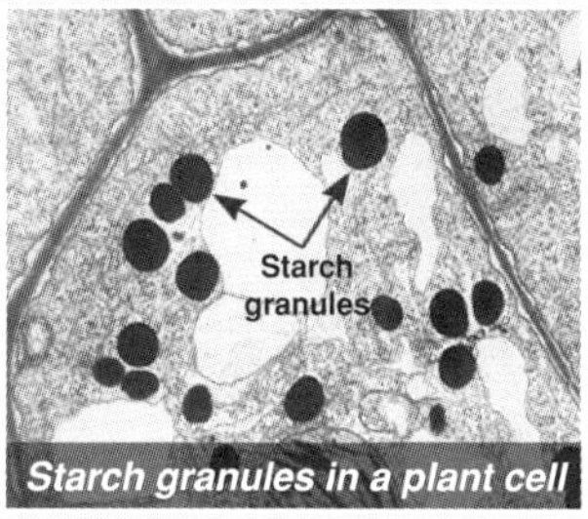
Starch granules

Starch granules in a plant cell

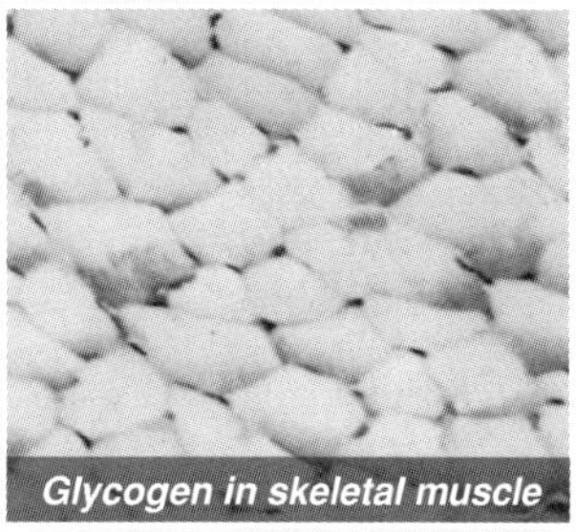

Glycogen in skeletal muscle

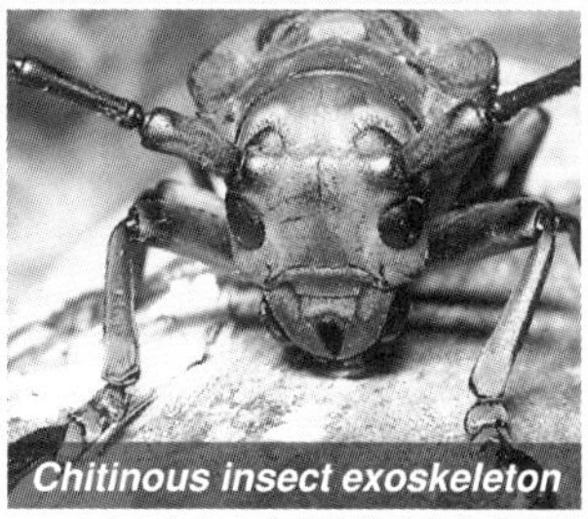

Chitinous insect exoskeleton

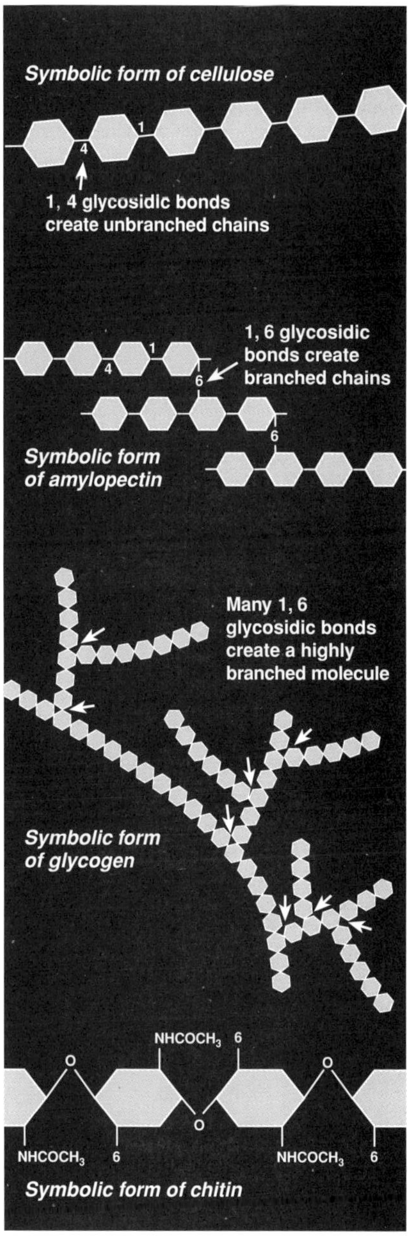
Symbolic form of cellulose
1
4
1, 4 glycosidic bonds create unbranched chains
1, 6 glycosidic bonds create branched chains
1
4
6
6
Symbolic form of amylopectin
Many 1, 6 glycosidic bonds create a highly branched molecule
Symbolic form of glycogen
NHCOCH3 6
O
O
O
NHCOCH3 6
NHCOCH3 6
Symbolic form of chitin

1. Why are polysaccharides such a good source of energy?

2. Discuss the structural differences between the polysaccharides starch and glycogen, explaining how the differences in structure contribute to the functional properties of the molecule:

ISBN: 978-1-927173-73-2

Related activities: *Condensation and Hydrolysis of Sugars*

Lipids

Lipids are a diverse group of chemicals that lack an affinity for water, i.e. they are **hydrophobic**. They consist mainly of covalently bonded hydrogen and carbon molecules. Lipids can be divided into fats (comprising fatty acids and glycerol), phospholipids, and steroids. They can be solids or liquids at room temperature depending on the length of their carbon chains.

Neutral Fats and Oils

The most abundant lipids in living things are neutral fats. They make up the fats and oils found in plants and animals. Fats are an economical way to store fuel reserves because they yield more than twice as much energy as the same quantity of carbohydrate. **Neutral fats** are composed of a glycerol molecule attached to one (monoglyceride), two (diglyceride) or three (triglyceride) fatty acids. The fatty acid chains may be saturated or unsaturated (see below). Waxes are similar in structure to fats and oils, but they are formed with a complex alcohol instead of glycerol.

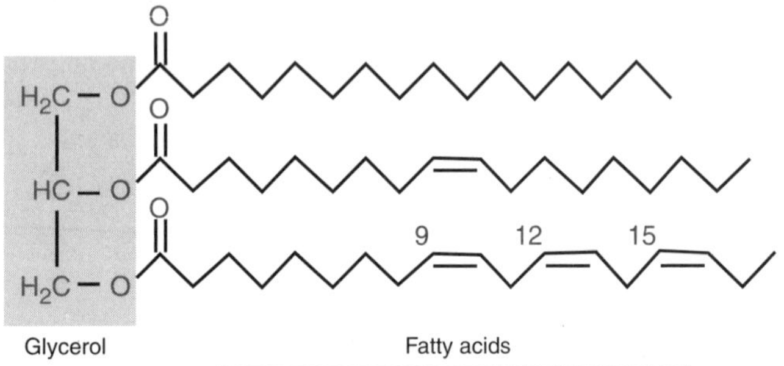

9
12
15
Glycerol
Fatty acids

Triglyceride: an example of a neutral fat

Condensation

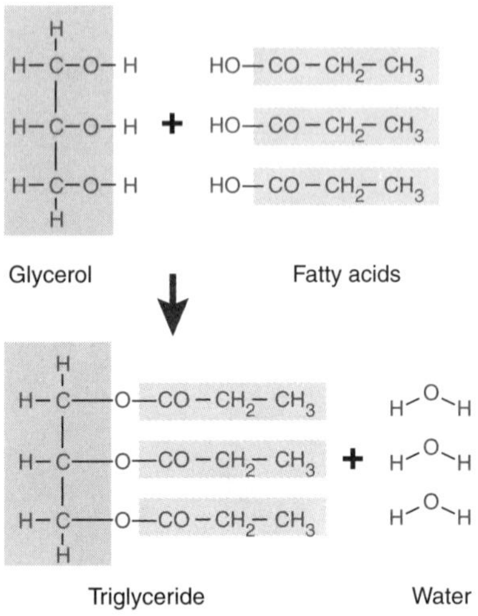

Glycerol
Fatty acids
Triglyceride
Water

Triglycerides form when glycerol bonds with three fatty acids. Glycerol is an alcohol containing three carbons. Each of these carbons is bonded to a hydroxyl (-OH) group.

When glycerol bonds with the fatty acid, an ester bond is formed and water is released. Three separate condensation reactions are involved in producing a triglyceride.

Saturated and Unsaturated Fatty Acids

Fatty acids are a major component of **neutral fats** and **phospholipids**. About 30 different kinds are found in animal lipids. **Saturated fatty acids** contain the maximum number of hydrogen atoms. **Unsaturated fatty acids** contain some carbon atoms that are double-bonded with each other and are not fully saturated with hydrogens. Lipids containing a high proportion of saturated fatty acids tend to be solids at room temperature (e.g. butter). Lipids with a high proportion of unsaturated fatty acids are oils and tend to be liquid at room temperature. This is because the unsaturation causes kinks in the straight chains so that the fatty acids do not pack closely together. Regardless of their degree of saturation, fatty acids yield a large amount of energy when oxidised.

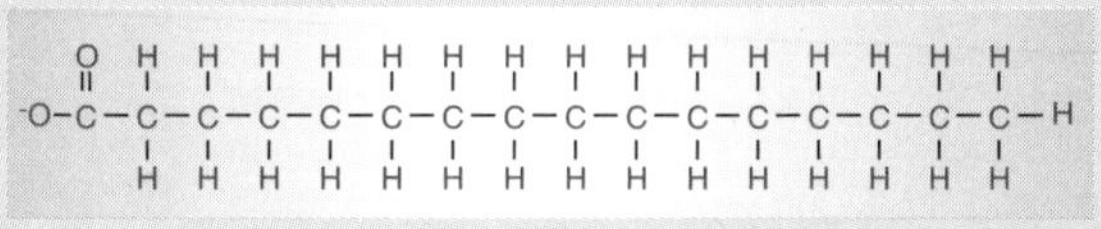

Formula (above) and molecular model (below) for **palmitic acid** (a saturated fatty acid)

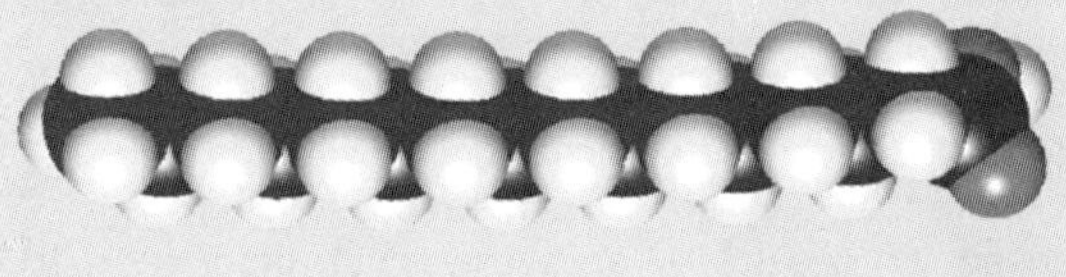

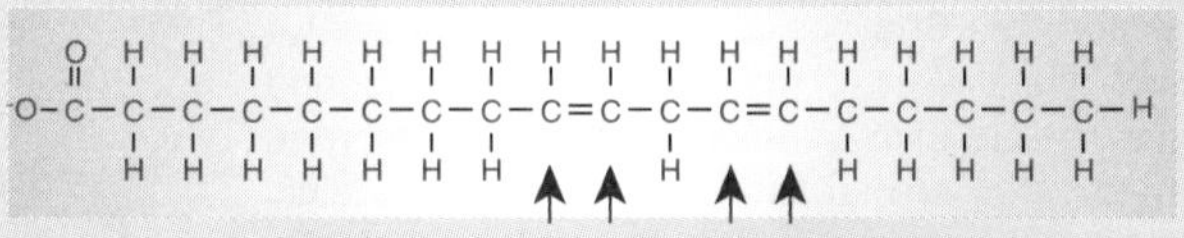

Formula (above) and molecular model (right) for **linoleic acid** (an unsaturated fatty acid). The arrows indicate double bonded carbon atoms that are not fully saturated with hydrogens.

1. (a) Distinguish between saturated and unsaturated fatty acids: ______________________________

____

____

(b) Explain how the type of fatty acid present in a neutral fat or phospholipid is related to that molecule's properties:

____

____

____

2. Describe two examples of steroids. For each example, describe its physiological function:

(a) ______________________________

(b) ______________________________

ISBN: 978-1-927173-73-2

Phospholipids

Phospholipids are the main component of cellular membranes. They consist of a glycerol attached to two fatty acid chains and a phosphate (PO_4^{3-}) group. The phosphate end of the molecule is attracted to water (it is hydrophilic) while the fatty acid end is repelled (hydrophobic). The hydrophobic ends turn inwards in the membrane to form a **phospholipid bilayer.**

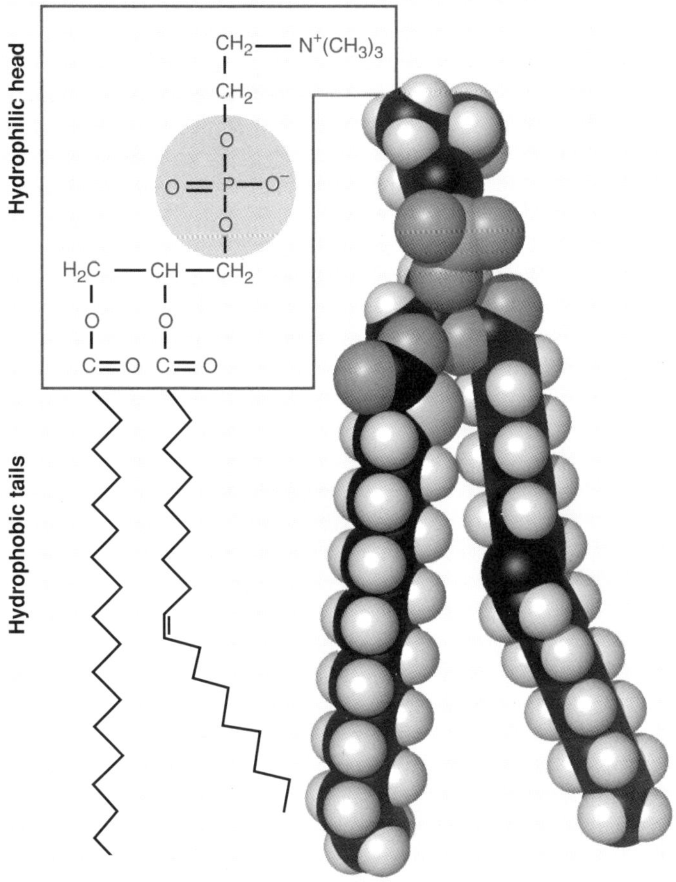

Hydrophilic head
Hydrophobic tails
CH2— N+(CH3)3
CH2
O
O=P—O-
O
H2C —CH —CH2
O O
C=O C=O

Steroids and Cholesterol

Although steroids are classified as lipids, their structure is quite different to that of other lipids. Steroids have a basic structure of three rings made of 6 carbon atoms each and a fourth ring containing 5 carbon atoms. Examples of steroids include the male and female sex hormones (testosterone and estrogen), and the hormones cortisol and aldosterone.

Cholesterol, while not a steroid itself, is a sterol lipid and is a precursor to several steroid hormones. It is present in the plasma membrane, where it regulates membrane fluidity by preventing the phospholipids from packing too closely together.

Like phospholipids, cholesterol is **amphipathic**. The hydroxyl (-OH) group on cholesterol interacts with the polar head groups of the membrane phospholipids, while the steroid ring and hydrocarbon chain tuck into the hydrophobic portion of the membrane. This helps to stabilize the outer surface of the membrane and reduce its permeability to small water-soluble molecules.

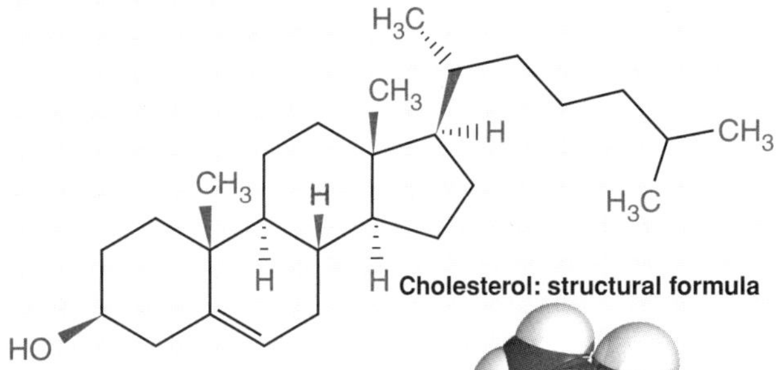

H3C
CH3
H
CH3
CH3
H
H3C
H
H
HO

Cholesterol: structural formula

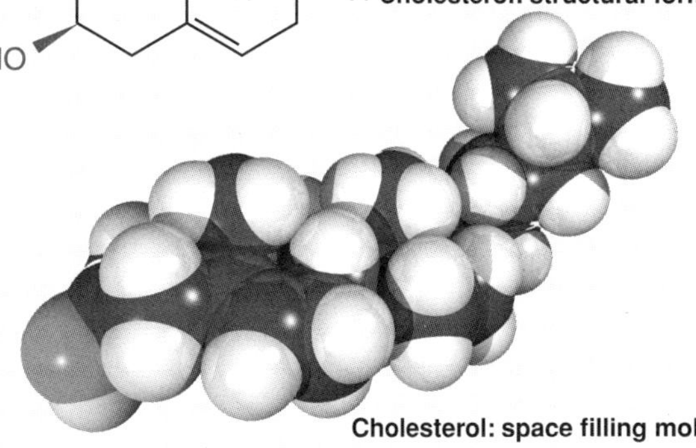

Cholesterol: space filling molecule

3. Outline the key **chemical** difference between a phospholipid and a triglyceride: ______

4. Explain why saturated fats (e.g. lard) are solid at room temperature: ______

5. (a) Relate the structure of phospholipids to their chemical properties and their functional role in cellular membranes:

   (b) Suggest how the cell membrane structure of an Arctic fish might differ from that of tropical fish species:

6. Explain how the structure of cholesterol enables it to perform structural and functional roles within membranes:

ISBN: 978-1-927173-73-2

Biological Functions of Lipids

Lipids are a group of organic compounds with an oily, greasy, or waxy consistency. They are relatively insoluble in water and tend to be water-repelling (e.g. cuticle on leaf surfaces). Lipids are important biological fuels, some are hormones, and some serve as structural components in plasma membranes. Proteins and carbohydrates may be converted into fats by enzymes and stored within cells of adipose tissue. During times of plenty, this store is increased, to be used during times of food shortage.

Important Biological Functions of Lipids

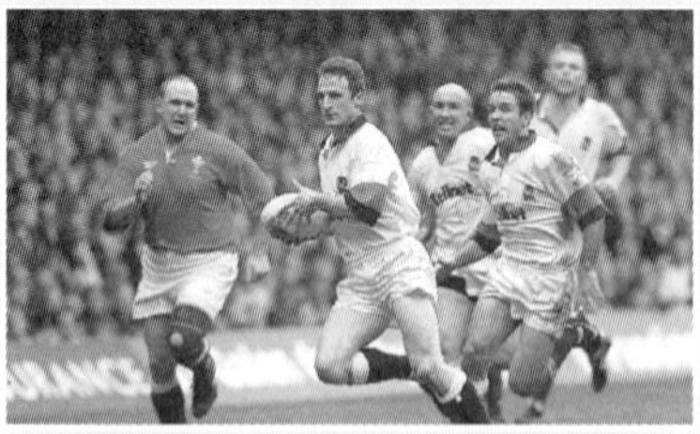

Lipids are concentrated sources of energy and provide fuel for aerobic respiration.

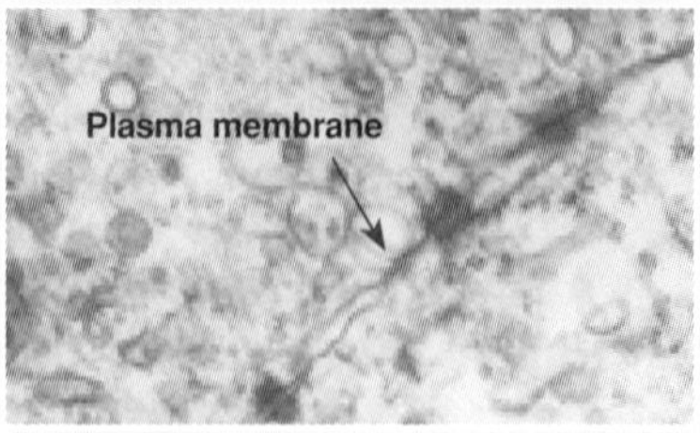
Plasma membrane

WMU

Phospholipids form the structural framework of cellular membranes.

Waxes and oils secreted onto surfaces provide waterproofing in plants and animals.

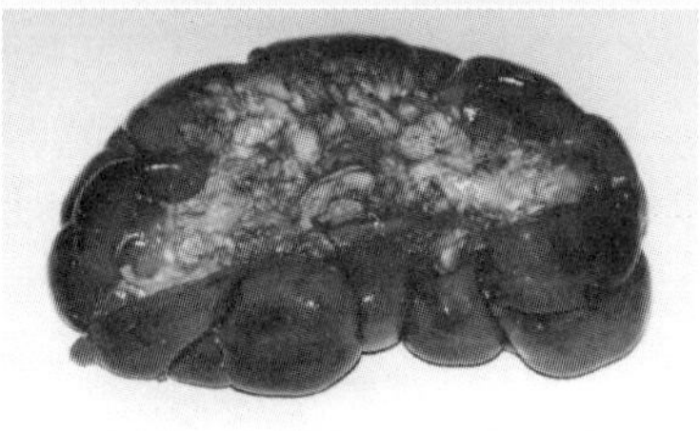

TG

Fat absorbs shocks. Organs that are prone to bumps and shocks (e.g. kidneys) are cushioned with a relatively thick layer of fat.

Lipids are a source of metabolic water. During respiration stored lipids are metabolized for energy, producing water and carbon dioxide.

Stored lipids provide insulation. Increased body fat levels in winter reduce heat losses to the environment.

1. Explain how fats can provide an animal with:

   (a) Energy: ______________________________

   (b) Water: ______________________________

   (c) Insulation: ______________________________

2. Explain why marine mammals (e.g. whales and seals) have thick layers of fat, or blubber, surrounding their bodies:

3. Oils and waxes are water repelling. Give two examples in animals or plants where this property would be useful:

4. Phospholipids have a polar head and non-polar tail. Explain how this allows them to spontaneously form the plasma membrane of a cell.

KNOW

Related activities: *Lipids*
Weblinks: *Biomolecules: Lipids*

ISBN: 978-1-927173-73-2

Nucleic Acids

Nucleic acids are a special group of chemicals in cells concerned with the transmission of inherited information. They have the capacity to store the information that controls cellular activity. The central nucleic acid is called **deoxyribonucleic acid** (DNA). DNA is a major component of chromosomes and is found primarily in the nucleus, although a small amount is found in mitochondria and chloroplasts. Other **ribonucleic acids** (RNA) are involved in the 'reading' of the DNA information. All nucleic acids are made up of simple repeating units called **nucleotides**, linked together to form chains or strands, often of great length. The strands vary in the sequence of the bases found on each nucleotide. It is this sequence which provides the 'genetic code' for the cell. In addition to nucleic acids, certain nucleotides and their derivatives are also important as suppliers of energy (**ATP**) or as hydrogen ion and electron carriers in respiration and photosynthesis (NAD, NADP, and FAD).

Chemical Structure of a Nucleotide

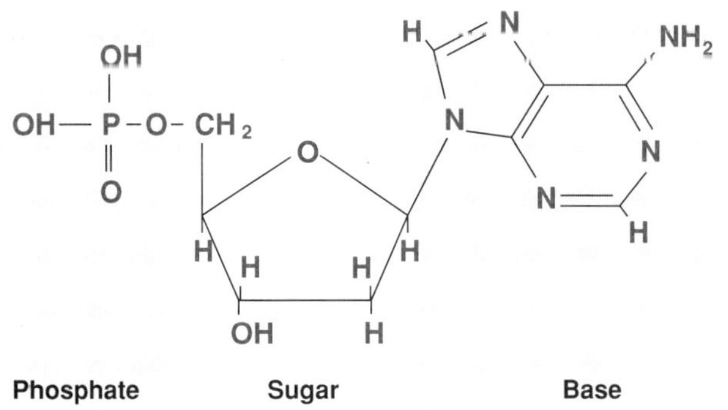
OH
OH— P–O– CH2
O
O
H
H
H
H
OH
H
N
H
N
NH_2
N
N
H
Phosphate
Sugar
Base

Symbolic Form of a Nucleotide

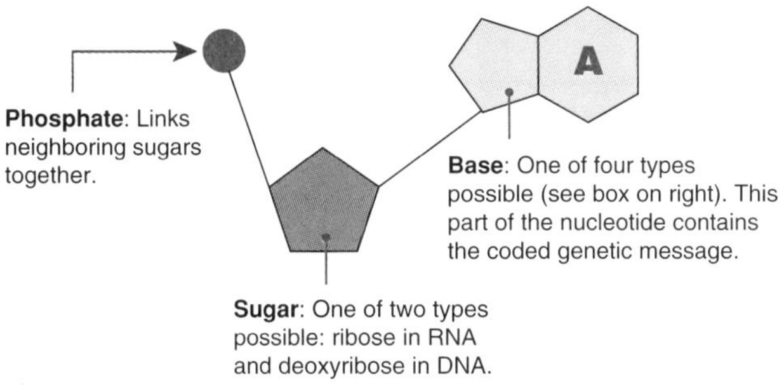
A
Phosphate: Links neighboring sugars together.
Base: One of four types possible (see box on right). This part of the nucleotide contains the coded genetic message.
Sugar: One of two types possible: ribose in RNA and deoxyribose in DNA.

Nucleotides are the building blocks of DNA. Their precise sequence in a DNA molecule provides the genetic instructions for the organism to which it governs. Accidental changes in nucleotide sequences are a cause of mutations, usually harming the organism, but occasionally providing benefits.

Bases

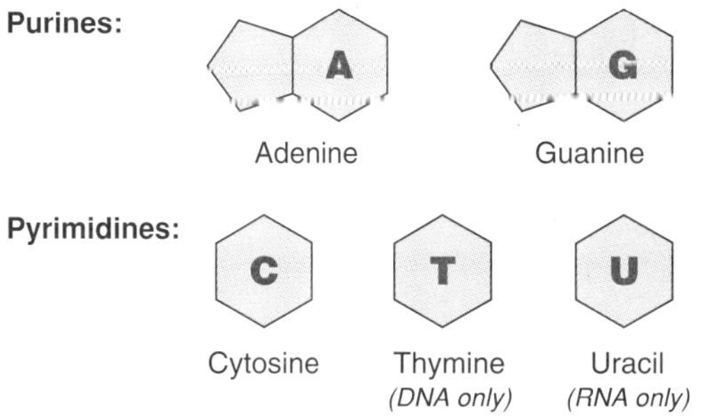
Purines:
A
G
Adenine
Guanine
Pyrimidines:
C
T
U
Cytosine
Thymine
(DNA only)
Uracil
(RNA only)

The two-ringed bases above are **purines**. The single-ringed bases are **pyrimidines**. Although only one of four kinds of base can be used in a nucleotide, **uracil** is found only in RNA, replacing **thymine**. DNA contains A, T, G, and C, while RNA contains A, U, G, and C.

Sugars

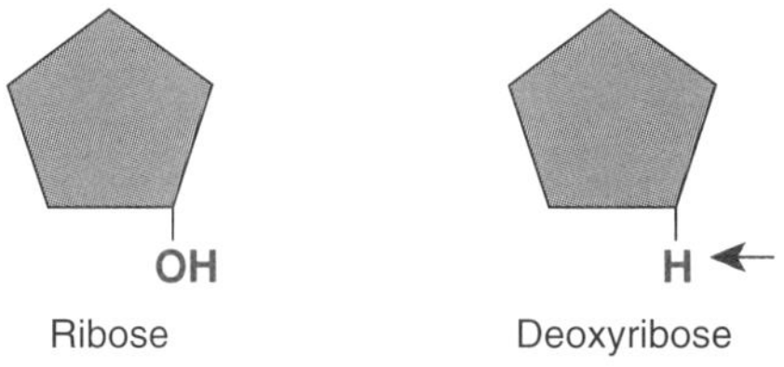
OH
H
Ribose
Deoxyribose

Deoxyribose sugar is found only in DNA. It differs from **ribose** sugar, found in RNA, by the lack of a single oxygen atom (arrowed).

RNA Molecule

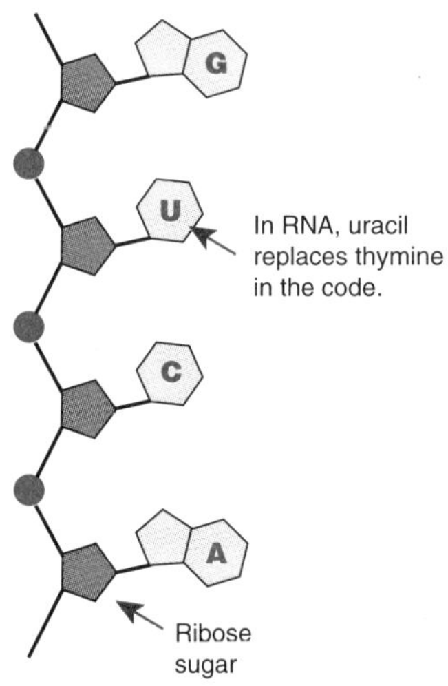
G
U
C
A
In RNA, uracil replaces thymine in the code.
Ribose sugar

Ribonucleic acid (RNA) comprises a *single strand* of nucleotides linked together.

DNA Molecule

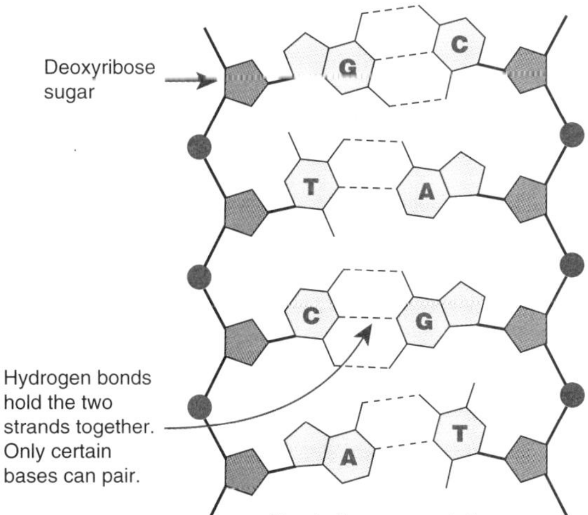
Deoxyribose sugar
G
C
T
A
C
G
A
T
Hydrogen bonds hold the two strands together. Only certain bases can pair.

Symbolic representation

DNA Molecule

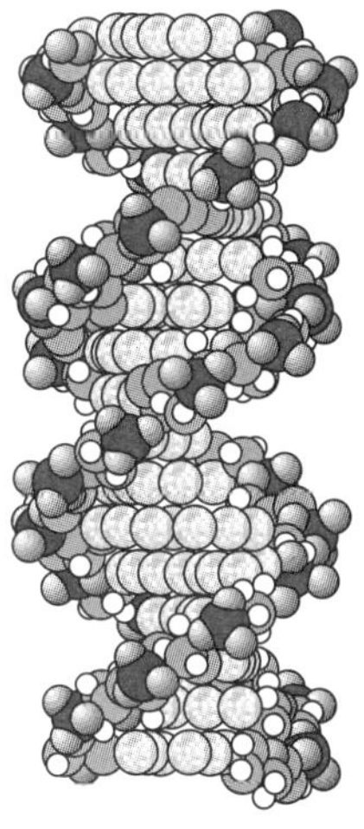

Space filling model

Deoxyribonucleic acid (DNA) comprises a *double strand* of nucleotides linked together. It is shown unwound in the symbolic representation (left). The DNA molecule takes on a twisted, double-helix shape as shown in the space filling model on the right.

ISBN: 978-1-927173-73-2

Related activities: *DNA Molecules*
Weblinks: *DNA Anatomy*

Formation of a nucleotide

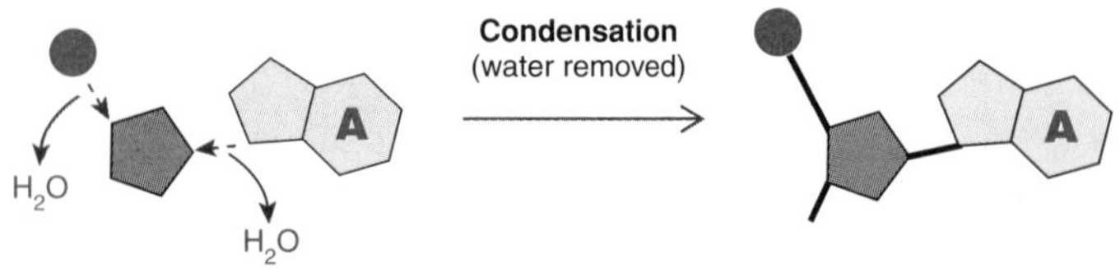

H_2O
H_2O
A
Condensation
(water removed)
A

A nucleotide is formed when phosphoric acid and a base are chemically bonded to a sugar molecule. In both cases, water is given off, and they are therefore condensation reactions. In the reverse reaction, a nucleotide is broken apart by the addition of water **(hydrolysis)**.

Formation of a dinucleotide

Two nucleotides are linked together by a condensation reaction between the phosphate of one nucleotide and the sugar of another.

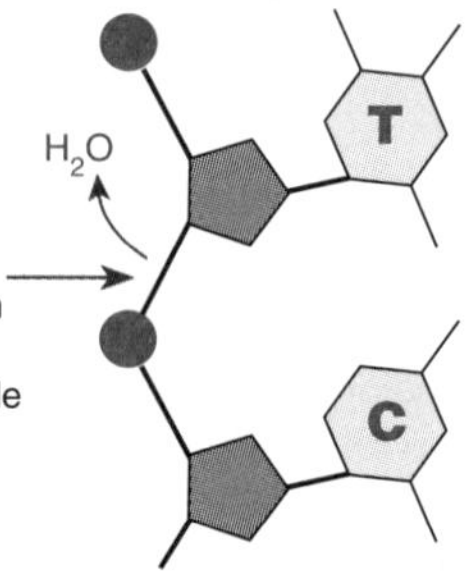

H_2O
T
C

Double-Stranded DNA

The double-helix structure of DNA is like a ladder twisted into a corkscrew shape around its longitudinal axis. It is 'unwound' here to show the relationships between the bases.

- The DNA backbone is made up from alternating phosphate and sugar molecules, giving the DNA molecule an asymmetrical structure.
- The asymmetrical structure gives a DNA strand a **direction**. Each strand runs in the opposite direction to the other.
- The ends of a DNA strand are labeled the 5' (five prime) and 3' (three prime) ends. The **5'** end has a terminal phosphate group (off carbon 5), the **3'** end has a terminal hydroxyl group (off carbon 3).
- The way the pairs of bases come together to form hydrogen bonds is determined by the number of bonds they can form and the configuration of the bases.

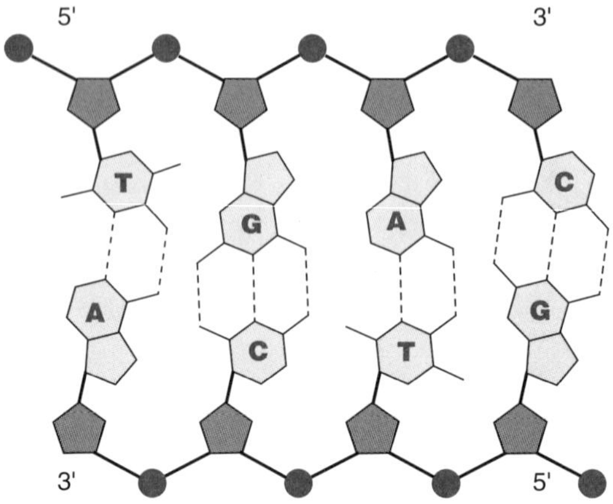

5'
3'
T
G
A
C
A
C
G
T
3'
5'

1. The diagram above depicts a double-stranded DNA molecule. Label the following parts on the diagram:
   (a) **Sugar** (deoxyribose)
   (b) **Phosphate**
   (c) **Hydrogen bonds** (between bases)
   (d) **Purine** bases
   (e) **Pyrimidine** bases

2. (a) Explain the **base-pairing rule** that applies in double-stranded DNA: ____________________

   ____

   (b) How is the base-pairing rule for mRNA different? ____________________

   (c) What is the purpose of the hydrogen bonds in double-stranded DNA? ____________________

   ____

3. Describe the functional role of nucleotides: ____________________

   ____

4. (a) Why do the DNA strands have an asymmetrical structure? ____________________

   ____

   (b) What are the differences between the 5' and 3' ends of a DNA strand? ____________________

   ____

5. Complete the following table summarizing the differences between DNA and RNA molecules:

	DNA	**RNA**
Sugar present		
Bases present		
Number of strands		
Relative length		

Amino Acids

Amino acids are the basic units from which proteins are made. Plants can manufacture all the amino acids they require from simpler molecules, but animals must obtain a certain number of ready-made amino acids (called **essential amino acids**) from their diet. Which amino acids are essential varies from species to species, as different metabolisms are able to synthesize different substances. The distinction between essential and non-essential amino acids is somewhat unclear though, as some amino acids can be produced from others and some are interconvertible by the urea cycle. Amino acids can combine to form peptide chains in a **condensation reaction**. The reverse reaction, which breaks up peptide chains, uses water and is called **hydrolysis**.

Structure of Amino Acids

There are over 150 amino acids found in cells, but only 20 occur commonly in proteins. The remaining, non-protein amino acids have roles as intermediates in metabolic reactions, or as neurotransmitters and hormones. All amino acids have a common structure (see right). The only difference between the different types lies with the 'R' group in the general formula. This group is variable, which means that it is different in each kind of amino acid.

General structure of an amino acid

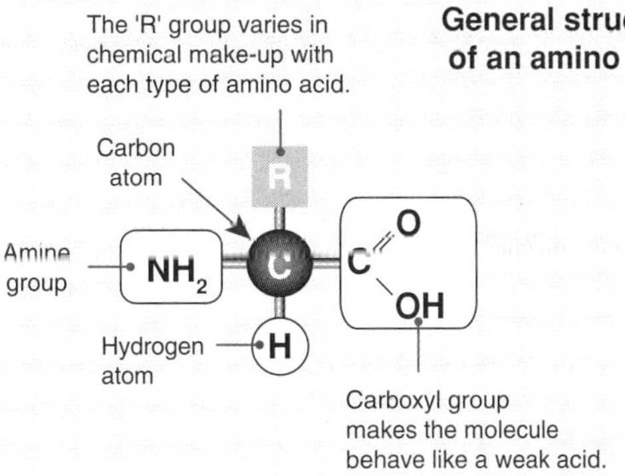

The 'R' group varies in chemical make-up with each type of amino acid.
Carbon atom
R
Amine group
NH2
C
C
O
OH
Hydrogen atom
H
Carboxyl group makes the molecule behave like a weak acid.

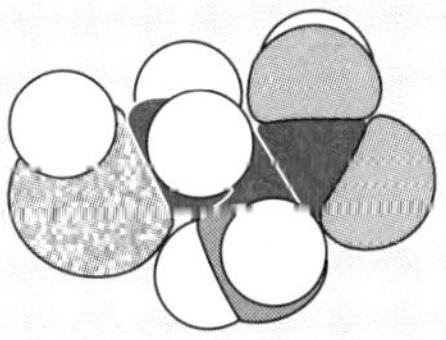

Example of an amino acid shown as a space filling model: cysteine.

Properties of Amino Acids

Three examples of amino acids with different chemical properties are shown right, with their specific 'R' groups outlined. The 'R' groups can have quite diverse chemical properties.

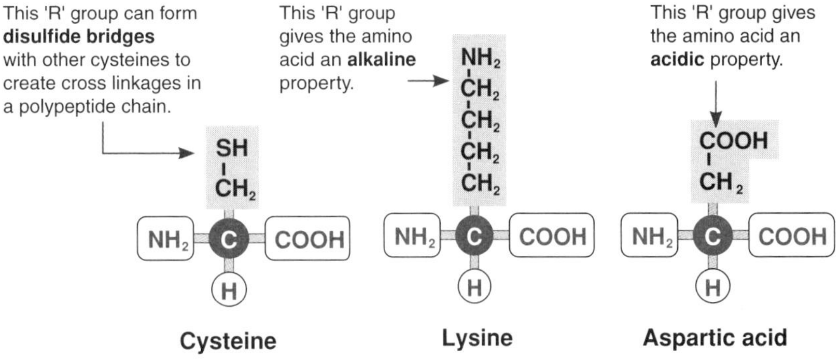

This 'R' group can form **disulfide bridges** with other cysteines to create cross linkages in a polypeptide chain.
This 'R' group gives the amino acid an **alkaline** property.
This 'R' group gives the amino acid an **acidic** property.
SH
CH2
NH2
CH2
CH2
CH2
CH2
COOH
CH2
NH2
C
COOH
H
Cysteine
Lysine
Aspartic acid

A polypeptide chain

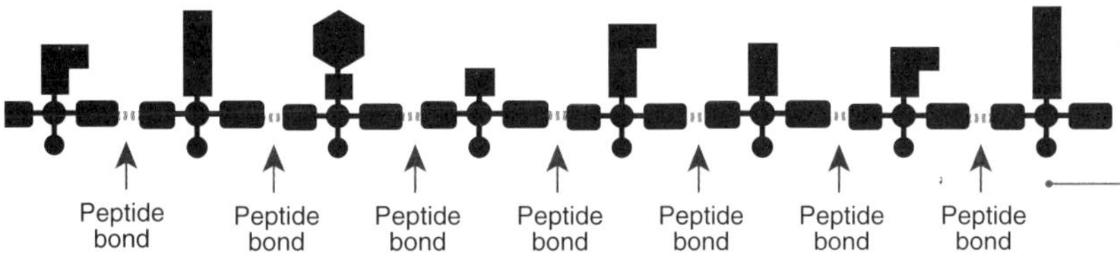

Peptide bond
Peptide bond
Peptide bond
Peptide bond
Peptide bond
Peptide bond
Peptide bond

The order of amino acids in a protein is determined by the order of nucleotides in DNA and mRNA.

Peptide bonds link amino acids together in long polymers called polypeptide chains.

The amino acids are linked together by peptide bonds to form long chains of up to several hundred amino acids (called polypeptide chains). These chains may be functional units (complete by themselves) or they may need to be joined to other polypeptide chains before they can carry out their function. In humans, not all amino acids can be manufactured by our body: ten must be taken in with our diet (eight in adults). These are the 'essential amino acids'. They are indicated by the symbol ♦ on the right. Those indicated with as asterisk (*) are also required by infants.

Amino acids occurring in proteins

Alanine	Glutamine	Leucine ♦	Serine
Arginine *	Glutamic acid	Lysine ♦	Threonine ♦
Asparagine	Glycine	Methionine ♦	Tryptophan ♦
Aspartic acid	Histidine *	Phenylalanine ♦	Tyrosine
Cysteine	Isoleucine ♦	Proline	Valine ♦

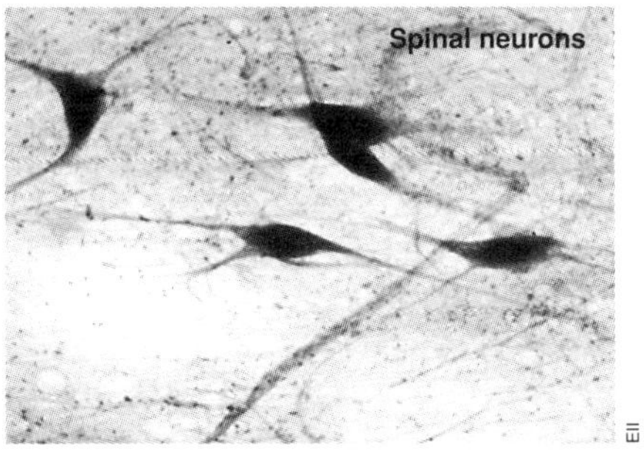

Spinal neurons
EII

Several amino acids act as neurotransmitters in the central nervous system. Glutamic acid and GABA (gamma amino butyric acid) are the most common neurotransmitters in the brain. Others, such as glycine, are restricted to the spinal cord.

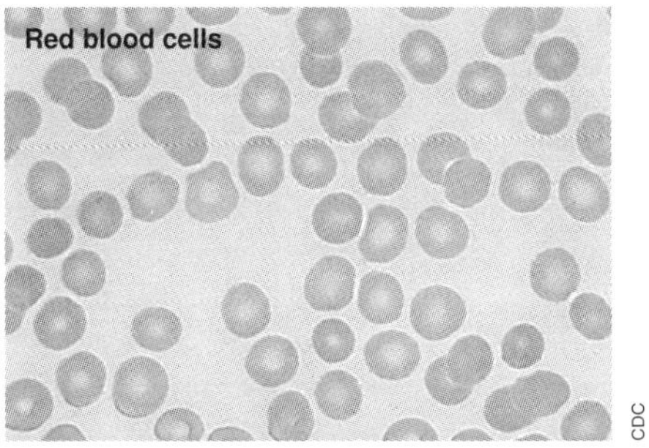

Red blood cells
CDC

Amino acids tend to stabilize the pH of solutions in which they are present (e.g. blood and tissue fluid) because they will remove excess H^+ or OH^- ions. They retain this buffer capacity even when incorporated into peptides and proteins.

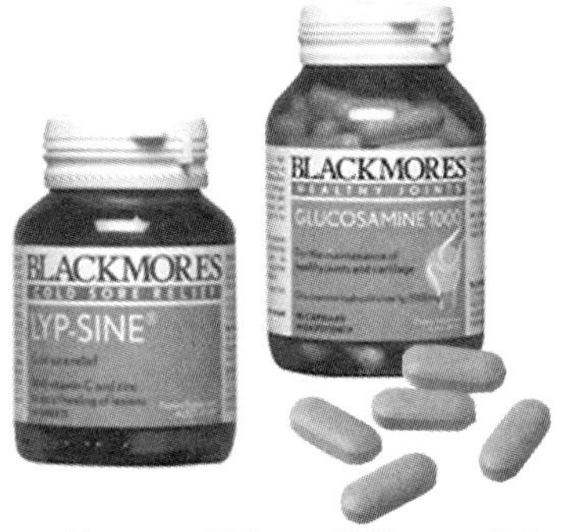

BLACKMORES
LYP-SINE
BLACKMORES
GLUCOSAMINE 1000

Amino acids are widely available as dietary supplements for specific purposes. Lysine is sold as relief for herpes infections and glucosamine supplements are used for alleviating the symptoms of arthritis and other joint disorders.

ISBN: 978-1-927173-73-2

Related activities: Proteins
Weblinks: Amino Acids and Peptide Bond Formation

Condensation and Hydrolysis Reactions

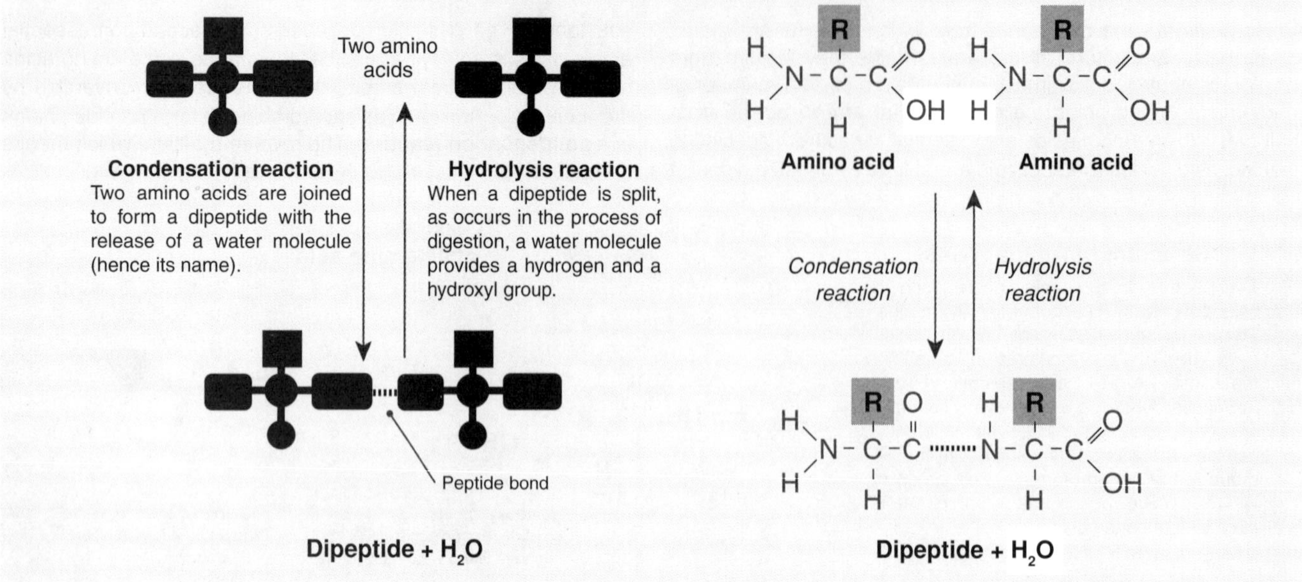
Two amino acids
Condensation reaction
Two amino acids are joined to form a dipeptide with the release of a water molecule (hence its name).
Hydrolysis reaction
When a dipeptide is split, as occurs in the process of digestion, a water molecule provides a hydrogen and a hydroxyl group.
Peptide bond
Dipeptide + H_2O
Amino acid
Amino acid
Condensation reaction
Hydrolysis reaction
Dipeptide + H_2O

1. Discuss the biological roles of amino acids: ______________________________

____

____

____

____

____

____

2. Describe what makes each of the 20 amino acids found in proteins unique: ______________________________

____

____

3. Describe the process that determines the sequence of amino acids in a polypeptide chain: ______________________________

____

____

4. Explain how the chemistry of amino acids enables them to act as buffers in biological tissues: ______________________________

____

____

5. Giving examples, explain what is meant by an **essential amino acid**: ______________________________

____

____

6. Describe the processes by which amino acids are joined together and broken down: ______________________________

____

____

____

____

____

ISBN: 978-1-927173-73-2

Proteins

Proteins are large, complex **macromolecules**, built up from a linear sequence of repeating units called **amino acids**. Proteins are molecules of central importance in the chemistry of life. They account for more than 50% of the dry weight of most cells, and they are important in virtually every cellular process. The folding of a protein into its functional form creates a three dimensional arrangement of the active 'R' groups. It is this **tertiary structure** that gives a protein its unique chemical properties. If a protein loses this precise structure (through **denaturation**), it is usually unable to carry out its biological function.

Primary Structure - 1°
(amino acid sequence)

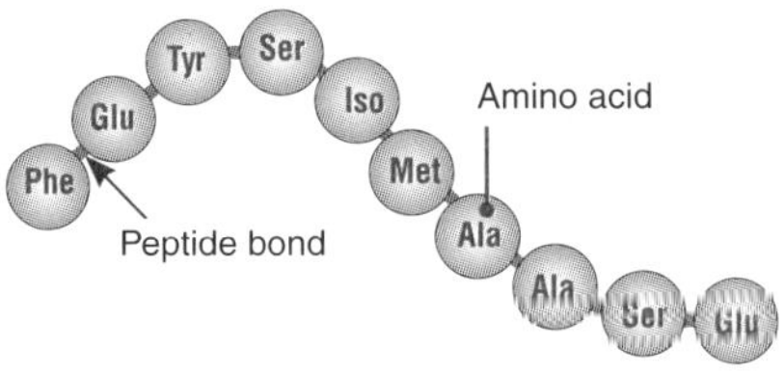
Phe
Glu
Tyr
Ser
Iso
Met
Ala
Ala
Ser
Glu
Amino acid
Peptide bond

Hundreds of amino acids are linked together by peptide bonds to form polypeptide chains. The attractive and repulsive charges on the amino acids determines how the protein is organized, and its biological function.

Secondary Structure - 2°
(α-helix or β-pleated sheet)

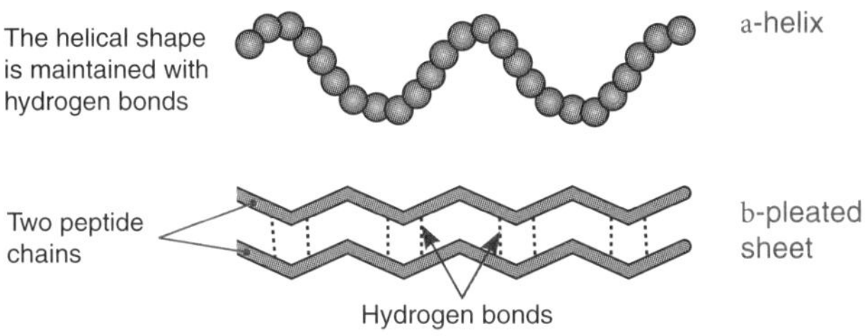
The helical shape is maintained with hydrogen bonds
a-helix
Two peptide chains
b-pleated sheet
Hydrogen bonds

Polypeptides fold into a secondary (2°) structure, usually either a coiled α-**helix** or a β-**pleated sheet**. Secondary structures are maintained with hydrogen bonds between neighboring CO and NH groups.

Tertiary Structure - 3°
(folding of the **2°** structure)

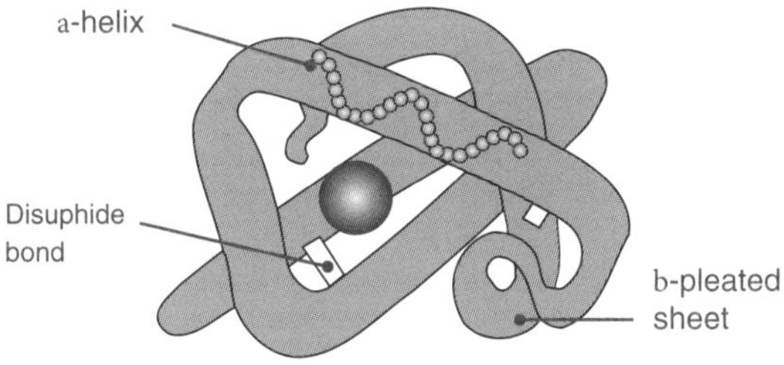
a-helix
Disuphide bond
b-pleated sheet

The tertiary structure of a protein is its three-dimensional structure, formed when the secondary structure folds up. Chemical bonds such as disulfide bridges between cysteine amino acids, ionic bonds, hydrogen bonds, and hydrophobic interactions result in folding of the protein. These bonds can be destroyed by the presence of heavy metals or some solvents, and unfavourable conditions such as pH and temperature.

Quaternary Structure - 4°

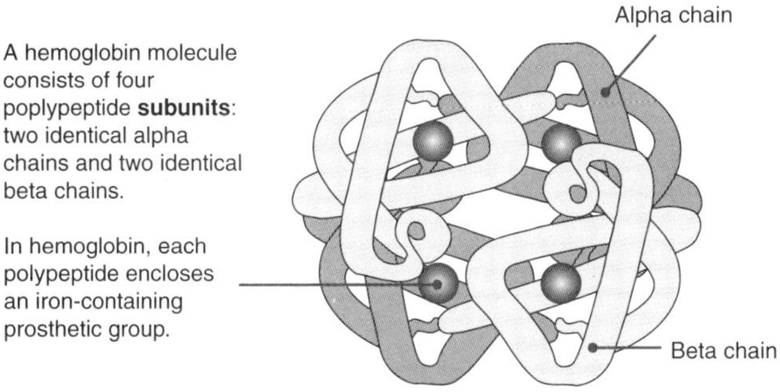
A hemoglobin molecule consists of four poplypeptide **subunits**: two identical alpha chains and two identical beta chains.
In hemoglobin, each polypeptide encloses an iron-containing prosthetic group.
Alpha chain
Beta chain

Many complex proteins exist as groups of polypeptide chains. The arrangement of the polypeptide chains into a functional protein is termed the quaternary structure. The example (above) shows hemoglobin.

1. Describe briefly the four main structures of a protein, and name any key factors contributing to the formation of each structure:

   (a) Primary structure: ______________________

   (b) Secondary structure: ______________________

   (c) Tertiary structure: ______________________

   (d) Quaternary structure: ______________________

2. How are proteins built up into a functional structure?

____

ISBN: 978-1-927173-73-2

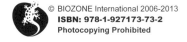

Related activities: *Protein Structure and Function*
Weblinks: *Amino Acids and Proteins*

Protein Structure and Function

Proteins can be classified according to their structure or their function. **Globular proteins** are roughly spherical and soluble in water. Many globular proteins are **enzymes** and have a **catalytic** role in regulating metabolic pathways. **Fibrous proteins** have an elongated structure and are not water soluble. They are often made up of repeating units and provide stiffness and rigidity to the more fluid components of cells and tissues. They have important **structural** and **contractile** roles.

Globular Proteins

Properties
- Easily water soluble
- Tertiary structure critical to function
- Polypeptide chains folded into a spherical shape

Function
- Catalytic *e.g. enzymes*
- Regulatory *e.g. hormones such as insulin*
- Transport *e.g. hemoglobin*
- Protective *e.g. antibodies*

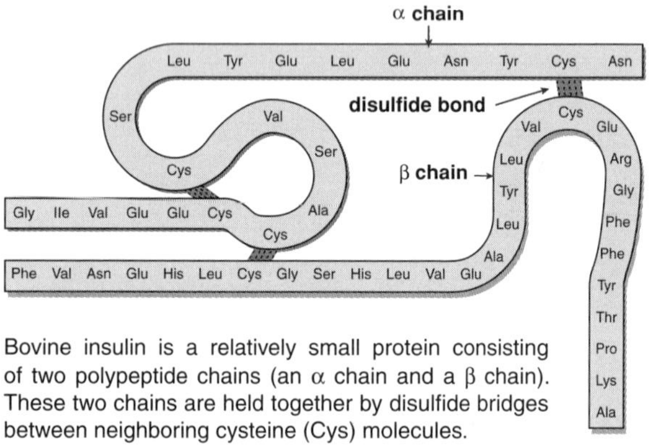
α chain
Leu Tyr Glu Leu Glu Asn Tyr Cys Asn
disulfide bond
Ser Val Ser Cys Ala Cys
Gly Ile Val Glu Glu Cys
β chain
Val Cys Glu Leu Tyr Leu Arg Gly Phe Phe Tyr Thr Pro Lys Ala
Phe Val Asn Glu His Leu Cys Gly Ser His Leu Val Glu Ala

Bovine insulin is a relatively small protein consisting of two polypeptide chains (an α chain and a β chain). These two chains are held together by disulfide bridges between neighboring cysteine (Cys) molecules.

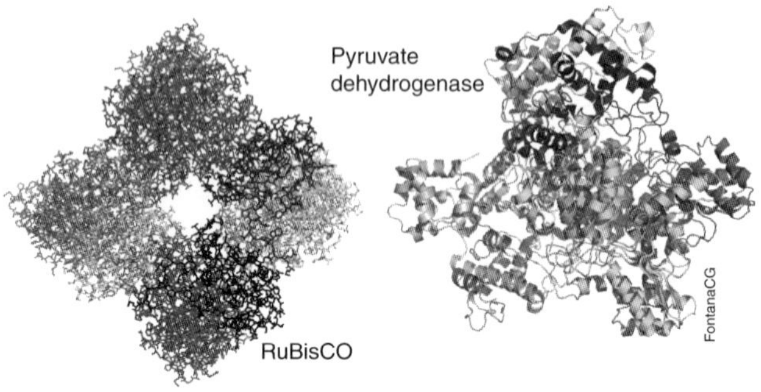
Pyruvate dehydrogenase
RuBisCO
FontanaCG

Pyruvate dehydrogenase is an enzyme involved in the conversion of pyruvate to acetyl-CoA, and so links the glycolysis pathway to the Krebs cycle. The enzyme **RuBisCo** is found in green plants and catalyzes the first step of carbon fixation in the Calvin cycle. RuBisCO is the most abundant protein in the world.

Fibrous Proteins

Properties
- Water insoluble
- Very tough physically; may be supple or stretchy
- Parallel polypeptide chains in long fibers or sheets

Function
- Structural role in cells and organisms e.g. *collagen found in connective tissue, cartilage, bones, tendons, and blood vessel walls.*
- Contractile e.g. *myosin, actin*

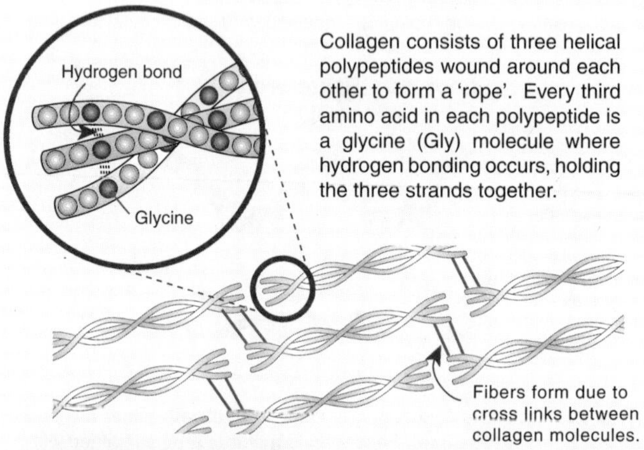
Hydrogen bond
Glycine
Fibers form due to cross links between collagen molecules.

Collagen consists of three helical polypeptides wound around each other to form a 'rope'. Every third amino acid in each polypeptide is a glycine (Gly) molecule where hydrogen bonding occurs, holding the three strands together.

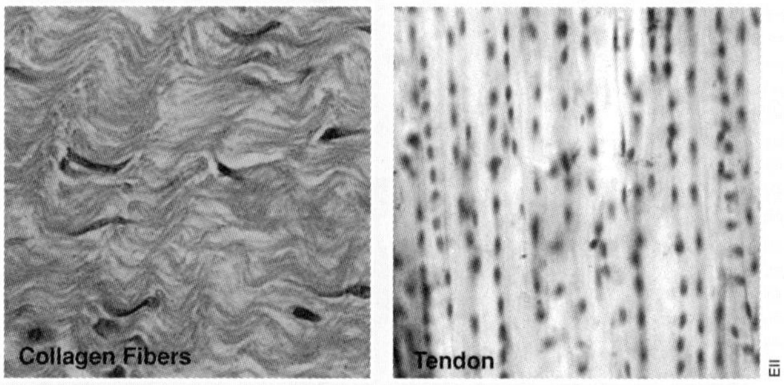
Collagen Fibers
Tendon
EII

Collagen is the main component of connective tissue, and is mostly found in fibrous tissues (e.g. tendons, ligaments, and skin). **Tendons** connect muscle to bone and tendons are composed of closely packed collagen fibers lined parallel to each other.

1. How are proteins involved in the following roles? Give examples to help illustrate your answer:

   (a) Structural tissues of the body: ______________________________

   ____

   ____

   (b) Catalyzing metabolic reactions in cells: ______________________________

   ____

   ____

2. How does the shape of a fibrous protein relate to its functional role? ______________________________

   ____

3. How does the shape of a catalytic protein (enzyme) relate to its functional role? ______________________________

   ____

ISBN: 978-1-927173-73-2

Modification of Proteins

Proteins may be modified after they have been produced by the ribosomes. This is termed **post translational modification**. Two important modifications are the addition of carbohydrates or lipids to the protein. **Glycoproteins** are formed by adding carbohydrates to proteins once they pass into the interior of rough endoplasmic reticulum. The carbohydrates may help position and orientate the glycoproteins in membranes, they may help guide a protein to its final destination, and they have roles in intercellular recognition and cell signaling. Other proteins may have fatty acids added to them to form **lipoproteins**. These modified proteins transport lipids in the plasma between various organs in the body (e.g. gut, liver, and adipose tissue). Other common post-translational modifications include degradation, cleavage, and phosphorylation (below).

Cleaving: Polypeptide chains may be cleaved to give smaller chains, which then fold or join to give the functional protein. An example is human insulin which is transcribed as one long polypeptide chain before being cleaved in two places to form two shorter chains that form the functional protein.

Glycosylation (adding carbohydrate groups): This is used to add an ID tag to the protein that will allow the cell to recognize its use and where it is to be transported (2a). The resulting glycoprotein may be used in the cell membrane or secreted. The carbohydrate tag may help position the glycoprotein within the membrane (2b).

Phosphorylation (the addition of phosphate groups). This may contribute to the protein's three dimensional structure, or help with cell signalling.

Lipid attachment: Proteins may have lipids attached to them which anchor the protein to the plasma membrane.

Degradation: Some polypeptide chains may be tagged for degradation when they are no longer useful and their amino acids reused in the formation of other proteins.

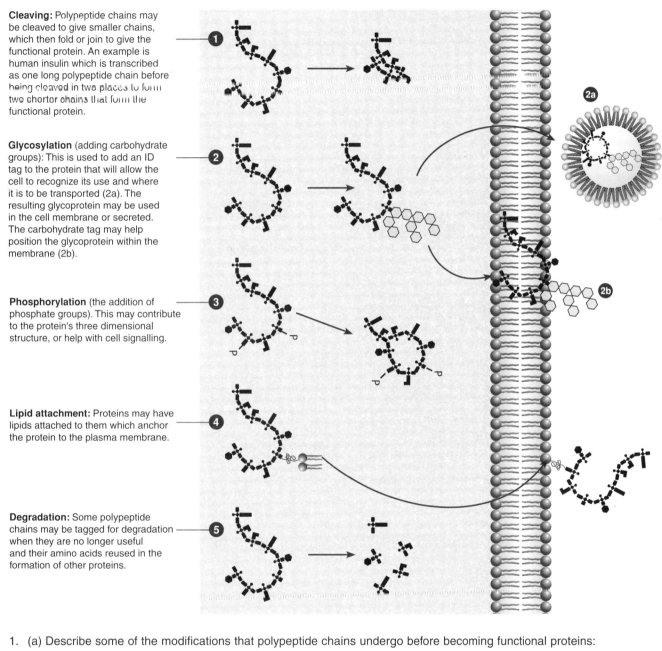

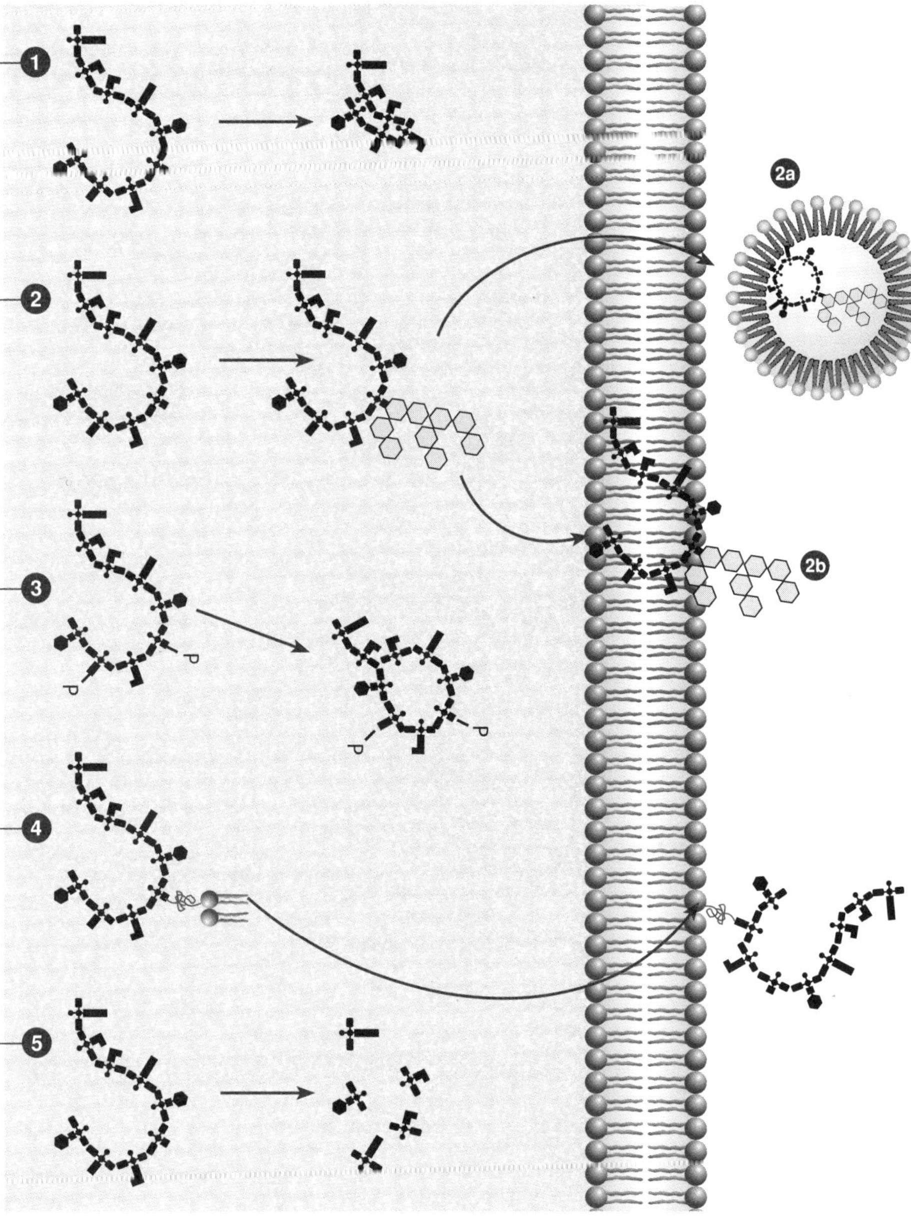

1
2
2a
2b
3
P
P
P
P
4
5

1. (a) Describe some of the modifications that polypeptide chains undergo before becoming functional proteins:

____

____

____

(b) Explain why these changes are necessary: ____

____

____

2. Explain why the orientation of a protein in the plasma membrane might be important: ____

____

ISBN: 978-1-927173-73-2

Biochemical Tests

Biochemical tests are used to detect molecules such as lipids, proteins, and carbohydrates. For tests where the presence of a substance is indicated by a color change, **colorimetric analysis** of a known dilution series (e.g. five prepared dilutions of glucose) can be used to produce a **calibration curve**. This curve can then be used to quantify that substance in samples of unknown concentration. Simple biochemical tests are useful, but they are crude. To analyze a mix of substances, a technique such as chromatography is required. For example, a positive Benedict's test indicates the presence of reducing sugar(s), but chromatography will distinguish different sugars (e.g. fructose and glucose).

Simple Food Tests

Proteins: The Biuret Test

Reagent: Biuret solution.
Procedure: A sample is added to biuret solution and gently heated.
Positive result: Solution turns from blue to lilac.

Starch: The Iodine Test

Reagent: Iodine.
Procedure: Iodine solution is added to the sample.
Positive result: Blue-black staining occurs.

Lipids: The Emulsion Test

Reagent: Ethanol.
Procedure: The sample is shaken with ethanol. After settling, the liquid portion is distilled and mixed with water.
Positive result: The solution turns into a cloudy-white emulsion of suspended lipid molecules.

Sugars: The Benedict's Test

Reagent: Benedict's solution.
Procedure: Non-reducing sugars: The sample is boiled with dilute hydrochloric acid (acid hydrolysis), then cooled and neutralised. A test for reducing sugars is then performed.
Reducing sugar: Benedict's solution is added, and the sample is placed in a water bath.
Positive result: Solution turns from blue to orange to red-brown.

Colorimetric Analysis of Glucose

Prepare glucose standards

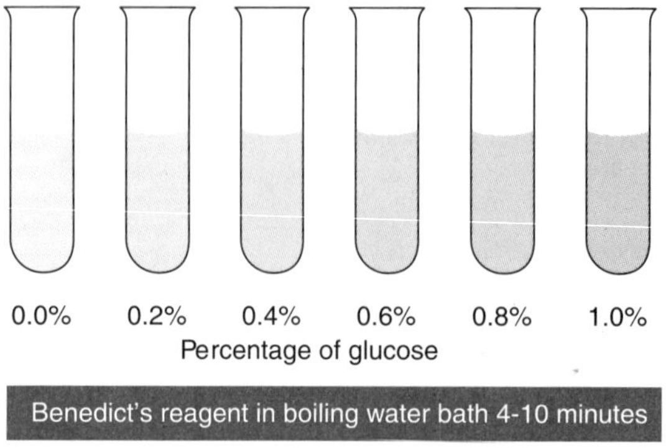
0.0%
0.2%
0.4%
0.6%
0.8%
1.0%
Percentage of glucose
Benedict's reagent in boiling water bath 4-10 minutes

Produce the calibration curve

Cool and filter samples as required. Using a red filter, measure the absorbance (at 735 nm) for each of the known dilutions and use these values to produce a calibration curve for glucose.

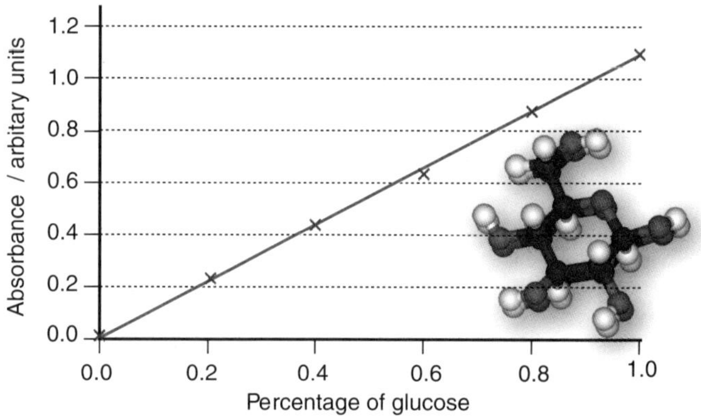
Absorbance / arbitary units
1.2
1.0
0.8
0.6
0.4
0.2
0.0
0.0
0.2
0.4
0.6
0.8
1.0
Percentage of glucose

1. Explain why lipids must be mixed in ethanol before they will form an emulsion in water:

2. (a) Explain how you could quantify the amount of glucose in a range of commercially available glucose drinks:

   (b) Explain how you would proceed if the absorbance values you obtained for most of your 'unknowns' were outside the range of your calibration curve:

3. Explain the purpose of acid hydrolysis of a non-reducing sugar before testing with Benedict's reagent:

4. Explain why the emulsion of lipids, ethanol, and water appears cloudy:

ISBN: 978-1-927173-73-2

Paper Chromatography

There are a number of simple biochemical tests used to detect the presence of certain molecules, but they provide limited information. **Chromatography** is a more useful technique because it can be used to separate a mixture of molecules and to distinguish between specific molecules (e.g. between fructose or glucose). It is useful for small samples and is widely used in the pharmaceutical and food industries for purification and analysis. Chromatography is based on passing a mixture dissolved in a mobile phase (a solvent) through a stationary phase. The stationary phase can separate molecules based on a number of characteristics including size and charge. **Paper chromatography** is a simple technique in which porous paper serves as the stationary phase, and a solvent, either water or ethanol, serves as the mobile phase.

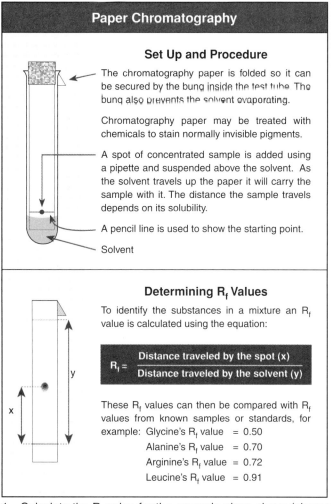

Paper Chromatography

Set Up and Procedure

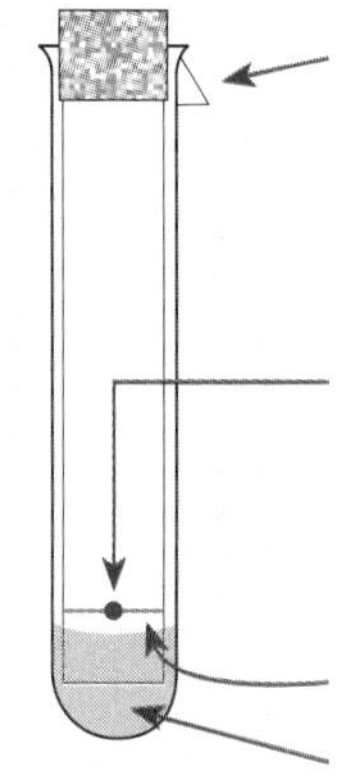

The chromatography paper is folded so it can be secured by the bung inside the test tube. The bung also prevents the solvent evaporating.

Chromatography paper may be treated with chemicals to stain normally invisible pigments.

A spot of concentrated sample is added using a pipette and suspended above the solvent. As the solvent travels up the paper it will carry the sample with it. The distance the sample travels depends on its solubility.

A pencil line is used to show the starting point.

Solvent

Determining R_f Values

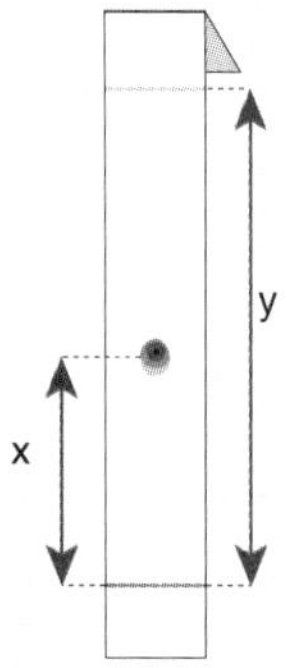

y
x

To identify the substances in a mixture an R_f value is calculated using the equation:

$$R_f = \frac{\text{Distance traveled by the spot (x)}}{\text{Distance traveled by the solvent (y)}}$$

These R_f values can then be compared with R_f values from known samples or standards, for example:

- Glycine's R_f value = 0.50
- Alanine's R_f value = 0.70
- Arginine's R_f value = 0.72
- Leucine's R_f value = 0.91

Separation of Photosynthetic Pigments

The four primary pigments of green plants can easily be separated and identified using paper chromatography. The pigments from the leaves are extracted with acetone before being separated. During paper chromatography the pigments separate according to differences in their relative solubilities. Two major classes of pigments are detected: the two greenish chlorophyll pigments and two yellowish carotenoid pigments.

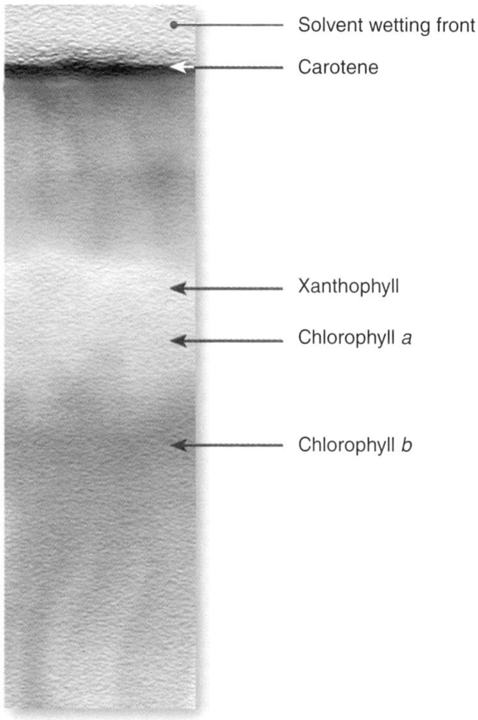

Solvent wetting front
Carotene
Xanthophyll
Chlorophyll a
Chlorophyll b

1. Calculate the R_f value for the example given above (show your working): ______

2. Why is the R_f value of a substance always less than 1? ______

3. When is it appropriate to use chromatography instead of a simple biochemical test? ______

4. Predict what would happen if a sample was immersed in the chromatography solvent, instead of suspended above it: ______

5. With reference to their R_f values, rank the four amino acids (listed above) in terms of their solubility: ______

6. Why must lipids be mixed in ethanol before they will form an emulsion in water? ______

ISBN: 978-1-927173-73-2

Enzymes

Most **enzymes** are proteins. They are capable of catalyzing (speeding up) biochemical reactions and are therefore called biological **catalysts**. Enzymes act on one or more compounds (called the **substrate**). They may break down a single substrate molecule into simpler substances, or join two or more substrate molecules together. The enzyme itself is unchanged in the reaction; its presence merely allows the reaction to take place more rapidly. The part of the enzyme into which the substrate binds and undergoes the reaction is the **active site**. It is a function of the polypeptide's complex tertiary structure.

Enzyme Structure

The model on the right illustrates the enzyme *Ribonuclease S*, which breaks up RNA molecules. It is a typical enzyme, being a globular protein and composed of up to several hundred atoms. The darkly shaded areas are part of the **active site** and make up the **cleft**; the region into which the substrate molecule(s) are drawn.

The correct positioning of these sites is critical for the catalytic reaction to occur. The substrate (RNA in this case) is drawn into the cleft by the active sites. By doing so, it puts the substrate molecule under stress, causing the reaction to proceed more readily.

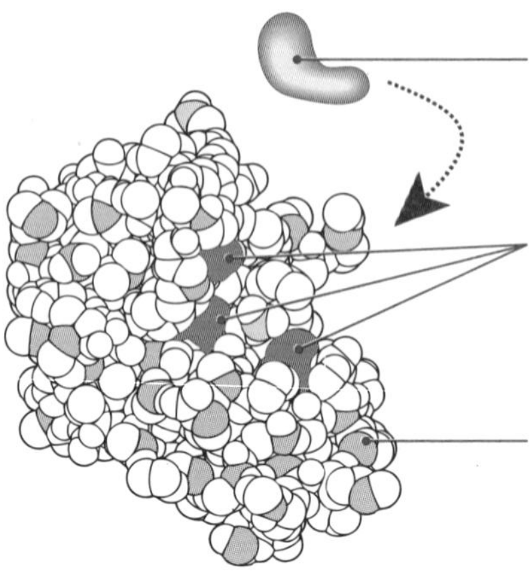
Substrate molecule: Substrate molecules are the chemicals that an enzyme acts on. They are drawn into the cleft of the enzyme.
Active site: These attraction points draw the substrate to the enzyme's surface. Substrate molecule(s) are positioned in a way to promote a reaction: either joining two molecules together or splitting up a larger one (as in this case).
Enzyme molecule: The complexity of the active site is what makes each enzyme so specific for the substrate it acts on.

Source: After *Biochemistry*, (1981) by Lubert Stryer

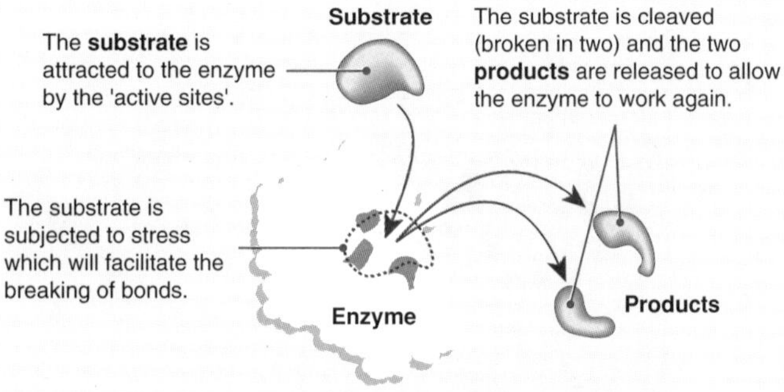
Substrate
The **substrate** is attracted to the enzyme by the 'active sites'.
The substrate is cleaved (broken in two) and the two **products** are released to allow the enzyme to work again.
The substrate is subjected to stress which will facilitate the breaking of bonds.
Enzyme
Products

Catabolic reactions

Some enzymes can cause a single substrate molecule to be drawn into the active site. Chemical bonds are broken, causing the substrate molecule to break apart to become two separate molecules. Catabolic reactions break down complex molecules into simpler ones and involve a net release of energy, so they are called exergonic. **Examples**: *hydrolysis, cellular respiration.*

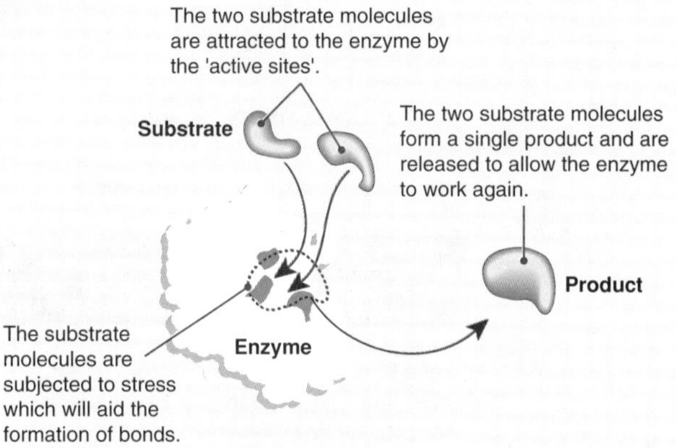
The two substrate molecules are attracted to the enzyme by the 'active sites'.
Substrate
The two substrate molecules form a single product and are released to allow the enzyme to work again.
Product
The substrate molecules are subjected to stress which will aid the formation of bonds.
Enzyme

Anabolic reactions

Some enzymes can cause two substrate molecules to be drawn into the active site. Chemical bonds are formed, causing the two substrate molecules to form bonds and become a single molecule. Anabolic reactions involve a net use of energy (they are endergonic) and build more complex molecules and structures from simpler ones. **Examples:** *protein synthesis*, *photosynthesis.*

1. Explain what is meant by the active site of an enzyme and relate it to the enzyme's tertiary structure:

2. What might happen to an enzyme's activity if a mutation caused a change to the shape of the active site?

3. Distinguish between **catabolism** and **anabolism**, giving an example of each and identifying each reaction as **endergonic** or **exergonic**:

ISBN: 978-1-927173-73-2

How Enzymes Work

Chemical reactions in cells are accompanied by energy changes. The amount of energy released (-ΔG) or taken up (+ΔG) is directly related to the tendency of a reaction to run to completion (for all the reactants to form products). Any reaction, even an exergonic reaction, needs to raise the energy of the substrate to an unstable transition state before the reaction will proceed (below left). The amount of energy required to do this is the **activation energy** (*Ea*). Enzymes work by lowering the *Ea* for any given reaction. They do this by orienting the substrate, or by adding charges or otherwise inducing strain in the substrate so that bonds are destabilized and the substrate is more reactive. Our current 'induced-fit' model of enzyme function is supported by studies of enzyme inhibitors, which show that enzymes are flexible and change shape when interacting with the substrate.

How Enzymes Work

The **lock and key** model proposed earlier last century suggested that the (perfectly fitting) substrate was simply drawn into a matching cleft on the enzyme molecule (below). This model was supported by early X-ray crystallography but has since been modified to recognize the flexibility of enzymes (the **induced fit** model, right).

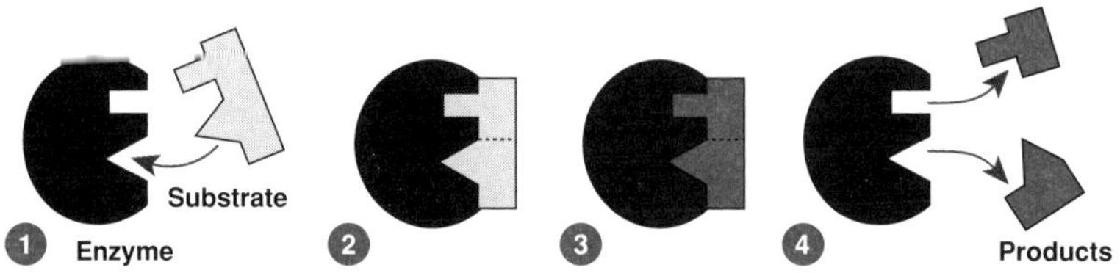
Substrate
1 Enzyme
2
3
4
Products

Lowering the Activation Energy

The presence of an enzyme simply makes it easier for a reaction to take place. All catalysts speed up reactions by influencing the stability of bonds in the reactants. They may also provide an alternative reaction pathway, thus lowering the activation energy (E_a) needed for a reaction to take place (see the graph below).

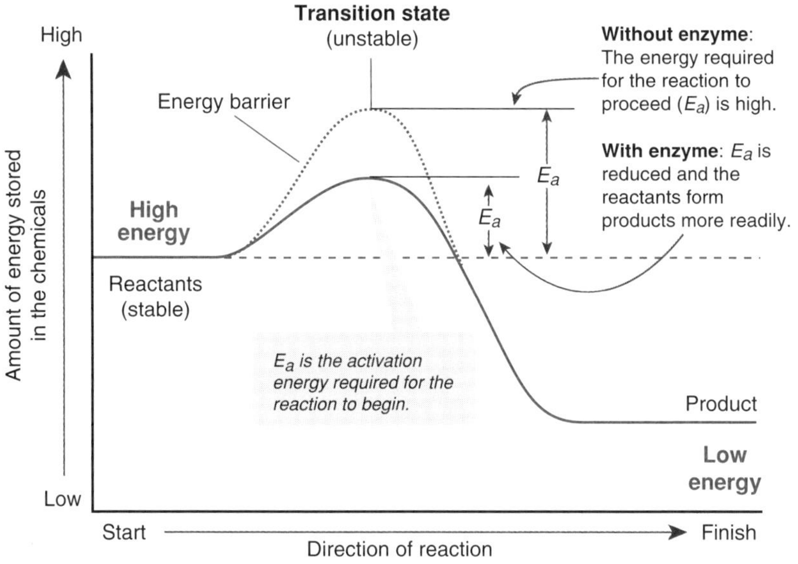
Transition state
(unstable)
High
Energy barrier
Without enzyme: The energy required for the reaction to proceed (E_a) is high.
With enzyme: E_a is reduced and the reactants form products more readily.
E_a
E_a
High energy
Reactants (stable)
Amount of energy stored in the chemicals
E_a is the activation energy required for the reaction to begin.
Product
Low energy
Low
Start
Finish
Direction of reaction

The Current Model: Induced Fit

An enzyme's interaction with its substrate is best regarded as an induced fit (below). The shape of the enzyme changes when the substrate fits into the cleft. The reactants become bound to the enzyme by weak chemical bonds. This binding can weaken bonds within the reactants themselves, allowing the reaction to proceed more readily.

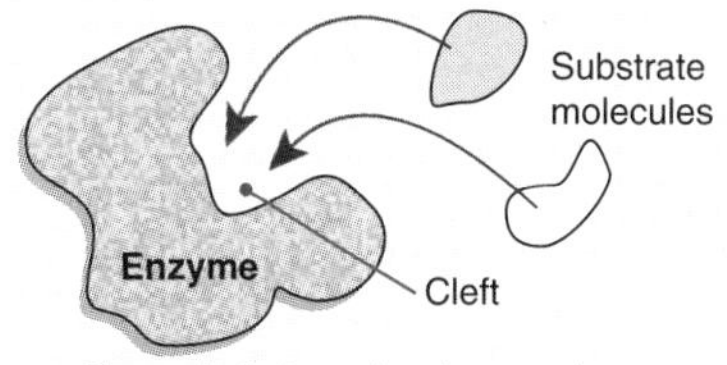
Substrate molecules
Enzyme
Cleft

1 Two substrate molecules are drawn into the cleft of the enzyme.

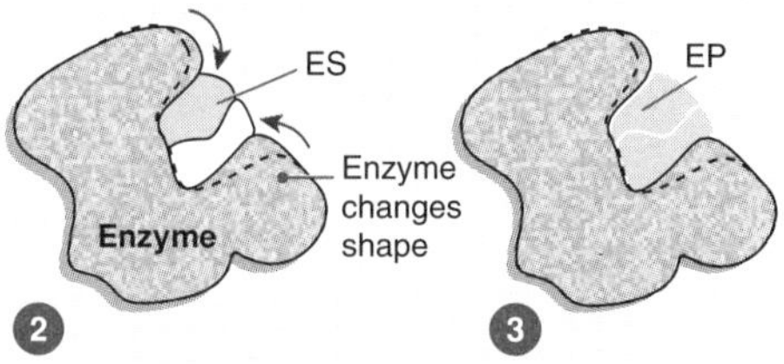
ES
EP
Enzyme changes shape
Enzyme
2
3

The enzyme changes shape as the substrate molecules bind in an enzyme-substrate complex (ES). The enzyme-substrate interaction results in an intermediate enzyme product (EP) complex.

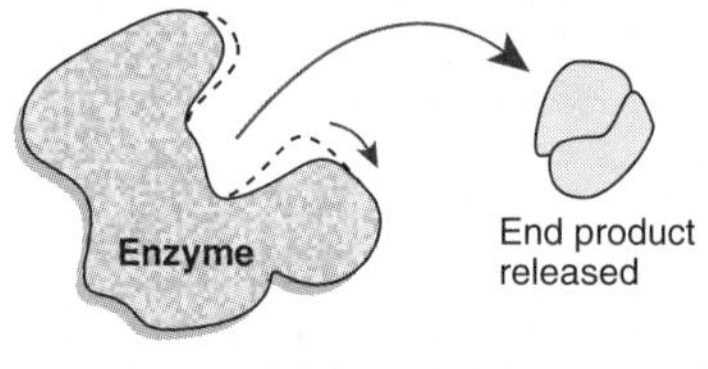
Enzyme
End product released

4 The end product is released and the enzyme returns to its previous shape.

1. Explain how enzymes act as **biological catalysts**: ______________________

2. Describe the key features of the '**lock and key**' model of enzyme action and explain its deficiencies as a working model:

3. Describe the current '**induced fit**' model of enzyme action, explaining how it differs from the lock and key model:

ISBN: 978-1-927173-73-2

Enzyme Reaction Rates

Enzymes often have a narrow range of conditions under which they operate properly. For most of the enzymes associated with plant and animal metabolism, there is little activity at low temperatures. As the temperature increases, so too does the enzyme activity, until the point is reached where the temperature is high enough to damage the enzyme's structure. At this point, the enzyme ceases to function. This phenomenon called **denaturation**. Extremes in pH can also cause denaturation. Poisons often work by denaturing enzymes or occupying the enzyme's active site so that it does not function. In some cases, enzymes will not function without cofactors, such as vitamins or trace elements. In the four graphs below, the *rate of reaction* or *degree of enzyme activity* is plotted against each of four factors that affect enzyme performance. Answer the questions relating to each graph:

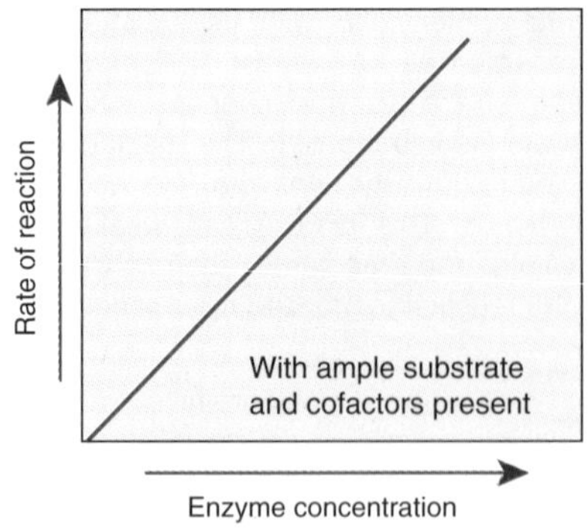
Rate of reaction
With ample substrate and cofactors present
Enzyme concentration

1. **Enzyme concentration**

(a) Describe the change in the rate of reaction when the enzyme concentration is increased (assuming there is plenty of the substrate present):

___

___

(b) Suggest how a cell may vary the amount of enzyme present in a cell:

___

___

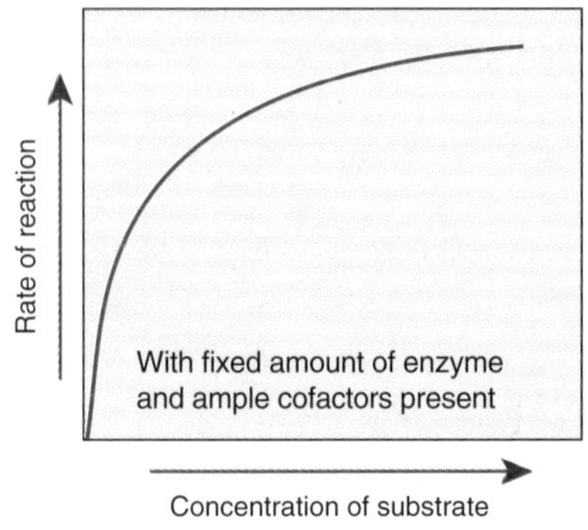
Rate of reaction
With fixed amount of enzyme and ample cofactors present
Concentration of substrate

2. **Substrate concentration**

(a) Describe the change in the rate of reaction when the substrate concentration is **increased** (assuming a fixed amount of enzyme and ample cofactors):

___

___

(b) Explain why the rate changes the way it does: ___

___

___

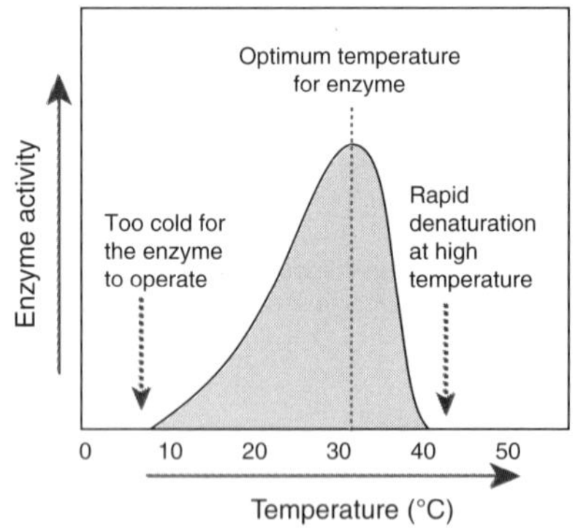
Optimum temperature for enzyme
Enzyme activity
Too cold for the enzyme to operate
Rapid denaturation at high temperature
0
10
20
30
40
50
Temperature (°C)

3. **Temperature**

Higher temperatures speed up all reactions, but few enzymes can tolerate temperatures higher than 50–60°C. The rate at which enzymes are **denatured** (change their shape and become inactive) increases with higher temperatures.

(a) Describe what is meant by an *optimum temperature* for enzyme activity:

___

___

(b) Explain why most enzymes perform poorly at low temperatures:

___

___

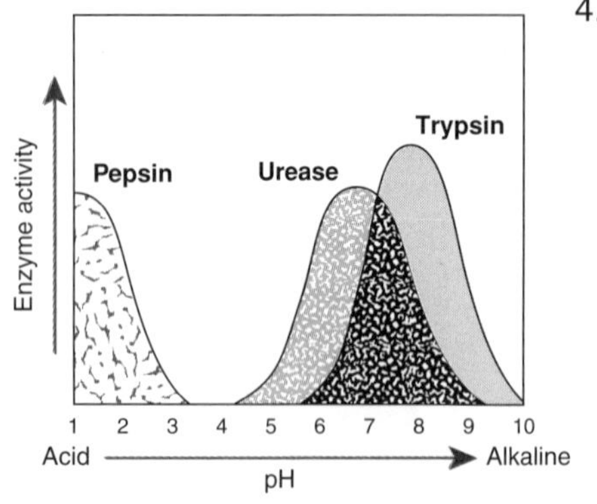
Enzyme activity
Pepsin
Urease
Trypsin
1
2
3
4
5
6
7
8
9
10
Acid
Alkaline
pH

4. **Acidity or Alkalinity (pH)**

Like all proteins, enzymes are **denatured** by *extremes* of **pH** (very acid or alkaline). Within these extremes, most enzymes are still influenced by pH. Each enzyme has a preferred pH range for optimum activity.

(a) State the optimum pH for each of the enzymes:

Pepsin: ___ Trypsin: ___ Urease: ___

(b) Pepsin acts on proteins in the stomach. Explain how its optimum pH is suited to its working environment:

___

___

ISBN: 978-1-927173-73-2

Enzyme Cofactors and Inhibitors

Nearly all enzymes are made of protein, although RNA has been demonstrated to have enzymatic properties. Some enzymes (e.g. pepsin) consist of only protein. Other enzymes require the addition of extra non-protein components to complete their catalytic properties. In these cases, the protein portion is called the **apoenzyme**, and the additional chemical component is called a **cofactor**. Neither one has catalytic activity on its own. Cofactors may be organic molecules (e.g. vitamin C) or inorganic ions (e.g. Ca^{2+}, Zn^{2+}). They may be tightly or loosely bound to the enzyme. Permanently bound cofactors are called **prosthetic groups**, whereas temporarily attached molecules, which detach after a reaction are called **coenzymes**. Some cofactors include both an organic and a non-organic component. Examples include the heme prosthetic groups, which consist of an iron atom in the centre of a porphyrin ring.

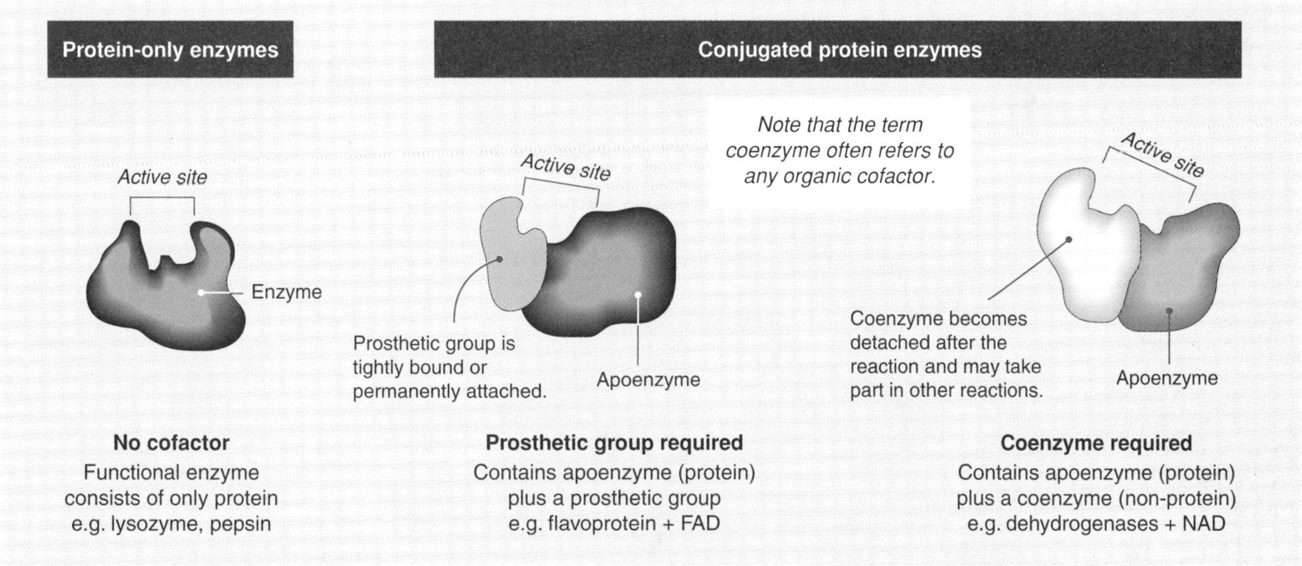

Protein-only enzymes
Conjugated protein enzymes
Note that the term coenzyme often refers to any organic cofactor.
Active site
Enzyme
Active site
Prosthetic group is tightly bound or permanently attached.
Apoenzyme
Active site
Coenzyme becomes detached after the reaction and may take part in other reactions.
Apoenzyme
No cofactor
Functional enzyme consists of only protein e.g. lysozyme, pepsin
Prosthetic group required
Contains apoenzyme (protein) plus a prosthetic group e.g. flavoprotein + FAD
Coenzyme required
Contains apoenzyme (protein) plus a coenzyme (non-protein) e.g. dehydrogenases + NAD

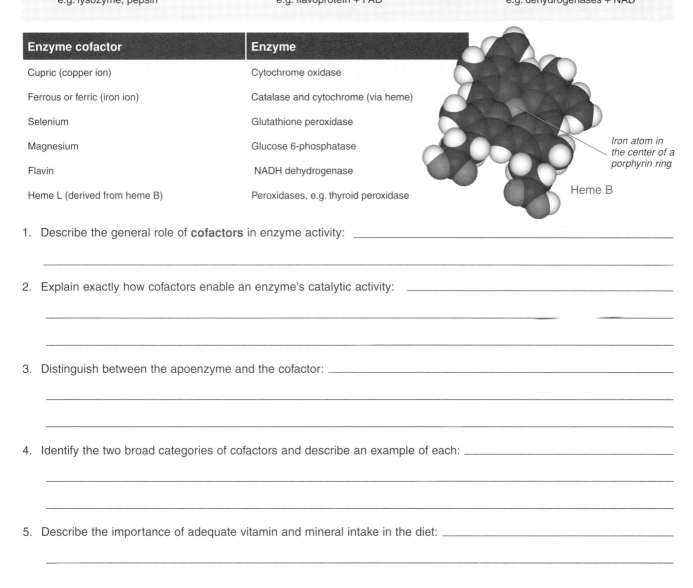

Enzyme cofactor	Enzyme
Cupric (copper ion)	Cytochrome oxidase
Ferrous or ferric (iron ion)	Catalase and cytochrome (via heme)
Selenium	Glutathione peroxidase
Magnesium	Glucose 6-phosphatase
Flavin	NADH dehydrogenase
Heme L (derived from heme B)	Peroxidases, e.g. thyroid peroxidase

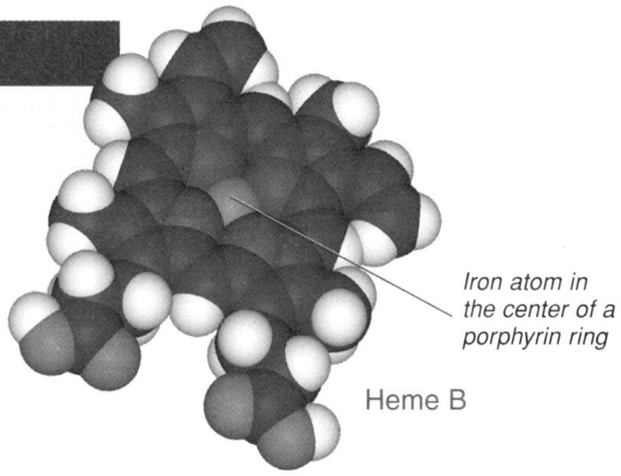

Iron atom in the center of a porphyrin ring
Heme B

1. Describe the general role of **cofactors** in enzyme activity: ____________________

2. Explain exactly how cofactors enable an enzyme's catalytic activity: ____________________

3. Distinguish between the apoenzyme and the cofactor: ____________________

4. Identify the two broad categories of cofactors and describe an example of each: ____________________

5. Describe the importance of adequate vitamin and mineral intake in the diet: ____________________

ISBN: 978-1-927173-73-2

Related activities: *Enzymes, Enzyme Reaction Rates*
Weblinks: *Science in the Box: Enzymes*

Competitive Inhibition

Competitive inhibitors compete with the normal substrate for the enzyme's active site.

A competitive inhibitor occupies the active site only temporarily and so the inhibition is reversible.

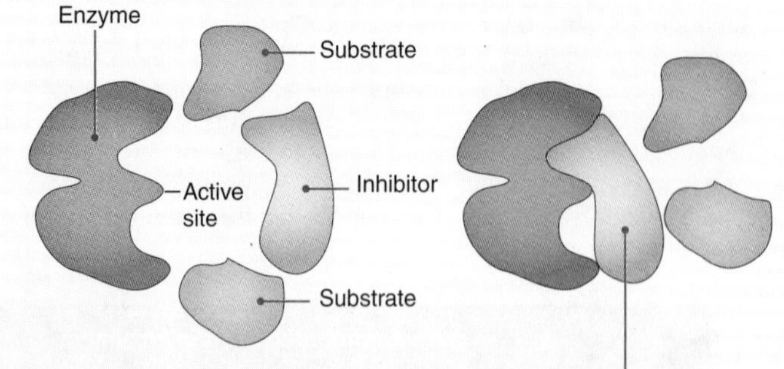
Enzyme
Substrate
Active site
Inhibitor
Substrate

1. Inhibitor is present in the cell (or solution) with the substrate
2. Inhibitor temporarily binds to the active site, blocking it so that the substrate cannot bind

Fig.1 Effect of competitive inhibition on enzyme reaction rate at different substrate concentration

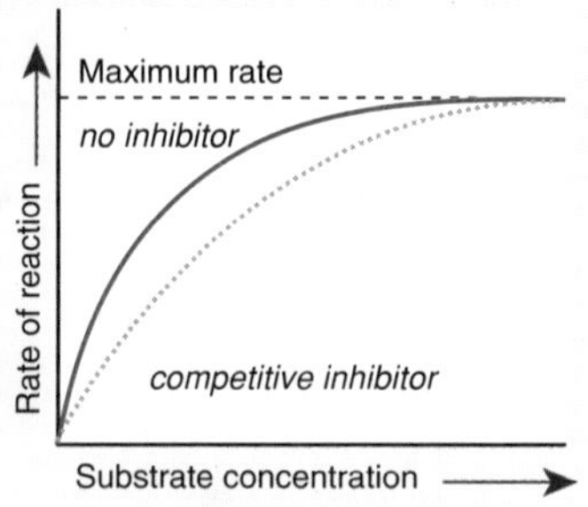
Maximum rate
no inhibitor
competitive inhibitor
Rate of reaction
Substrate concentration

Non-competitive Inhibition

Non-competitive inhibitors bind with the enzyme at a site other than the active site. They inactivate the enzyme by altering its shape.

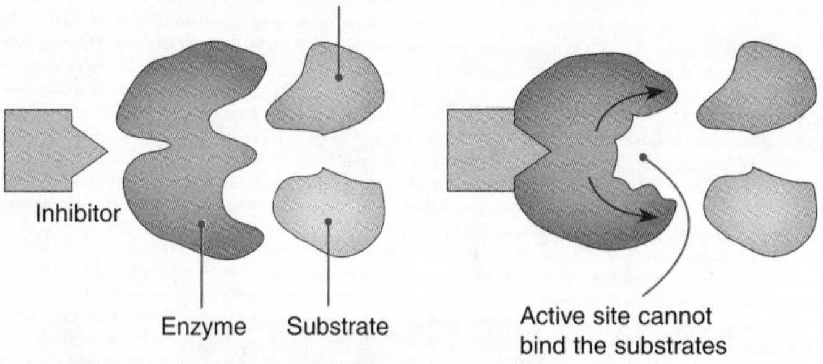
Substrate
Inhibitor
Enzyme
Substrate
Active site cannot bind the substrates

1. Without the inhibitor bound, the enzyme can bind the substrate
2. When the inhibitor binds, the enzyme changes shape.

Fig.2 Effect of non-competitive inhibition on enzyme reaction rate at different substrate concentration

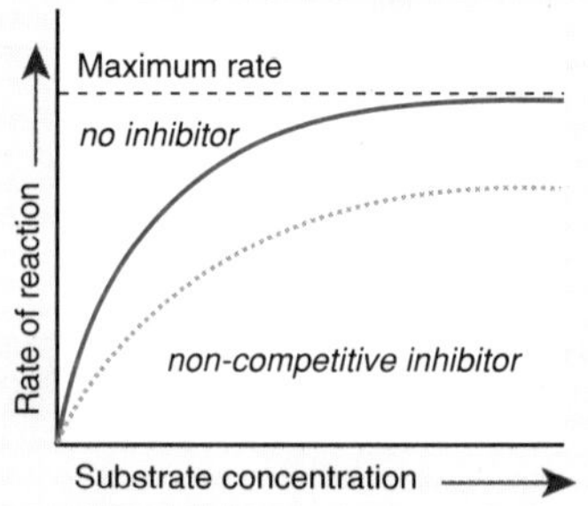
Maximum rate
no inhibitor
non-competitive inhibitor
Rate of reaction
Substrate concentration

Enzymes may be deactivated, temporarily or permanently, by chemicals called enzyme inhibitors. **Competitive inhibitors** compete directly with the substrate for the active site, and their effect can be overcome by increasing the concentration of available substrate. A **non-competitive inhibitor** does not occupy the active site, but distorts it so that the substrate and enzyme can no longer interact.

6. Distinguish between **competitive** and **non-competitive** inhibition: ______________________________

____

____

____

____

7. (a) Compare and contrast the effect of competitive and non-competitive inhibition on the relationship between the substrate concentration and the rate of an enzyme controlled reaction (figs 1 and 2 above):

____

____

____

____

____

(b) How could you distinguish between competitive and non-competitive inhibition in an isolated system?

____

____

____

ISBN: 978-1-927173-73-2

KEY TERMS: Mix and Match

INSTRUCTIONS: Test your vocabulary by matching each term to its correct definition, as identified by its preceding letter code.

activation energy ....
active site ....
amino acids ....
carbohydrate ....
cofactor ....
condensation ....
enzymes ....
fibrous proteins ....
globular proteins ....
hydrolysis ....
inorganic ion ....
induced fit model ....
lipids ....
monomers ....
monosaccharide ....
nucleic acid ....
organic molecule ....
primary structure ....
polymer ....
polysaccharide ....
proteins ....
Rf value ....
secondary structure ....
specificity ....
tertiary structure ....

A Substance required by an enzyme to enable its catalytic function.

B Proteins with a rod or wire-like structure that are important in structure.

C Water soluble proteins with a spherical tertiary structure. They are involved in many cellular functions including as catalysts and in transport and regulation.

D A charged molecule that does not contain carbon.

E The structure of a protein maintained by disulfide bonds and hydrophilic and hydrophobic interactions.

F A class of organic compounds with an oily, greasy, or waxy consistency. Important as energy storage molecules and as components of cellular membranes..

G An information-carrying macromolecule composed of chains of nucleotides.

H These are biological catalysts.

I Organic molecule consisting only of carbon, hydrogen, and oxygen that serves as a structural component in cells and as an energy source.

J A molecule that contains carbon.

K Organic compounds, usually linear polymers, made of amino acids linked together by peptide bonds.

L The term describing how only one enzyme can catalyze a particular reaction.

M The energy that must be overcome in order for a chemical reaction to occur.

N Long carbohydrate molecules of single sugar units joined by glycosidic bonds.

O A general term for a reaction in which water is released.

P The splitting of a molecule into smaller components by addition of a water molecule.

Q The repeating units of a large polymer molecule.

R The sequence of amino acids in a polypeptide.

S The currently accepted model for enzyme function.

T The region of an enzyme responsible for substrate binding and reaction catalysis.

U The building blocks of proteins.

V Large molecule made up from many repeating units.

W The general three-dimensional form of local segments of a protein, e.g. beta pleated sheet or alpha helix, maintained by hydrogen bonding.

X The basic structural unit of a carbohydrate.

Y A measure of the rate of migration of a compound relative to a solvent.

ISBN: 978-1-927173-73-2

Chapter 2

Cell Structure

Key terms

bacteria
cell wall
centrioles
chloroplast
cilia
contractile vacuole
cytoplasm
cytoskeleton
desmosome
electron microscope
endoplasmic reticulum (ER)
eukaryotic cell
flagellum
fungi
gap junction
Golgi apparatus
lysosome
magnification
mitochondrion
nuclear envelope
nuclear pore
nucleolus
nucleus
optical microscope
organelles
plasma membrane
plasmodesmata
prokaryotic cell
Protista
resolution
ribosome
rough ER
SEM
smooth ER
TEM
tight junction
vacuole

Weblinks:

www.thebiozone.com/weblink/Cellbio-3732/

BIOZONE APP:
Student Review Series
Cell Structure

Key concepts

- Cells are the fundamental units of life.
- There are distinguishing differences between the cells of different kingdoms.
- Microscopy can be used to understand cellular structure.
- Centrifugation is used to separate cell components.
- Multicellular organisms are organized according to a hierarchy of structural levels. New properties emerge with each level of organization.

Learning Objectives

☐ 1. Use the **KEY TERMS** to compile a glossary for this topic.

Features of Cells

pages 33-37

☐ 2. Describe the features of the **cell theory** and outline its development.

☐ 3. Explain why viruses do not fulfil the criteria for being living cells.

☐ 4. Compare and contrast features of different cell types including **eukaryotic** vs **prokaryotic cells**, and protistan, fungal, plant, and animal cells.

☐ 5. Describe the range of cell sizes. Express cell sizes in different units of measurement (mm, µm, nm).

Cell Structure and Microscopy

pages 38-57

☐ 6. Describe the structure and basic principles of **light** (optical) **microscopes**.

☐ 7. Distinguish between the structure and use of **compound** and **dissecting** (stereo) light microscopes. Use **dissecting** and **compound light microscopes** to locate material and focus images.

☐ 8. Explain the difference between **magnification** and **resolution**. Calculate the **linear magnification** of images viewed with a microscope. Compare the magnification and resolution achieved using different microscopes.

☐ 9. Use diagrams and electron micrographs to describe the **organelles** of **eukaryotic cells**. Describe the functions of the organelles identified.

☐ 10. Use drawings and electron micrographs to compare and contrast the structure of **prokaryotic cells** and eukaryotic cells.

☐ 11. Use drawings and photomicrographs to compare and contrast the structure and ultrastructure of **plant cells** and **animal cells**.

Specialization and Tissues

pages 58-62

☐ 12. Define the terms **cellular differentiation** and **specialized cell**.

☐ 13. Recognize the hierarchy of organization in multicellular organisms: molecular, organelle, cell, tissue, organ.

☐ 14. Describe examples of tissues in plants and animals.

Separating Cell Fractions

page 63

☐ 15. Describe the principles of **cell fractionation**. Identify the components of the four fractions obtained from differential centrifugation: the **nuclear fraction**, **mitochondrial fraction**, **microsomal fraction**, and **soluble fraction**

The Cell Theory

The idea that all living things are composed of cells developed over many years and is strongly linked to the invention and refinement of the microscope. Early microscopes in the 1600s (such as Leeuwenhoek's below) opened up a whole new field of biology; the study of cell biology and microorganisms. The cell theory is a fundamental idea of biology.

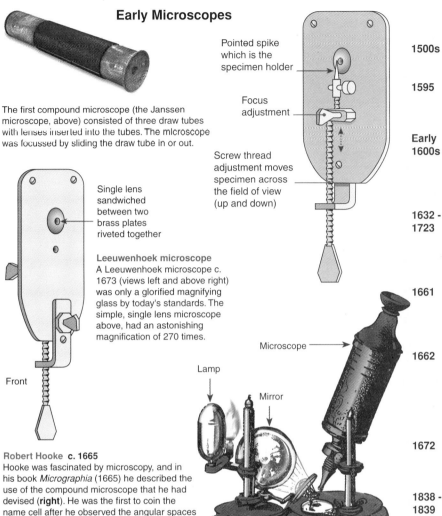

Early Microscopes

The first compound microscope (the Janssen microscope, above) consisted of three draw tubes with lenses inserted into the tubes. The microscope was focussed by sliding the draw tube in or out.

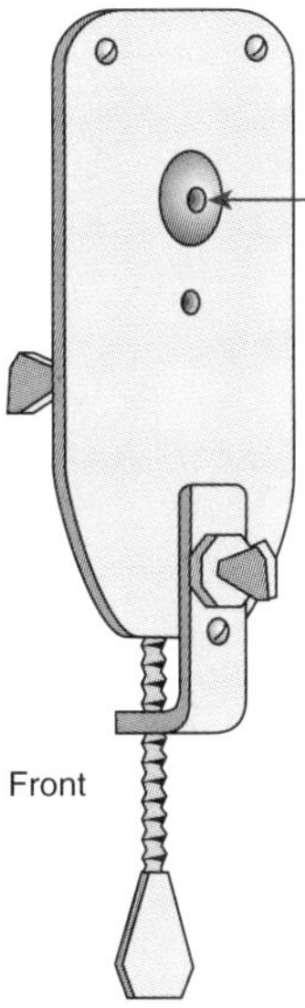
Single lens sandwiched between two brass plates riveted together
Front

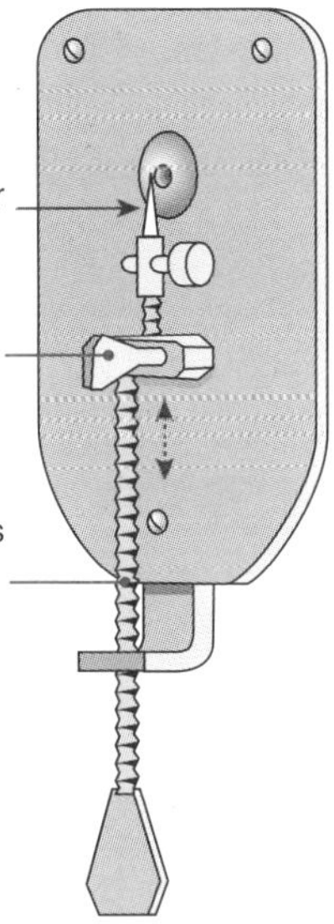
Pointed spike which is the specimen holder
Focus adjustment
Screw thread adjustment moves specimen across the field of view (up and down)

Leeuwenhoek microscope
A Leeuwenhoek microscope c. 1673 (views left and above right) was only a glorified magnifying glass by today's standards. The simple, single lens microscope above, had an astonishing magnification of 270 times.

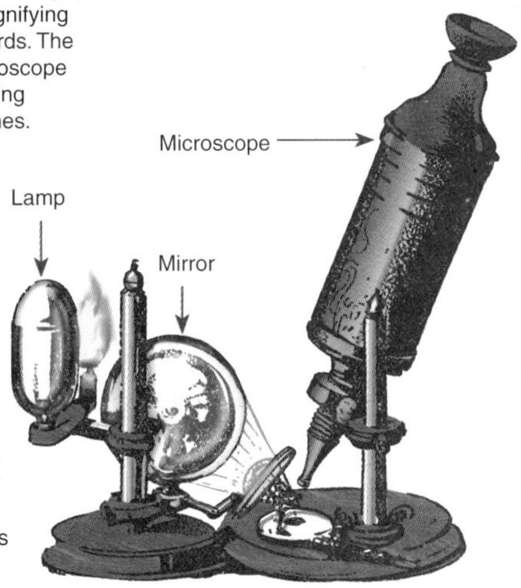
Microscope
Lamp
Mirror

Robert Hooke c. 1665
Hooke was fascinated by microscopy, and in his book *Micrographia* (1665) he described the use of the compound microscope that he had devised (**right**). He was the first to coin the name cell after he observed the angular spaces that he saw in a thin section of cork.

The Cell Theory

The idea that cells are fundamental units of life is part of the cell theory. The basic principles of the theory (as developed by early biologists) are:

- All living things are composed of cells and cell products.
- New cells are formed only by the division of preexisting cells.
- The cell contains inherited information (genes) that are used as instructions for growth, functioning, and development.
- The cell is the functioning unit of life; the chemical reactions of life take place within cells.

Milestones in Cell Biology

1500s Convex lenses with a magnification greater than x5 became available.

1595 **Zacharias Janssen** of Holland has been credited with the first compound microscope (more than one lens).

Early 1600s First compound microscopes used in Europe (used two convex lenses to make objects look larger). Suffered badly from color distortion; an effect called 'spherical aberration'.

1632 - 1723 **Antoni van Leeuwenhoek** of Holland produced over 500 single lens microscopes, discovering bacteria, human blood cells, spermatozoa, and protozoa. Friend of Robert Hooke.

1661 **Marcello Malpighi** used lenses to study insects. Discovered capillaries and may have described cells in writing of 'globules' and 'saccules'.

1662 **Robert Hooke** of England used the term 'cell' in describing the microscopic structure of cork. He believed that the cell walls were the important part of otherwise empty structures. Published *Micrographia* in 1665.

1672 **Nehemlah Grew** wrote the first of two well-illustrated books on the microscopic anatomy of plants.

1838 - 1839 Botanist **Matthias Schleiden** and zoolozgist **Theodor Schwann** proposed the cell theory based on their observations of plant and animal cells.

1855 **Rudolph Virchow** extended the cell theory by stating that "new cells are formed only by the division of previously existing cells".

1880 **August Weismann** added to Virchow's idea by pointing out that "all the cells living today can trace their ancestry back to ancient times", thus making the link between cell theory and evolution.

Cell Structure

1. What impact do you think the invention of microscopes has had on biology? ______________________

____

____

2. Before the development of the cell theory, it was commonly believed that living organisms could arise by spontaneous generation. What does this term mean and why has it been discredited as a theory?

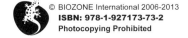

____

____

____

ISBN: 978-1-927173-73-2

Related activities: *Optical Microscopes*

Characteristics of Life

With each step in the hierarchy of biological order, new properties emerge that were not present at simpler levels of organization. Life itself is associated with numerous **emergent properties**, including metabolism and growth. The cell is the functioning unit structure from which living organisms are made. Viruses and cells are profoundly different. Viruses are non-cellular, lack the complex structures found in cells, and show only some of the properties we associate with living things. The traditional view of viruses is as a minimal particle, although the identification in 2004 of a new family of viruses, called mimiviruses, is forcing a rethink of this conservative view. Note the different scale to which the examples below are drawn. Refer to the scale bars for the comparative sizes (1000 nm = 1 μm = 0.001 mm).

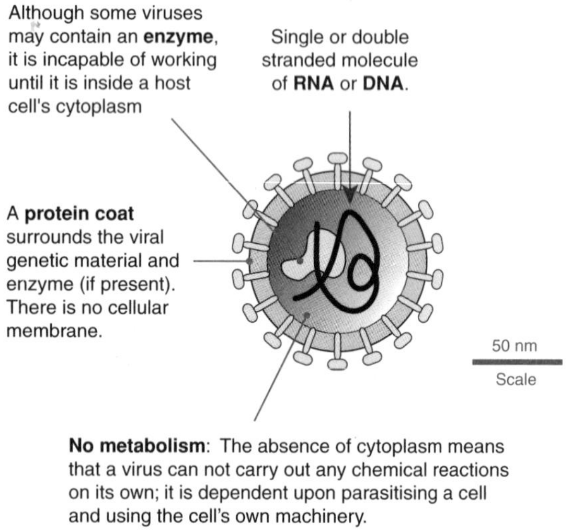
Although some viruses may contain an **enzyme**, it is incapable of working until it is inside a host cell's cytoplasm
Single or double stranded molecule of **RNA** or **DNA**.
A **protein coat** surrounds the viral genetic material and enzyme (if present). There is no cellular membrane.
50 nm
Scale
No metabolism: The absence of cytoplasm means that a virus can not carry out any chemical reactions on its own; it is dependent upon parasitising a cell and using the cell's own machinery.

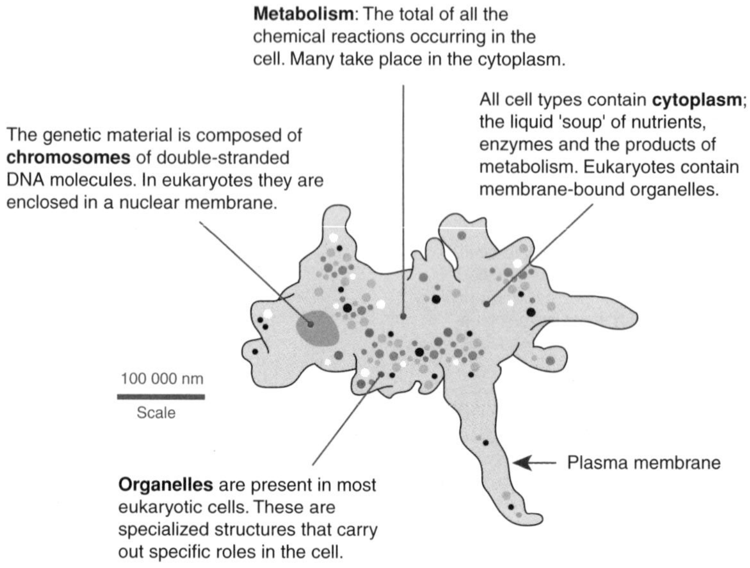
Metabolism: The total of all the chemical reactions occurring in the cell. Many take place in the cytoplasm.
The genetic material is composed of **chromosomes** of double-stranded DNA molecules. In eukaryotes they are enclosed in a nuclear membrane.
All cell types contain **cytoplasm**; the liquid 'soup' of nutrients, enzymes and the products of metabolism. Eukaryotes contain membrane-bound organelles.
100 000 nm
Scale
Plasma membrane
Organelles are present in most eukaryotic cells. These are specialized structures that carry out specific roles in the cell.

Virus
(*e.g. HIV*)

Viruses cannot become active outside a living host cell. They simply exist as inert virus particles called **virions**. Only when they invade a cell and take over the cell's metabolic machinery, can the virus carry out its 'living programme'.

Cell
(*e.g. Amoeba*)

Cells remain alive so long as their metabolic reactions in the cytoplasm are maintained. With a few rare exceptions (that involve freezing certain types of cells) if metabolism is halted, the cell dies.

1. Identify three features that all cells have in common: ______________________________

____

2. Describe how cells differ from viruses in the following aspects:

(a) Size: ______________________________

____

(b) Metabolism: ______________________________

____

(c) Organelles: ______________________________

____

(d) Genetic material: ______________________________

____

(e) Life cycle: ______________________________

____

3. Why are multicellular organisms said to show emergent properties? ______________________________

____

____

ISBN: 978-1-927173-73-2

Types of Living Things

Living things are known as organisms. Organisms are made up of one or more cells. Under the five kingdom system, cells can be divided into two broad groups, **prokaryotic** (bacterial) **cells** and the more complex **eukaryotic cells**. Eukaryotic cells are further organised according to their basic cell type (protist, fungus, plant, or animal). Viruses are non-cellular and have no cellular machinery of their own. All cells need energy to carry out their metabolic processes. **Autotrophs** (including unicellular autotrophs) are able to meet their energy requirements using light or chemical energy from the physical environment. **Heterotrophs** obtain their energy from other living or dead organisms.

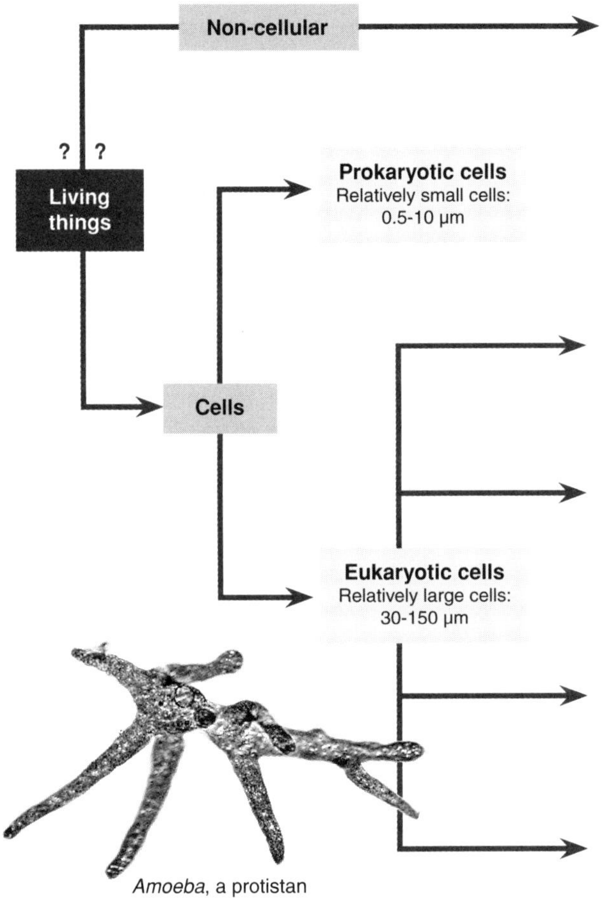

Non-cellular
? ?
Living things
Prokaryotic cells
Relatively small cells:
0.5-10 µm
Cells
Eukaryotic cells
Relatively large cells:
30-150 µm

Amoeba, a protistan

Viruses

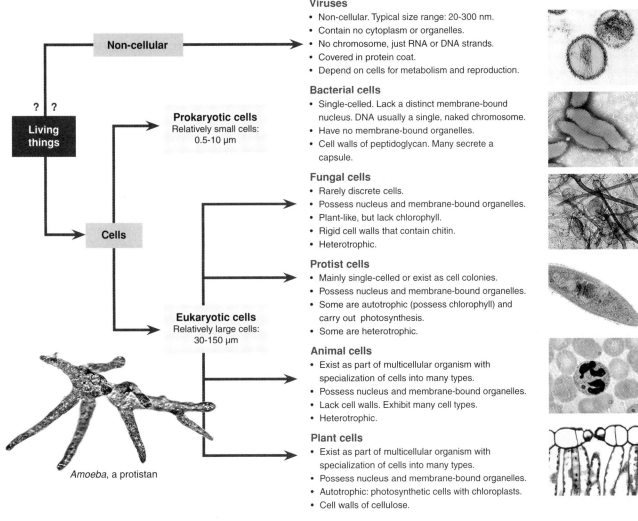

- Non-cellular. Typical size range: 20-300 nm.
- Contain no cytoplasm or organelles.
- No chromosome, just RNA or DNA strands.
- Covered in protein coat.
- Depend on cells for metabolism and reproduction.

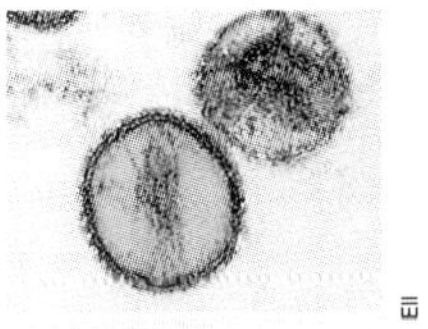
EII

Bacterial cells

- Single-celled. Lack a distinct membrane-bound nucleus. DNA usually a single, naked chromosome.
- Have no membrane-bound organelles.
- Cell walls of peptidoglycan. Many secrete a capsule.

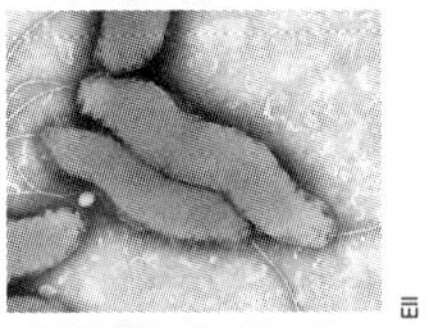
EII

Fungal cells

- Rarely discrete cells.
- Possess nucleus and membrane-bound organelles.
- Plant-like, but lack chlorophyll.
- Rigid cell walls that contain chitin.
- Heterotrophic.

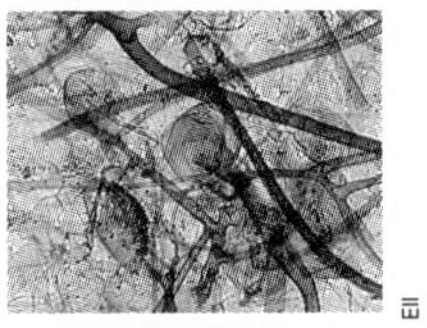
EII

Protist cells

- Mainly single-celled or exist as cell colonies.
- Possess nucleus and membrane-bound organelles.
- Some are autotrophic (possess chlorophyll) and carry out photosynthesis.
- Some are heterotrophic.

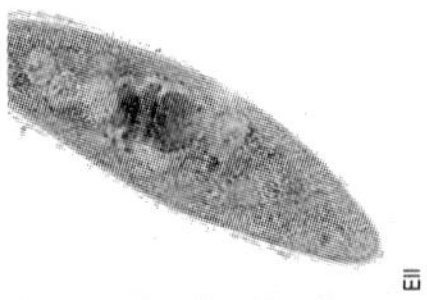
EII

Animal cells

- Exist as part of multicellular organism with specialization of cells into many types.
- Possess nucleus and membrane-bound organelles.
- Lack cell walls. Exhibit many cell types.
- Heterotrophic.

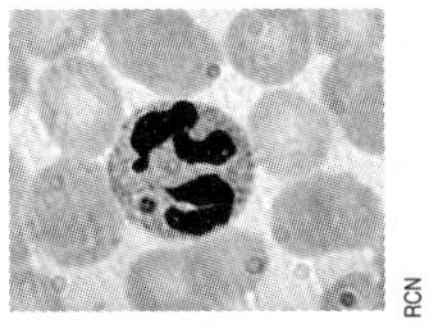
RCN

Plant cells

- Exist as part of multicellular organism with specialization of cells into many types.
- Possess nucleus and membrane-bound organelles.
- Autotrophic: photosynthetic cells with chloroplasts.
- Cell walls of cellulose.

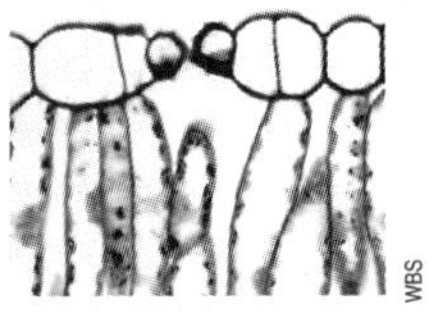
WBS

Cell Structure

1. List the cell types above according to the way in which they obtain their energy. Include viruses in your answer as well:

   (a) Autotrophic: ____________________

   (b) Heterotrophic: ____________________

2. Consult the diagram above and describe the two main features distinguishing **eukaryotic** cells from **prokaryotic** cells:

   (a) ____________________

   (b) ____________________

3. (a) Why do you think fungi were once classified as belonging to the plant kingdom? ____________________

   (b) Why, in terms of the distinguishing features of fungi, was this classification incorrect? ____________________

4. Why have the protists traditionally been a difficult group to classify? ____________________

ISBN: 978-1-927173-73-2

***Related activities:** Bacterial Cells, Plant Cells, Animal Cells, Unicellular Eukaryotes*

KNOW

Cell Sizes

Cells are extremely small and they can only be seen properly when viewed through the magnifying lenses of a microscope. The diagrams and photographs below show a variety of cell types, together with a virus and a microscopic animal for comparison. For each of these images, note the scale and relate this to the type of microscopy used.

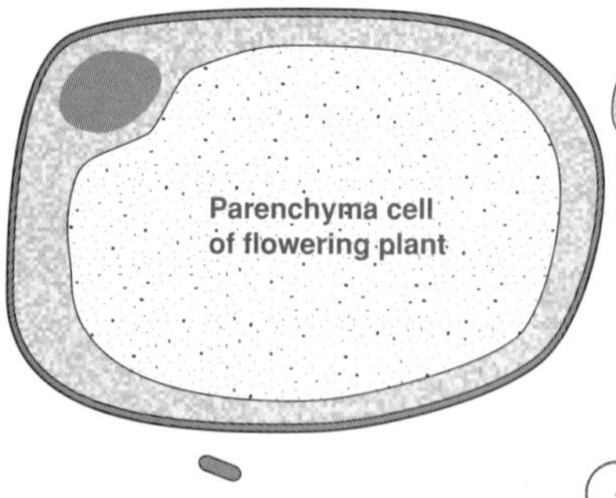
Parenchyma cell
of flowering plant

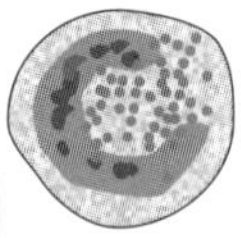

Human white blood cell

Eukaryotic cells
(e.g. plant and animal cells)
Size: 10-100 μm diameter. Cellular organelles may be up to 10 μm.

Prokaryotic cells
Size: Typically 2-10 μm length, 0.2-2 μm diameter. Upper limit 30 μm long.

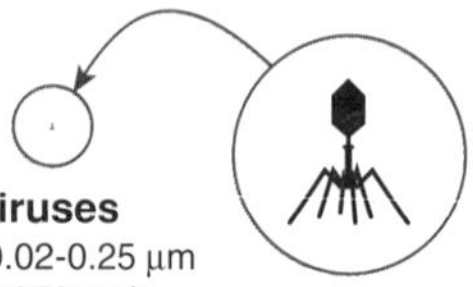

Viruses
Size: 0.02-0.25 μm (20-250 nm)

Unit of length (International System)		
Unit	**Meters**	**Equivalent**
1 meter (m)	1 m	= 1000 millimeters
1 millimeter (mm)	10^{-3} m	= 1000 micrometers
1 micrometer (μm)	10^{-6} m	= 1000 nanometers
1 nanometer (nm)	10^{-9} m	= 1000 picometers

Micrometers are sometime referred to as **microns**. Smaller structures are usually measured in nanometers (nm) e.g. molecules (1 nm) and plasma membrane thickness (10 nm).

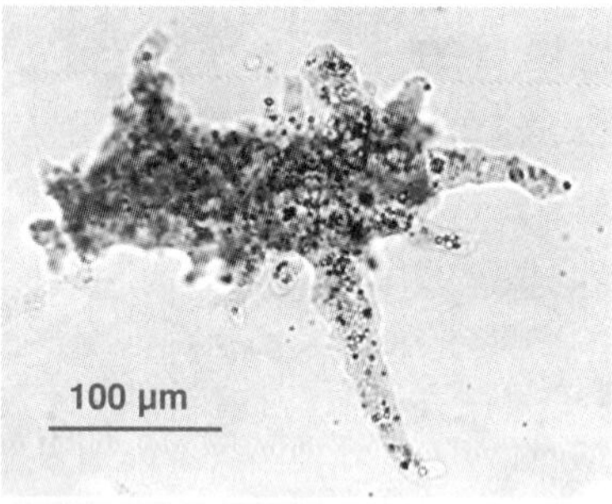
100 μm

RCN

An ***Amoeba*** showing extensions of the cytoplasm called pseudopodia. This protoctist changes its shape, exploring its environment.

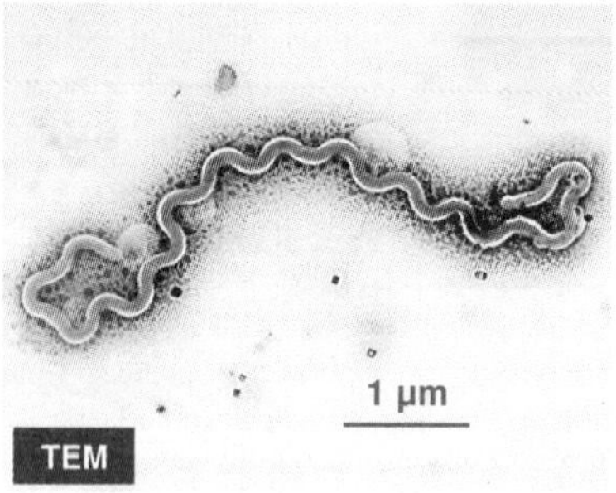
1 μm
TEM

WMU

A long thin cell of the spirochete bacterium ***Leptospira pomona***, which causes the disease leptospirosis.

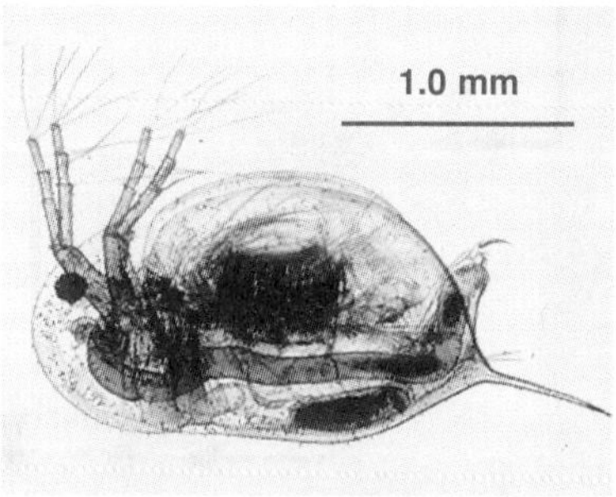
1.0 mm

RCN

Daphnia showing its internal organs. These freshwater microcrustaceans are part of the zooplankton found in lakes and ponds.

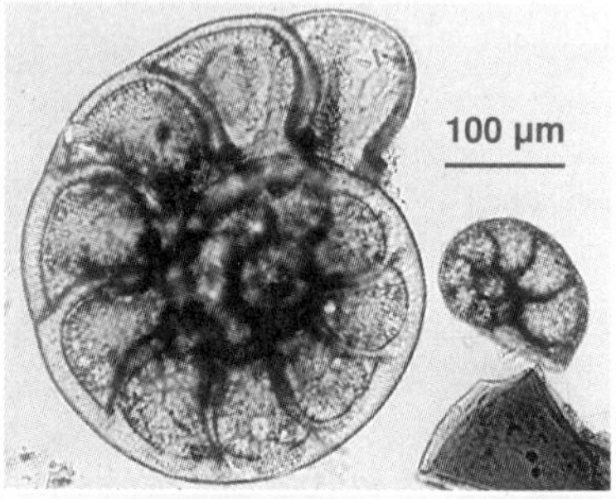
100 μm

RCN

A **foraminiferan** showing its chambered, calcified shell. These single-celled protozoans are marine planktonic amoebae.

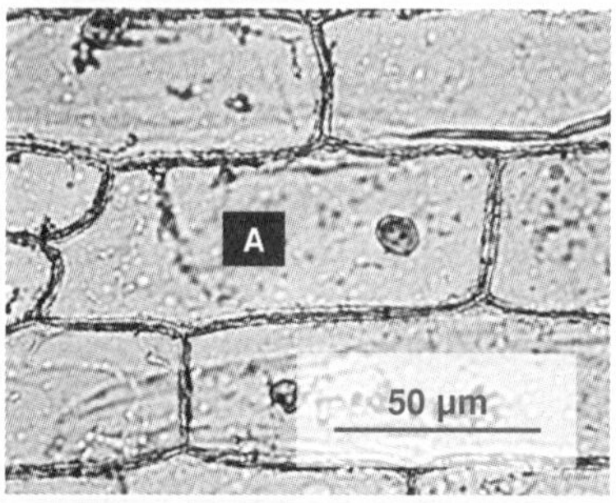
A
50 μm

RCN

Epidermal cells (skin) from an onion bulb showing the nucleus, cell walls and cytoplasm. Organelles are not visible at this resolution.

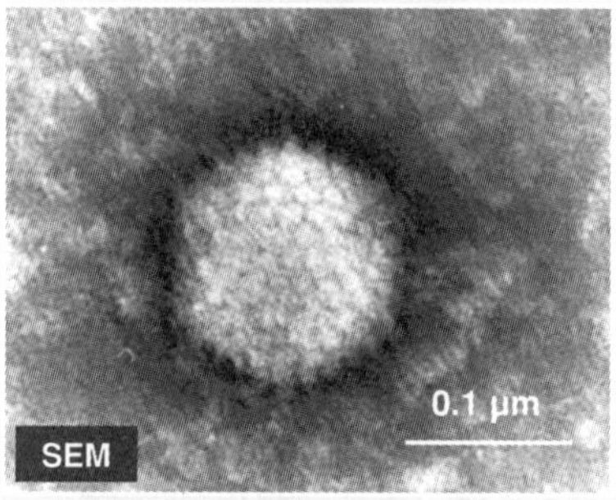
0.1 μm
SEM

WMU

Papillomavirus (human wart virus) showing its polyhedral protein coat (20 triangular faces, 12 corners) made of ball-shaped structures.

1. Using the measurement scales provided on each of the photographs above, determine the longest dimension (length or diameter) of the cell/animal/virus in μm and mm (choose the cell marked 'A' for epidermal cells):

   (a) *Amoeba*: ________ μm ________ mm
   (b) Foraminiferan: ________ μm ________ mm
   (c) *Leptospira*: ________ μm ________ mm
   (d) Epidermis: ________ μm ________ mm
   (e) *Daphnia*: ________ μm ________ mm
   (f) *Papillomavirus*: ________ μm ________ mm

2. List these six organisms in order of size, from the smallest to the largest: ________________

   ____

3. Study the scale of your ruler and state which of these six organisms you would be able to see with your unaided eye:

   ____

4. Calculate the equivalent length in millimeters (mm) of the following measurements:

   (a) 0.25 μm: ________ (b) 450 μm: ________ (c) 200 nm: ________

Related activities: *Optical Microscopes, Electron Microscopes*

ISBN: 978-1-927173-73-2

Cellular Environments

All organisms need a relatively stable internal environment in which to function effectively. Yet organisms survive in a wide variety of environments, some of which are more challenging to cell survival than others. Marine environments most closely resemble the osmolarity of a cell's cytoplasm, although this does not mean that the ionic composition is the same. Environments that depart from these isotonic conditions in any way will each present their own difficulties. Cells in freshwater must cope with influxes of water, whereas those in terrestrial environments risk dehydration. The evolution of multicellularity provided some independence from the external environment, because specialised cells could be organized into protective tissues, such as skin. Cell specialization and organization has enabled multicellular organisms to grow larger and provide the cells within their bodies with the optimum environment for cellular function.

Typical ion concentrations in cytosol and blood of a mammal (millimolar)

Ion	Concentration in cytosol (*mM*)	Concentration in blood (*mM*)
Potassium	139	4
Sodium	12	145
Chloride	4	116
Bicarbonate	12	29
Amino acids	138	9
Magnesium	0.8	1.5
Calcium	<0.0002	1.8

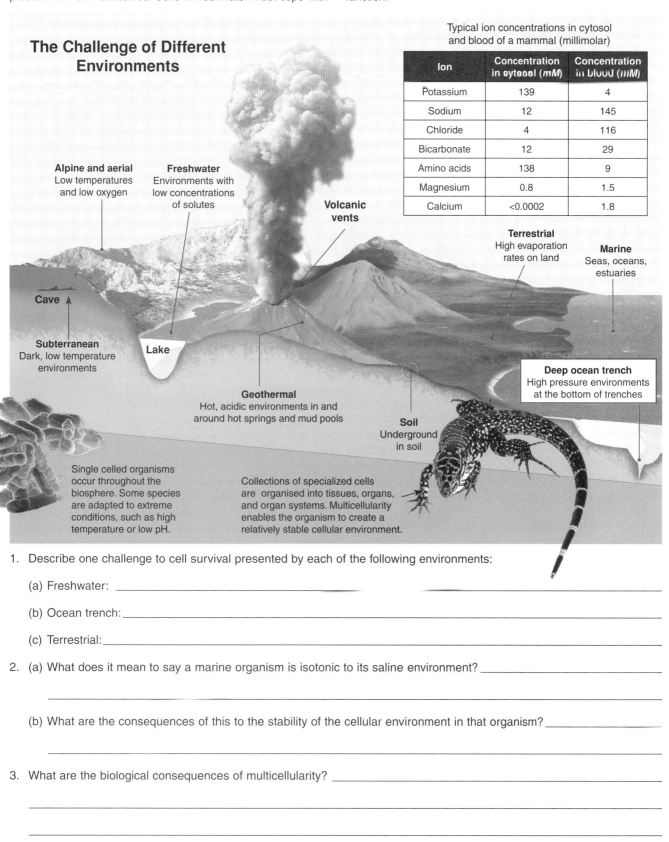

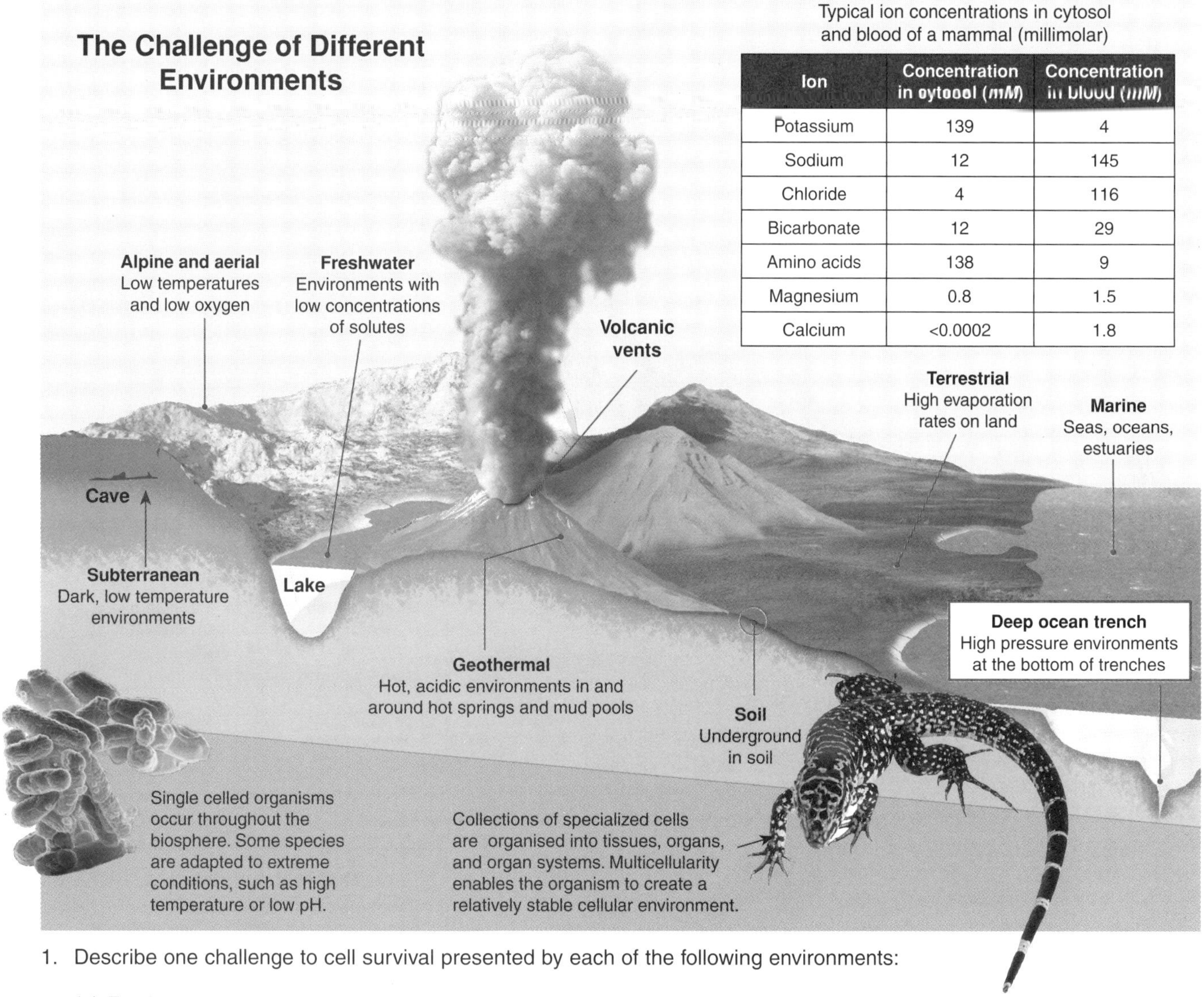
The Challenge of Different Environments
Alpine and aerial
Low temperatures and low oxygen
Freshwater
Environments with low concentrations of solutes
Volcanic vents
Terrestrial
High evaporation rates on land
Marine
Seas, oceans, estuaries
Cave
Subterranean
Dark, low temperature environments
Lake
Geothermal
Hot, acidic environments in and around hot springs and mud pools
Soil
Underground in soil
Deep ocean trench
High pressure environments at the bottom of trenches
Single celled organisms occur throughout the biosphere. Some species are adapted to extreme conditions, such as high temperature or low pH.
Collections of specialized cells are organised into tissues, organs, and organ systems. Multicellularity enables the organism to create a relatively stable cellular environment.

1. Describe one challenge to cell survival presented by each of the following environments:

   (a) Freshwater: ______________________

   (b) Ocean trench: ______________________

   (c) Terrestrial: ______________________

2. (a) What does it mean to say a marine organism is isotonic to its saline environment? ______________________

   (b) What are the consequences of this to the stability of the cellular environment in that organism? ______________________

3. What are the biological consequences of multicellularity? ______________________

Cell Structure

ISBN: 978-1-927173-73-2

Optical Microscopes

The light (optical) microscope is an important tool in biology and using it correctly is an essential skill. High power **compound light microscopes** (below) use a combination of lenses to magnify objects up to several hundred times. A specimen viewed with this type of microscope must be thin and mostly transparent so that light can pass through it. No detail will be seen in specimens that are thick or opaque. Modern microscopes are binocular (have two adjustable eyepieces). Dissecting microscopes are a special type of binocular microscope used for observations at low total magnification (X4 to X50), where a large working distance between the objectives and stage is required. A dissecting microscope has two separate lens systems, one for each eye. Such microscopes produce a 3-D view of the specimen and are sometimes called stereo microscopes for this reason.

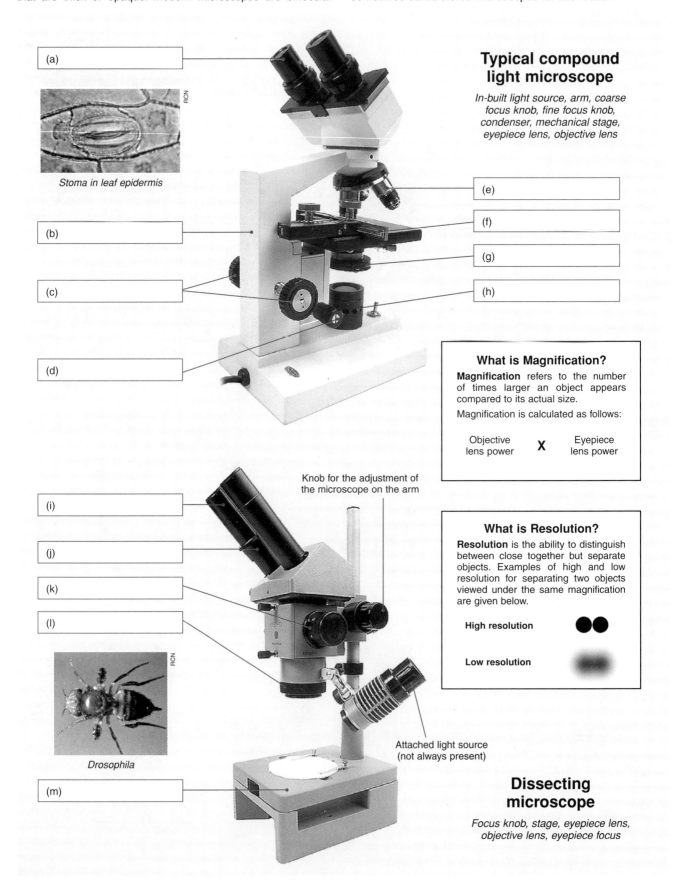

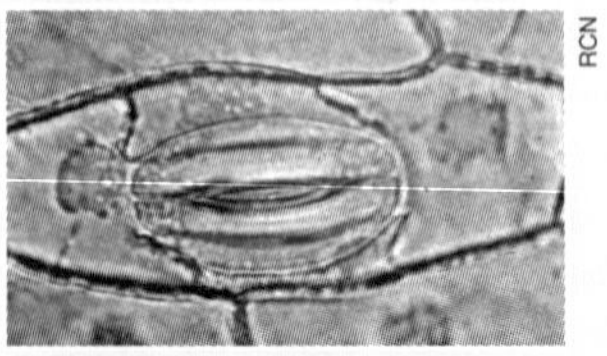
RCN

Stoma in leaf epidermis

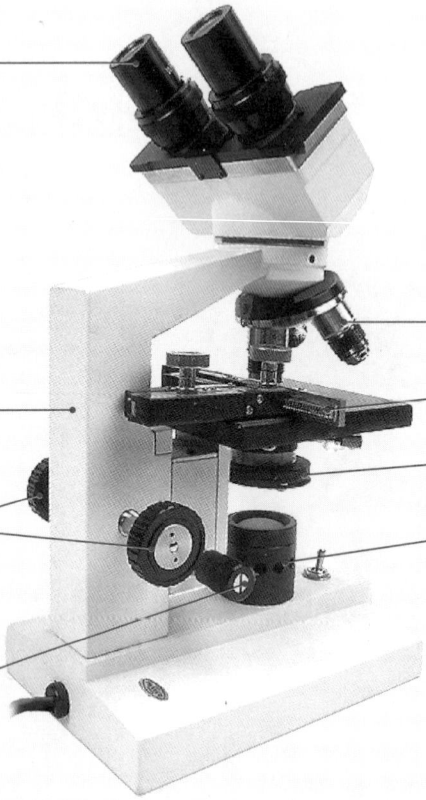
(a)
(b)
(c)
(d)
(e)
(f)
(g)
(h)

Typical compound light microscope

In-built light source, arm, coarse focus knob, fine focus knob, condenser, mechanical stage, eyepiece lens, objective lens

What is Magnification?

Magnification refers to the number of times larger an object appears compared to its actual size.

Magnification is calculated as follows:

Objective lens power **X** Eyepiece lens power

What is Resolution?

Resolution is the ability to distinguish between close together but separate objects. Examples of high and low resolution for separating two objects viewed under the same magnification are given below.

High resolution

Low resolution

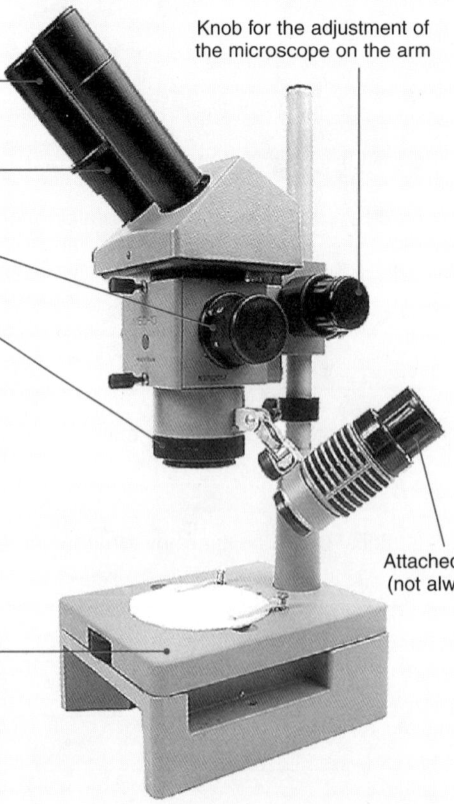
Knob for the adjustment of the microscope on the arm
(i)
(j)
(k)
(l)
(m)
Attached light source (not always present)

RCN

Drosophila

Dissecting microscope

Focus knob, stage, eyepiece lens, objective lens, eyepiece focus

ISBN: 978-1-927173-73-2

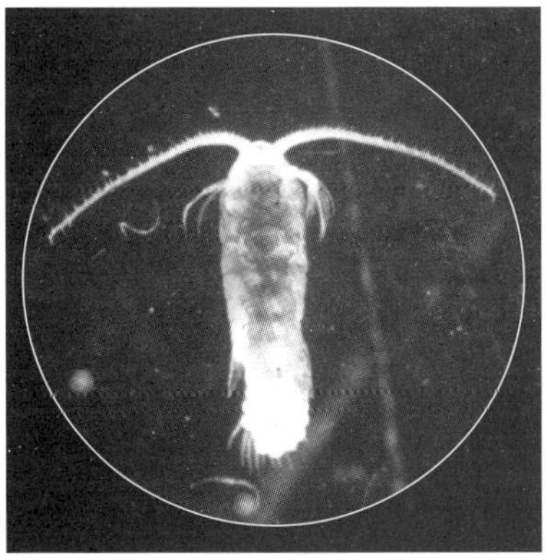
JDG

Dissecting microscopes are used for identifying and sorting organisms, observing microbial cultures, and dissections.

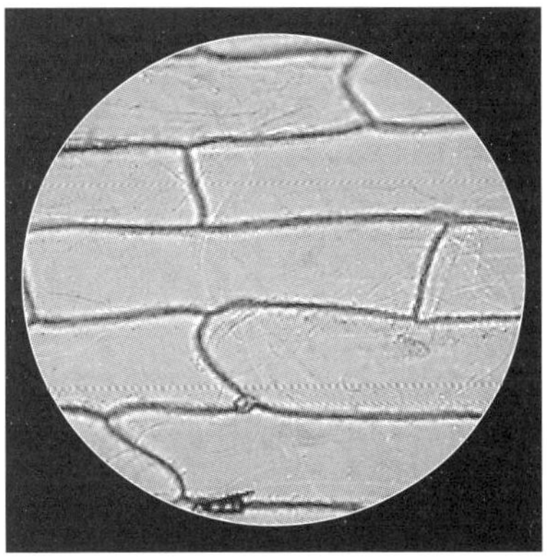

These onion epidermal cells are viewed with standard **bright field** lighting. Very little detail can be seen (only cell walls) and the cell nuclei are barely visible.

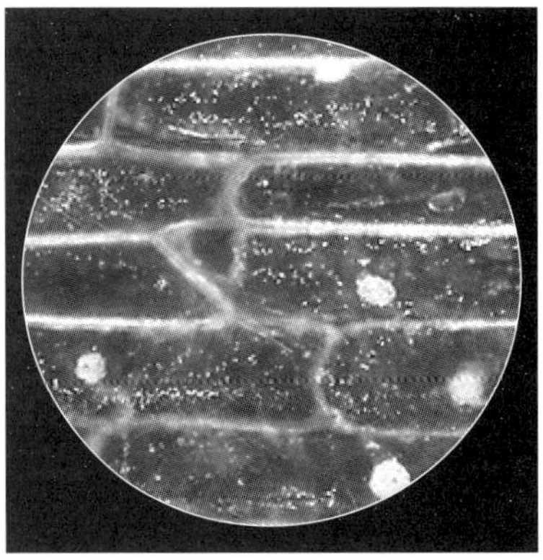

Dark field illumination is excellent for viewing specimens that are almost transparent. The nuclei of these onion epidermal cells are clearly visible.

1. Label the two photographs on the previous page, the compound light microscope (a) to (h) and the dissecting microscope (i) to (m). Use words from the lists supplied for each image.

2. Determine the magnification of a microscope using:

   (a) 15 X eyepiece and 40 X objective lens: __________ (b) 10 X eyepiece and 60 X objective lens: __________

3. Describe the main difference between a compound light microscope and a dissecting microscope: __________

4. What type of microscope would you use to:

   (a) Count stream invertebrates in a sample: __________ (b) Observe cells in mitosis: __________

5. (a) Distinguish between **magnification** and **resolution** (resolving power): __________

   (b) Explain the benefits of a higher resolution: __________

6. Below is a list of ten key steps taken to set up a microscope and optimally view a sample. The steps have been mixed up. Put them in their **correct order** by numbering each step:

☐ Focus and center the specimen using the high objective lens. Adjust focus using the fine focus knob only.

☐ Adjust the illumination to an appropriate level by adjusting the iris diaphragm and the condenser. The light should appear on the slide directly below the objective lens, and give an even amount of illumination.

☐ Rotate the objective lenses until the shortest lens is in place (pointing down towards the stage). This is the lowest / highest power objective lens (delete one).

☐ Place the slide on the microscope stage. Secure with the sample clips.

☐ Fine tune the illumination so you can view maximum detail on your sample.

☐ Focus and center the specimen using the medium objective lens. Focus firstly with the coarse focus knob, then with the fine focus knob (if needed).

☐ Turn on the light source.

☐ Focus and center the specimen using the low objective lens. Focus firstly with the coarse focus knob, then with the fine focus knob.

☐ Focus the eyepieces to adjust your view.

☐ Adjust the distance between the eyepieces so that they are comfortable for your eyes.

Cell Structure

ISBN: 978-1-927173-73-2

Electron Microscopes

Electron microscopes (EMs) use a beam of electrons, instead of light, to produce an image. The higher resolution of EMs is due to the shorter wavelengths of electrons. There are two basic types of electron microscope: **scanning electron microscopes** (SEM) and **transmission electron microscopes** (TEM). In SEMs, the electrons are bounced off the surface of an object to produce detailed images of the external appearance. TEMs produce very clear images of specially prepared thin sections.

Transmission Electron Microscope (TEM)

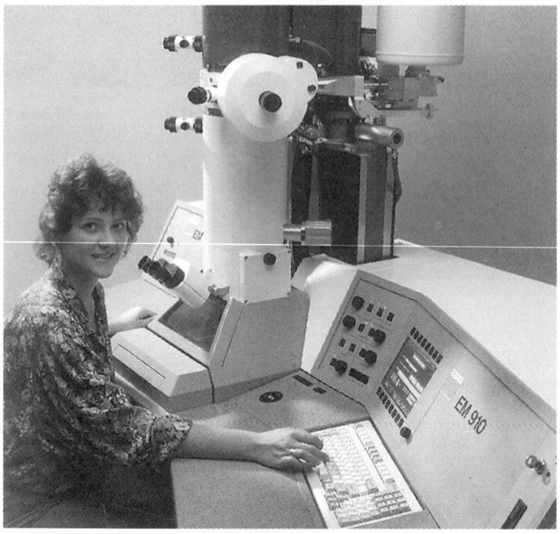
EM 910
WMU

The transmission electron microscope is used to view extremely thin sections of material. Electrons pass through the specimen and are scattered. Magnetic lenses focus the image onto a fluorescent screen or photographic plate. The sections are so thin that they have to be prepared with a special machine, called an **ultramicrotome**, that can cut wafers to just 30 thousandths of a millimeter thick. It can magnify several hundred thousand times.

Scanning Electron Microscope (SEM)

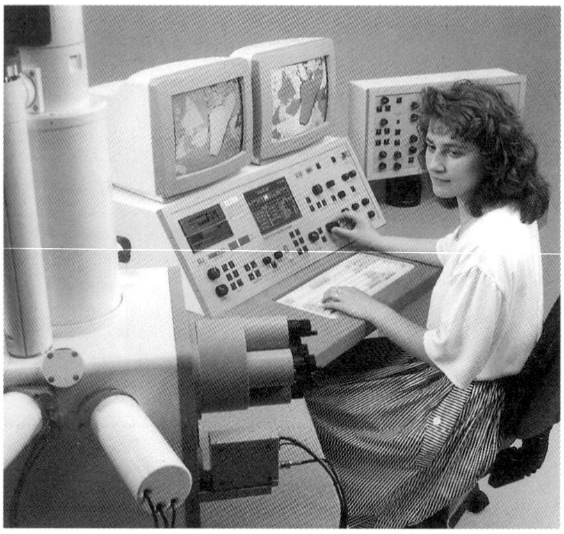
WMU

The scanning electron microscope scans a sample with a beam of primary electrons that knock electrons from its surface. These secondary electrons are picked up by a collector, amplified, and transmitted onto a viewing screen or photographic plate, producing a superb 3-D image. A microscope of this power can easily obtain clear pictures of organisms as small as bacteria and viruses. The image produced is of the outside surface only.

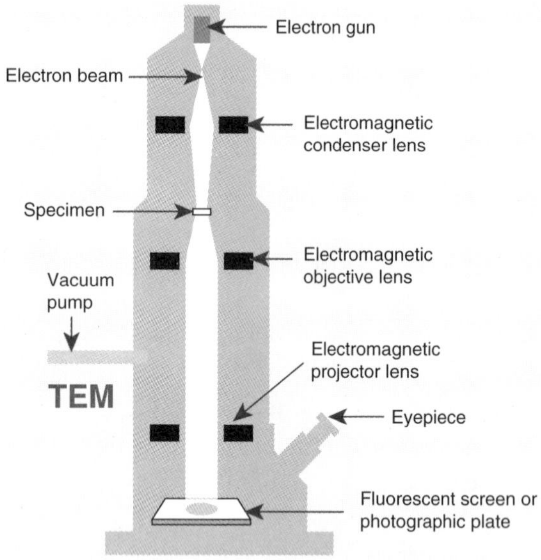
Electron gun
Electron beam
Electromagnetic condenser lens
Specimen
Electromagnetic objective lens
Vacuum pump
Electromagnetic projector lens
TEM
Eyepiece
Fluorescent screen or photographic plate

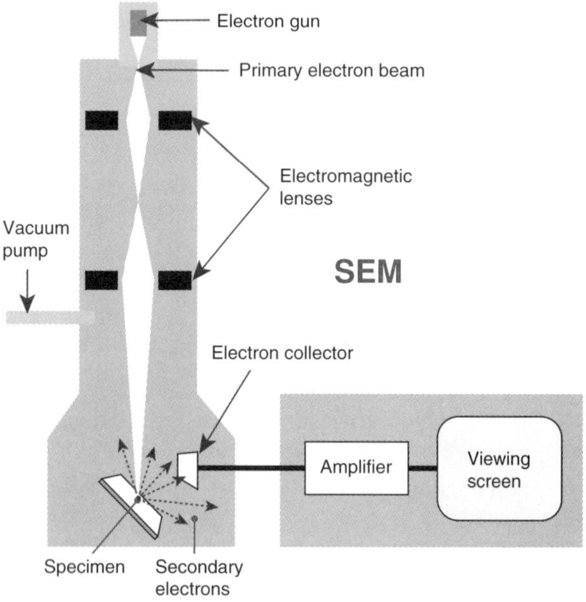
Electron gun
Primary electron beam
Electromagnetic lenses
Vacuum pump
SEM
Electron collector
Amplifier
Viewing screen
Specimen
Secondary electrons

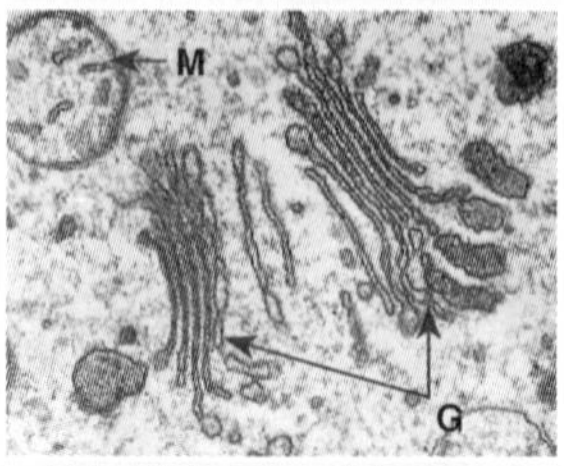
M
G
WMU
TEM photo showing the Golgi (**G**) and a mitochondrion (**M**).

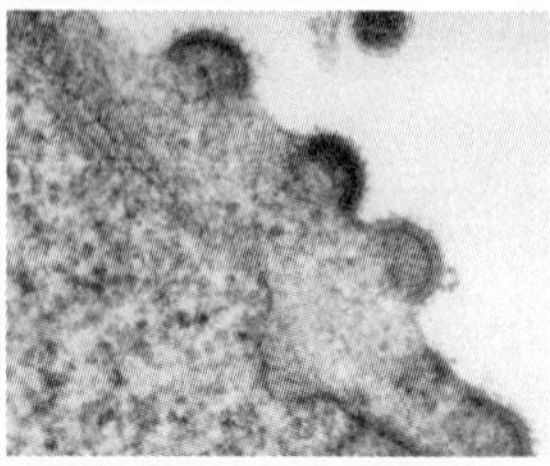
EII
Three HIV viruses budding out of a human lymphocyte (TEM).

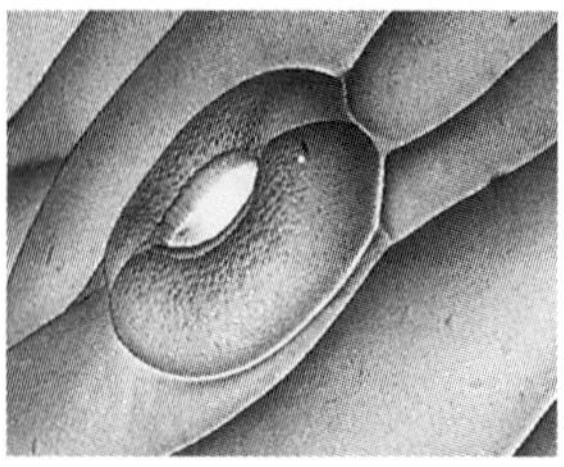
EII
SEM photo of stoma and epidermal cells on the upper surface of a leaf.

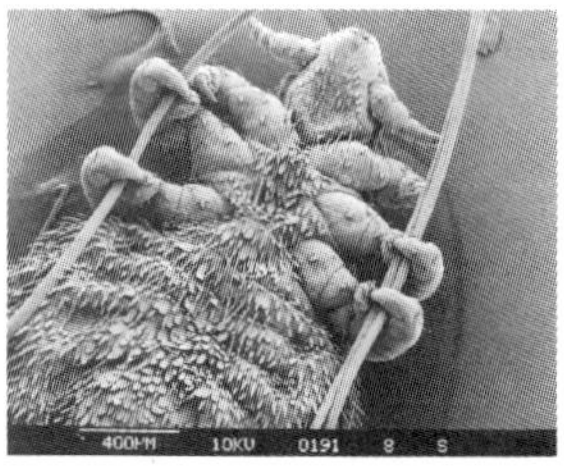
GW
Image of hair louse clinging to two hairs on a Hooker's sealion (SEM).

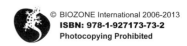

ISBN: 978-1-927173-73-2

	Light Microscope	Transmission Electron Microscope (TEM)	Scanning Electron Microscope (SEM)
Radiation source:	light	electrons	electrons
Wavelength:	400-700 nm	0.005 nm	0.005 nm
Lenses:	glass	electromagnetic	elcctromagnetic
Specimen:	living or non-living supported on glass slide	non-living supported on a small copper grid in a vacuum	non-living supported on a metal disc in a vacuum
Maximum resolution:	200 nm	1 nm	10 nm
Maximum magnification:	1500 x	250,000 x	100,000 x
Stains:	colored dyes	impregnated with heavy metals	coated with carbon or gold
Type of image:	colored	monochrome (black & white)	monochrome (black & white)

1. Explain why electron microscopes are able to resolve much greater detail than a light microscope:

____

____

____

2. Describe two typical applications for each of the following types of microscope:

   (a) Transmission electron microscope (TEM): ______________________________

   ____

   (b) Scanning electron microscope (SEM): ______________________________

   ____

   (c) Bright field microscope (thin section): ______________________________

   ____

   (d) Dissecting microscope: ______________________________

   ____

3. Identify which type of electron microscope (SEM or TEM) or optical microscope (compound light (bright field) microscope or dissecting microscope) was used to produce each of the images in the photos below (A-H):

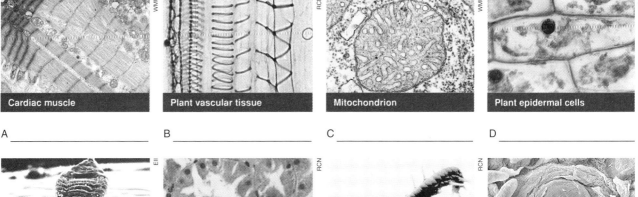

Cardiac muscle
WMU

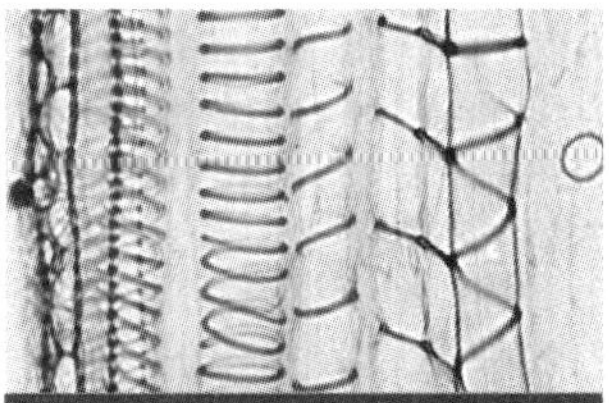
Plant vascular tissue
RCN

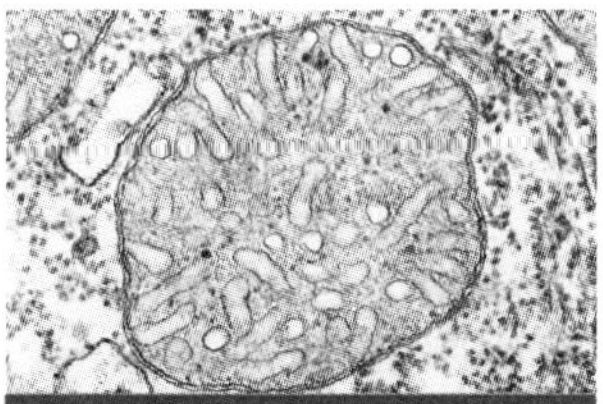
Mitochondrion
WMU

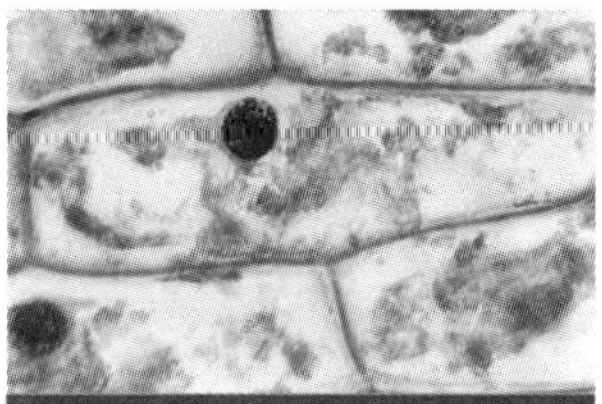
Plant epidermal cells
RCN

A ____________ B ____________ C ____________ D ____________

Head louse
EII

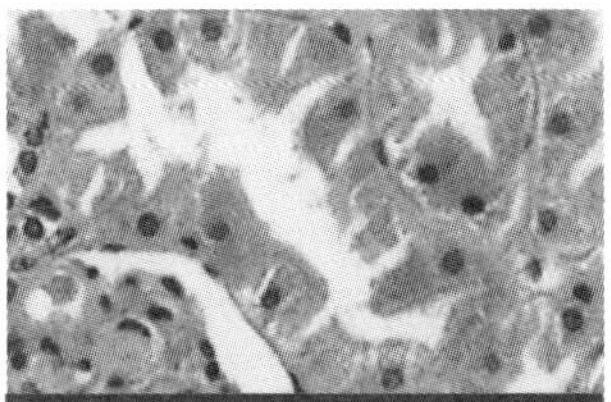
Kidney cells
RCN

Alderfly larva
RCN

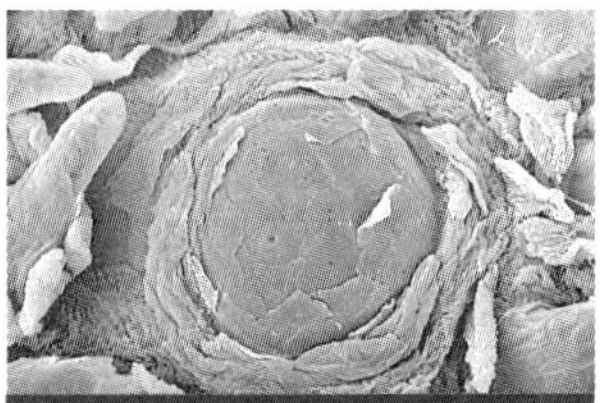
Tongue papilla
EII

E ____________ F ____________ G ____________ H ____________

ISBN: 978-1-927173-73-2

Calculating Linear Magnification

Microscopes produce an enlarged (magnified) image of an object allowing it to be observed in greater detail than is possible with the naked eye. **Magnification** refers to the number of times larger an object appears compared to its actual size. **Linear magnification** is calculated by taking a ratio of the image height to the object's actual height. If this ratio is greater than one, the image is enlarged, if it is less than one, it is reduced. To calculate magnification, all measurements should be converted to the same units. Most often, you will be asked to calculate an object's actual size, in which case you will be told the size of the object, as viewed through the microscope, and given the magnification.

Calculating Linear Magnification: A Worked Example

1. Measure the body length of the bed bug image (right). Your measurement should be 40 mm (***not*** including the body hairs and antennae).

2. Measure the length of the scale line marked 1.0 mm. You will find it is 10 mm long. The magnification of the scale line can be calculated using equation 1 (below right).

   The magnification of the scale line is **10** (10 mm / 1 mm)

   **NB: The magnification of the bed bug image will also be 10x because the scale line and image are magnified to the same degree.*

3. Calculate the actual (real) size of the bed bug using equation 2 (right):

   The actual size of the bed bug is **4 mm**
   (40 mm / 10 x magnification)

1.0 mm

Microscopy Equations

1. Magnification = $\frac{\text{size of the image}}{\text{actual size of object}}$

2. Actual object size = $\frac{\text{size of the image}}{\text{magnification}}$

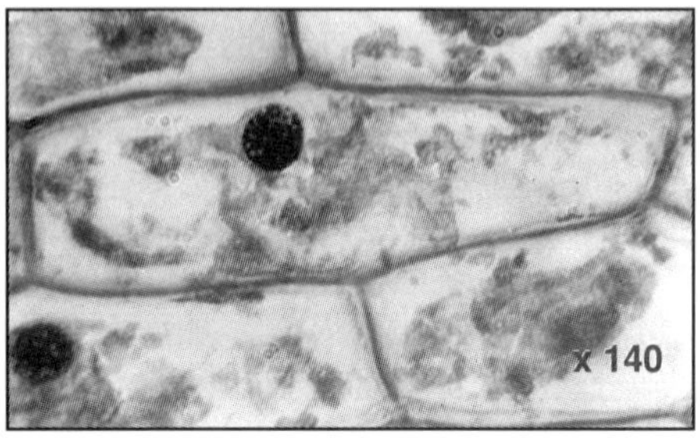
x 140

1. The bright field microscopy image on the left is of onion epidermal cells. The measured length of the onion cell in the center of the photograph is 52,000 µm (52 mm). The image has been magnified 140 x. Calculate the actual size of the cell:

___

___

___

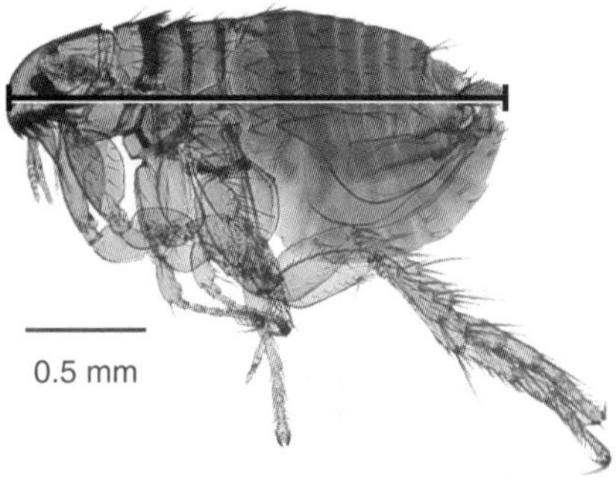
0.5 mm

2. The image of the flea (left) has been captured using light microscopy.

   (a) Calculate the magnification using the scale line on the image:

   ___

   ___

   ___

   (b) The body length of the flea is indicated by a line. Measure along the line and calculate the actual length of the flea:

   ___

   ___

   ___

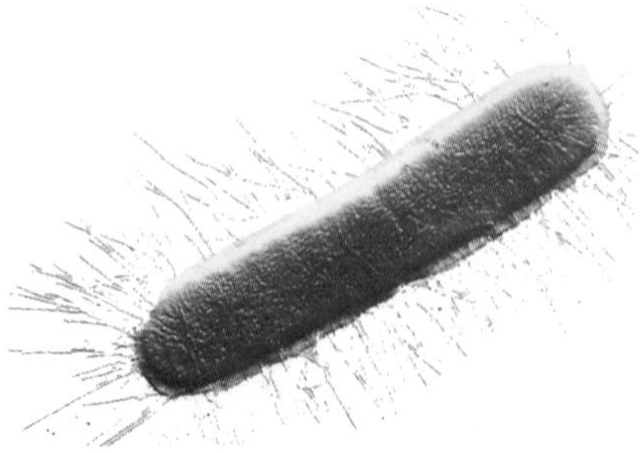

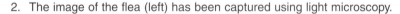

3. The image size of the *E.coli* cell (left) is 43 mm, and its actual size is 2 µm. Using this information, calculate the magnification of the image:

___

___

___

ISBN: 978-1-927173-73-2

Bacterial Cells

Bacterial (prokaryotic) cells are much smaller and simpler than the cells of eukaryotes. They lack many eukaryotic features (e.g. a distinct nucleus and membrane-bound cellular organelles). The bacterial cell wall is an important feature. It is a complex, multi-layered structure and often has a role in virulence. These pages illustrate some features of bacterial structure and diversity.

Structure of a Generalized Bacterial Cell

Plasmids: Small, circular DNA molecules which can reproduce independently of the main chromosome. They can move between cells, and even between species, by **conjugation**. This property accounts for the transmission of antibiotic resistance between bacteria. Plasmids are also used as vectors in recombinant DNA technology.

Fimbriae: Hairlike structures that are shorter, straighter, and thinner than flagella. They are used for attachment, not movement. Pili are similar to fimbriae, but are longer and less numerous. They are involved in bacterial conjugation (below) and as phage receptors.

The cell lacks a nuclear membrane, so there is no distinct nucleus and the chromosome is in direct contact with the cytoplasm. It is possible for free ribosomes to attach to mRNA while the mRNA is still in the process of being transcribed from the DNA.

Cell surface membrane: Similar in composition to eukaryotic membranes, although less rigid.

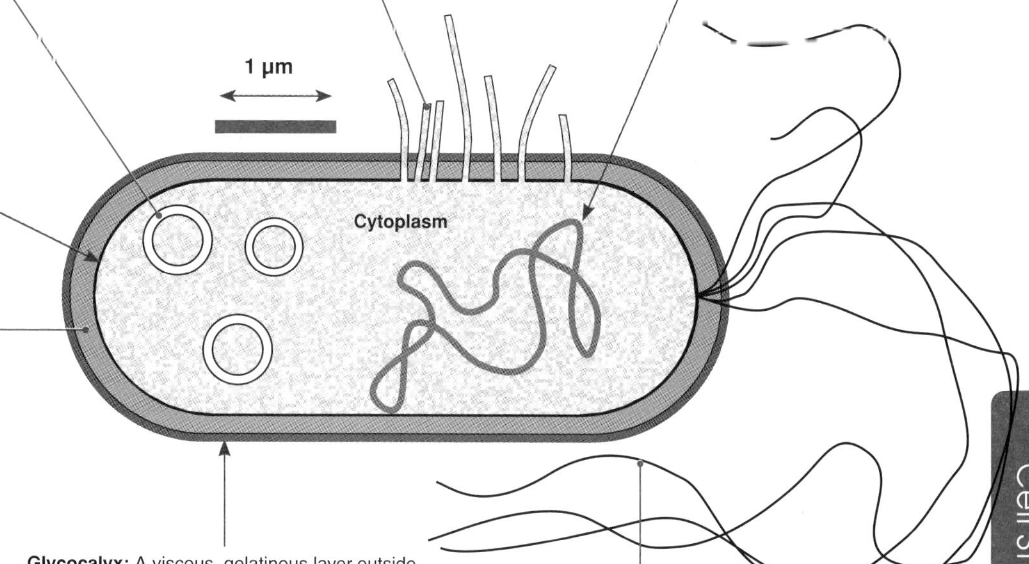
1 μm
Cytoplasm

Cell wall: A complex, semi-rigid structure that gives the cell shape, prevents rupture. The cell wall is composed of a macromolecule called **peptidoglycan**; repeating disaccharides attached by polypeptides to form a lattice. The wall also contains varying amounts of lipopolysaccharides and lipoproteins. The amount of peptidoglycan present in the wall forms the basis of the diagnostic **gram stain**. In many species, the cell wall contributes to their virulence (disease-causing ability).

Glycocalyx: A viscous, gelatinous layer outside the cell wall. It is composed of polysaccharide and/or polypeptide. If it is firmly attached to the wall, it is called a **capsule**. If loosely attached, it is called a **slime layer**. Capsules may contribute to virulence in pathogenic species, e.g. by protecting the bacteria from immune attack. In some species, the glycocalyx allows attachment to substrates.

Flagellum (pl. flagella): Some bacteria have long, filamentous appendages, called flagella, that are used for locomotion. There may be a single polar flagellum (monotrichous), one or more flagella at each end of the cell, or the flagella may be distributed over the entire cell (peritrichous).

Bacterial cell shapes

Most bacterial cells range between 0.20-2.0 μm in diameter and 2-10 μm length. Although they are a very diverse group, much of this diversity is in their metabolism. In terms of gross morphology, there are only a few basic shapes found (illustrated below). The way in which members of each group aggregate after division is often characteristic and is helpful in identifying certain species.

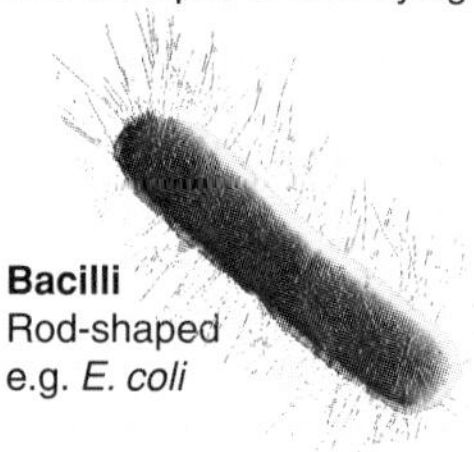

Bacilli
Rod-shaped
e.g. *E. coli*

Bacilli: Rod-shaped bacteria that divide only across their short axis. Most occur as single rods, although pairs and chains are also found. The term bacillus can refer (as here) to shape. It may also denote a genus.

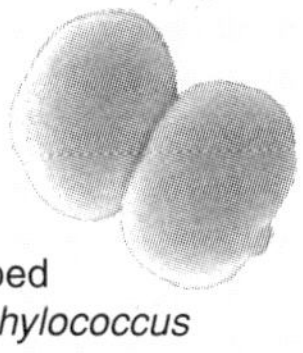

Cocci
Ball-shaped
e.g. *Staphylococcus*

Cocci: usually round, but sometimes oval or elongated. When they divide, the cells stay attached to each other and remain in aggregates e.g. pairs (diplococci) or clusters (staphylococci), that are usually a feature of the genus.

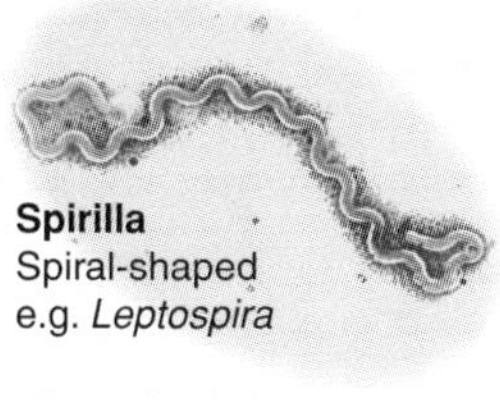

Spirilla
Spiral-shaped
e.g. *Leptospira*

Spirilla and vibrio: Bacteria with one or more twists. Spirilla bacteria have a helical (corkscrew) shape which may be rigid or flexible (as in spirochetes). Bacteria that look like curved rods (comma shaped) are called vibrios. Vibrio may also denote a genus.

Bacterial conjugation

The two bacteria below are involved in conjugation: a one-way exchange of genetic information from a donor cell to a recipient cell. The plasmid, which must be of the 'conjugative' type, passes through a tube called a sex pilus to the other cell. Which is donor and which is recipient appears to be genetically determined. Conjugation should not be confused with sexual reproduction, as it does not involve the fusion of gametes or formation of a zygote.

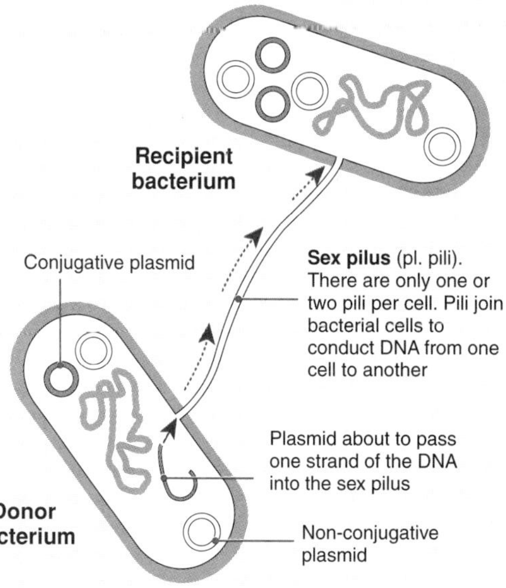
Recipient bacterium
Conjugative plasmid
Sex pilus (pl. pili). There are only one or two pili per cell. Pili join bacterial cells to conduct DNA from one cell to another
Plasmid about to pass one strand of the DNA into the sex pilus
Donor bacterium
Non-conjugative plasmid

ISBN: 978-1-927173-73-2

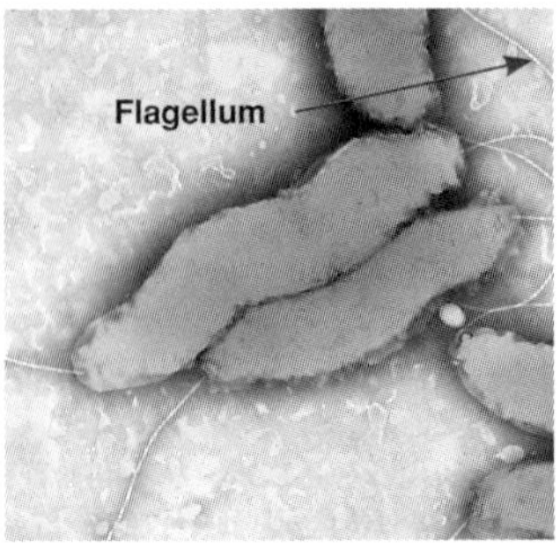
Flagellum

Campylobacter jejuni, a spiral bacterium responsible for foodborne intestinal disease. Note the single flagellum at each end (amphitrichous arrangement).

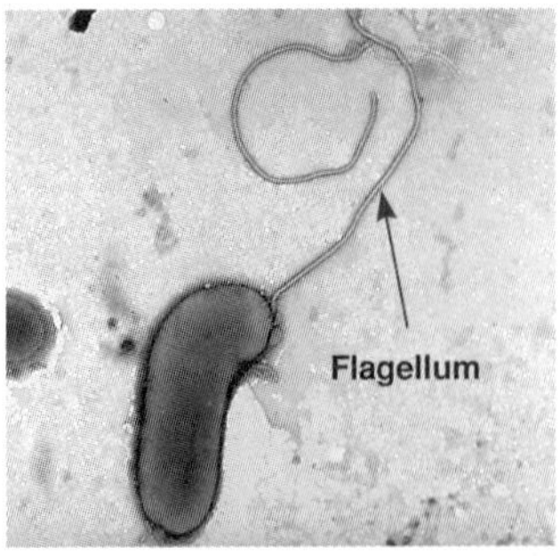
Flagellum

Helicobacter pylori, a comma-shaped vibrio bacterium that causes stomach ulcers in humans. This bacterium moves by means of multiple polar flagella.

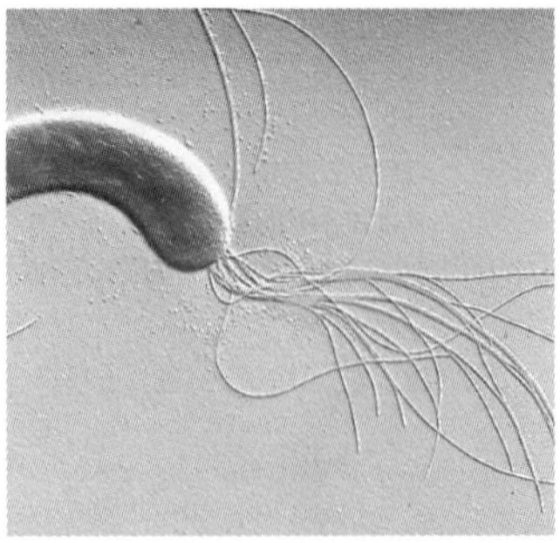

A species of *Spirillum,* a spiral shaped bacterium with a tuft of polar flagella. Most of the species in this genus are harmless aquatic organisms.

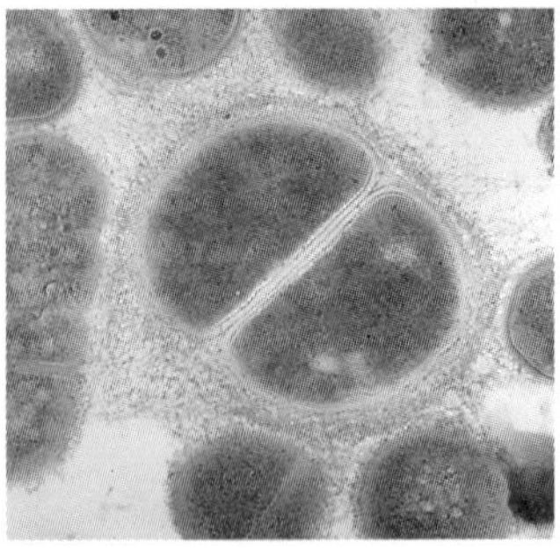

Bacteria usually divide by binary fission. During this process, DNA is copied and the cell splits into two cells, as in these gram positive cocci.

All photos this row: EII

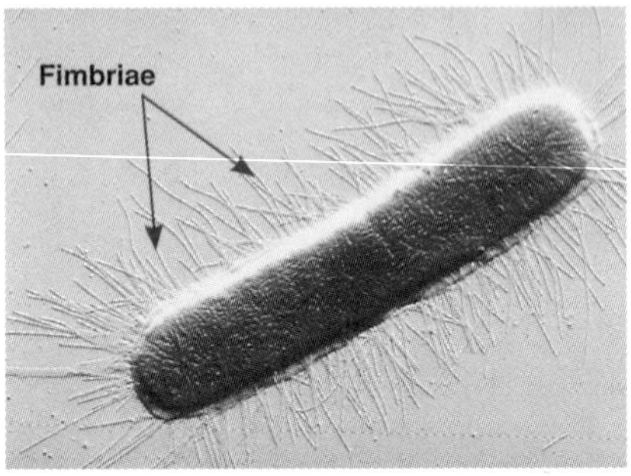
Fimbriae

EII

Escherichia coli, a common gut bacterium with **peritrichous** (around the entire cell) **fimbriae**. *E. coli* is a gram negative rod; it does not take up the gram stain but can be counter stained with safranin.

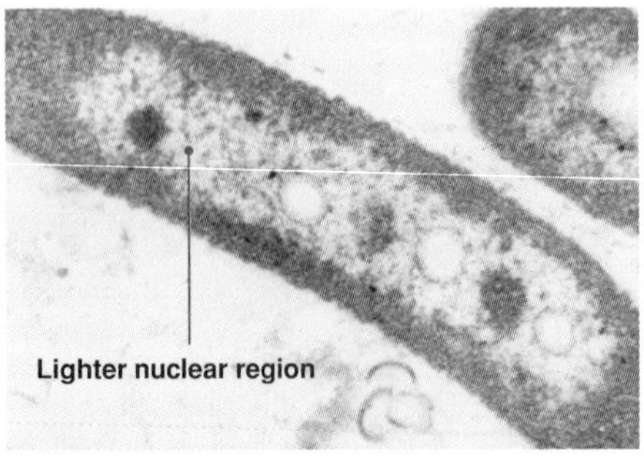
Lighter nuclear region

WMU

TEM showing *Enterobacter* bacteria, which belong to the family of gut bacteria commonly known as enterics. They are widely distributed in water, sewage, and soil. The family includes motile and non-motile species.

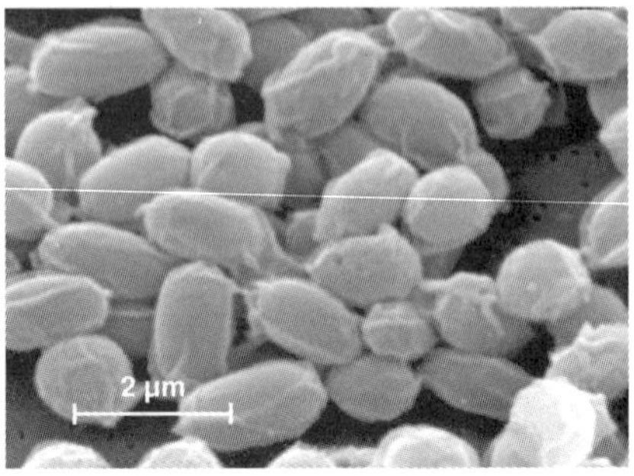
2 µm

CDC

SEM of endospores of *Bacillus anthracis* bacteria, which cause the disease anthrax. These heat-resistant spores remain viable for many years and enable the bacteria to survive in a dormant state.

1. Describe three features which distinguish prokaryotic cells from eukaryotic cells:

   (a) ______________________________

   (b) ______________________________

   (c) ______________________________

2. (a) Describe the function of flagella in bacteria: ______________________________

   (b) Explain how fimbriae differ structurally and functionally from flagella: ______________________________

3. (a) Describe the location and general composition of the bacterial cell wall: ______________________________

   (b) Describe how the glycocalyx differs from the cell wall: ______________________________

4. (a) Describe the main method by which bacteria reproduce: ______________________________

   (b) Explain how conjugation differs from this usual method: ______________________________

5. Briefly describe how the artificial manipulation of plasmids has been used for technological applications:

____

ISBN: 978-1-927173-73-2

Unicellular Eukaryotes

Unicellular (single-celled) **eukaryotes** comprise the majority of the diverse kingdom, **Protista**. They are found almost anywhere there is water, including within larger organisms (as parasites or symbionts). The protists are a diverse group, showing some features typical of generalized eukaryotic cells, as well as specialized features. Note that even within the genera below there is considerable variation in size and appearance. *Amoeba* and *Paramecium* are both heterotrophic, ingesting food, which accumulates inside a vacuole. *Euglena and Chlamydomonas* are autotrophic algae, although *Euglena* is heterotrophic when deprived of light. Other protists include the marine foraminiferans and radiolarians, specialized intracellular parasites such as *Plasmodium*, and zooflagellates such as the parasites *Trypanosoma* and *Giardia*.

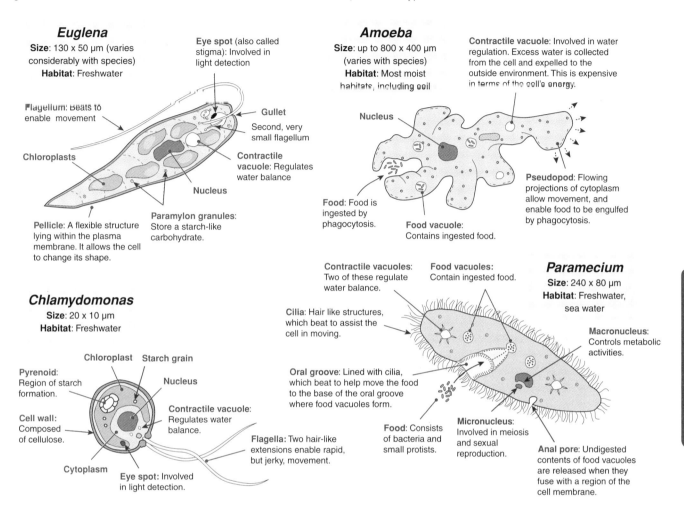

Euglena

Size: 130 x 50 μm (varies considerably with species)
Habitat: Freshwater

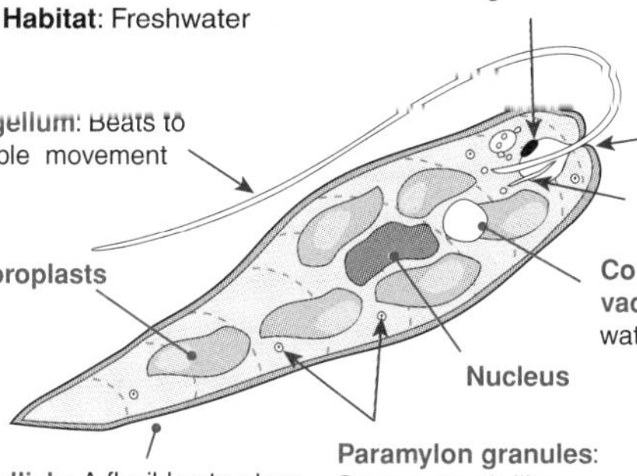

Eye spot (also called stigma): Involved in light detection
Flagellum: Beats to enable movement
Gullet
Second, very small flagellum
Chloroplasts
Contractile vacuole: Regulates water balance
Nucleus
Paramylon granules: Store a starch-like carbohydrate.
Pellicle: A flexible structure lying within the plasma membrane. It allows the cell to change its shape.

Amoeba

Size: up to 800 x 400 μm (varies with species)
Habitat: Most moist habitats, including soil

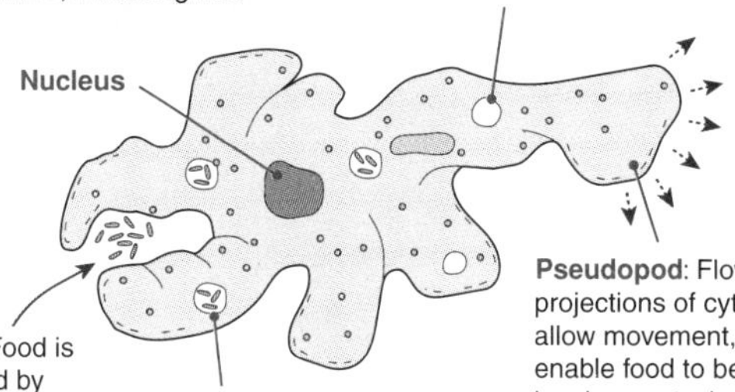

Contractile vacuole: Involved in water regulation. Excess water is collected from the cell and expelled to the outside environment. This is expensive in terms of the cell's energy.
Nucleus
Pseudopod: Flowing projections of cytoplasm allow movement, and enable food to be engulfed by phagocytosis.
Food: Food is ingested by phagocytosis.
Food vacuole: Contains ingested food.

Paramecium

Size: 240 x 80 μm
Habitat: Freshwater, sea water

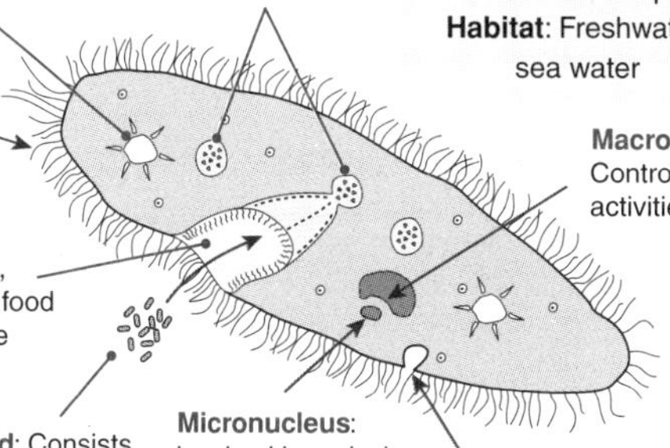

Contractile vacuoles: Two of these regulate water balance.
Food vacuoles: Contain ingested food.
Cilia: Hair like structures, which beat to assist the cell in moving.
Macronucleus: Controls metabolic activities.
Oral groove: Lined with cilia, which beat to help move the food to the base of the oral groove where food vacuoles form.
Food: Consists of bacteria and small protists.
Micronucleus: Involved in meiosis and sexual reproduction.
Anal pore: Undigested contents of food vacuoles are released when they fuse with a region of the cell membrane.

Chlamydomonas

Size: 20 x 10 μm
Habitat: Freshwater

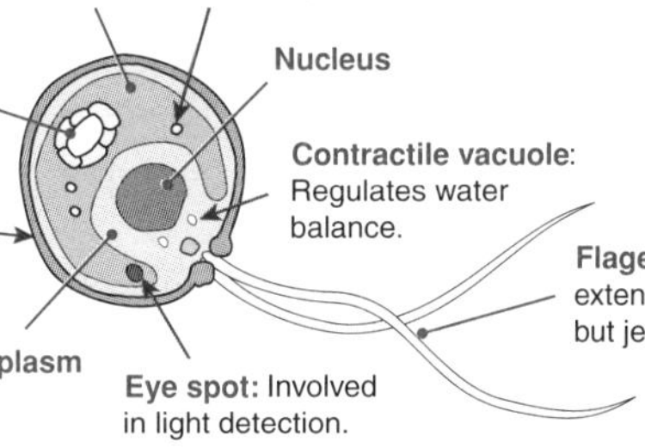

Chloroplast
Starch grain
Pyrenoid: Region of starch formation.
Nucleus
Contractile vacuole: Regulates water balance.
Cell wall: Composed of cellulose.
Flagella: Two hair-like extensions enable rapid, but jerky, movement.
Cytoplasm
Eye spot: Involved in light detection.

1. Fill in the table below to summarize differences in some of the features and life functions of the protists shown above:

Organism	Nutrition	Movement	Osmoregulation	Eye spot present / absent	Cell wall present / absent
Amoeba					
Paramecium					
Euglena					
Chlamydomonas					

2. List the four organisms shown above in order of size (largest first): ______________________________

____

3. Explain why an autotroph would have an eye spot: ______________________________

____

Cell Structure

ISBN: 978-1-927173-73-2

Related activities: *Calculating Linear Magnification*

KNOW

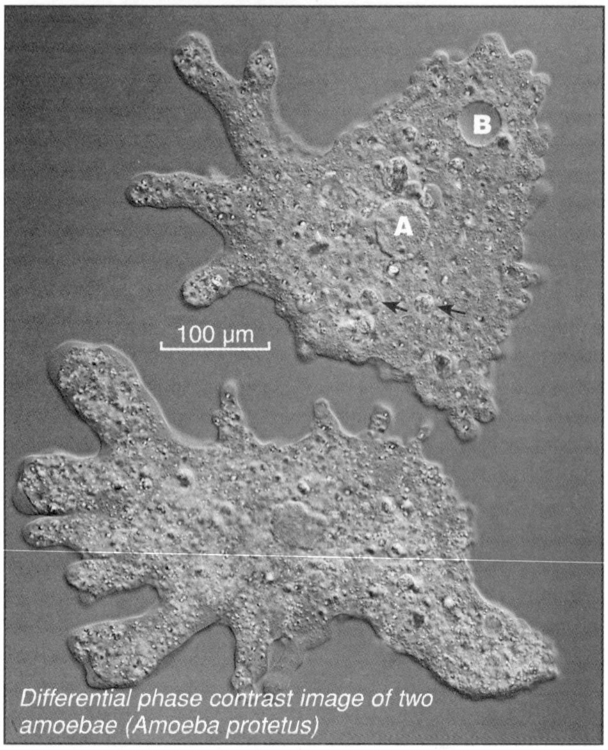
B
A
100 µm

Differential phase contrast image of two amoebae (Amoeba protetus)

istock

4. (a) Identify the structure labelled **A**:

(b) Circle the same structure in the unlabelled specimen:

(c) What feature(s) helped you identify this organelle?

(d) Identify the structure labelled **B**:

(e) Describe the function of this structure:

(f) Identify the structures labelled with arrows:

(g) Describe the function of these structures:

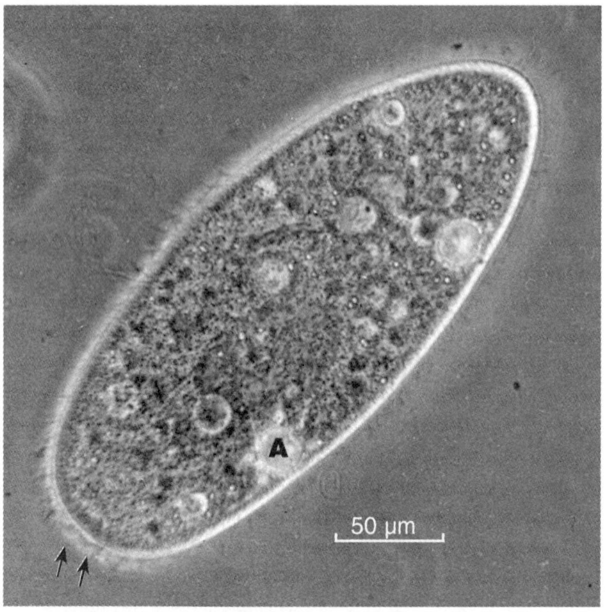
A
50 µm

Barfooz CC 3.0

5. (a) Identify this organism:

(b) What feature(s) helped you make your identification?

(c) Identify the organelle labelled **A**:

(d) Circle another organelle with the same function:

(e) Identify the structures indicated by the arrows and describe their purpose:

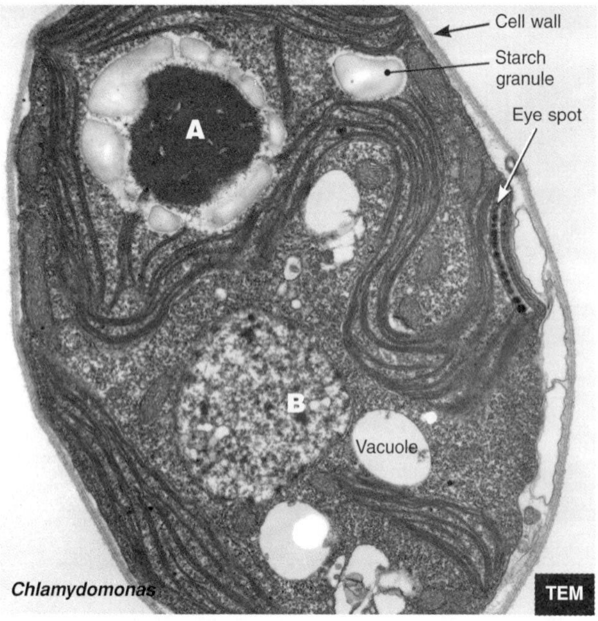
Cell wall
Starch granule
Eye spot
A
B
Vacuole
TEM

Chlamydomonas

Dartmouth College

6. (a) Identify the organelle labelled **A**:

(b) Describe the function of this organelle:

(c) Identify the organelle labelled B. What is the dark granular material you can see?

(d) Identify the ribbon-like structures in this image, and explain how you came to your conclusion about what they are:

ISBN: 978-1-927173-73-2

Fungal Cells

The fungi are a large, successful group of eukaryotes that includes the yeasts, molds, and fleshy fungi. The study of fungi is called **mycology**. All fungi are chemoheterotrophs: they lack chlorophyll and require organic compounds for a source of energy and carbon. Most fungi are also **saprophytic**, feeding on dead material, although some are parasitic or mutualistic. Fungal nutrition is absorptive and digestion is extracellular and takes place outside the fungal body. Of more than 100,000 fungal species, only about 100 are pathogenic to humans or other animals. However, many are plant pathogens and virtually every economically important plant species is attacked by one or more fungi. Note that the **lichens** have been reclassified into the fungal kingdom. They are dual organisms, formed by a mutualistic association between a green alga or a cyanobacterium, and a fungus (usually an ascomycete). Features of two fungal groups: yeasts and molds are described below.

Single Celled Fungi: Yeasts

Yeasts are nonfilamentous, unicellular fungi that are typically spherical or oval shaped. Yeasts reproduce asexually by fission or budding. They are facultative anaerobes, and are used in the brewing, wine making, and bread making industries.

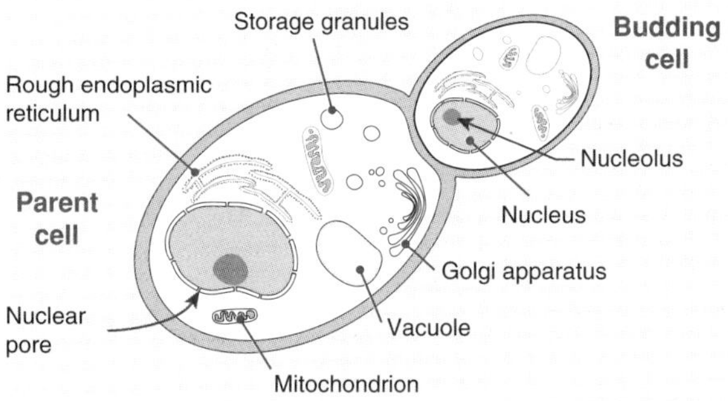

Storage granules
Budding cell
Rough endoplasmic reticulum
Nucleolus
Parent cell
Nucleus
Golgi apparatus
Nuclear pore
Vacuole
Mitochondrion

Filamentous Fungi: Molds

Molds are multicellular, filamentous fungi often divided by septa into uni-nucleate, cell-like units. When conditions are favorable, hyphae grow to form a filamentous mass called a **mycelium**.

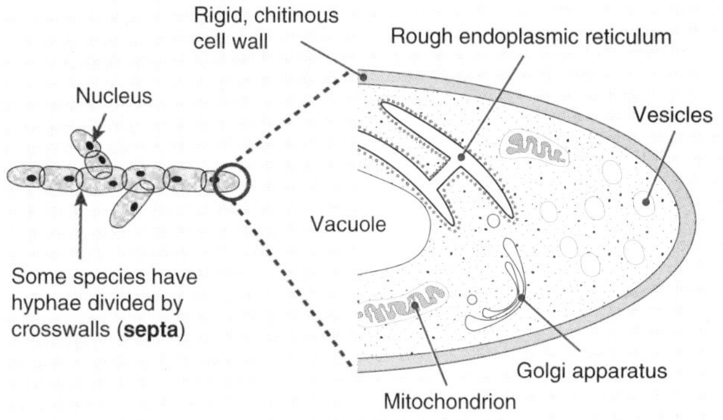

Rigid, chitinous cell wall
Rough endoplasmic reticulum
Nucleus
Vesicles
Vacuole
Some species have hyphae divided by crosswalls (septa)
Golgi apparatus
Mitochondrion

Reproduction in a Filamentous Fungus, *Rhizopus*

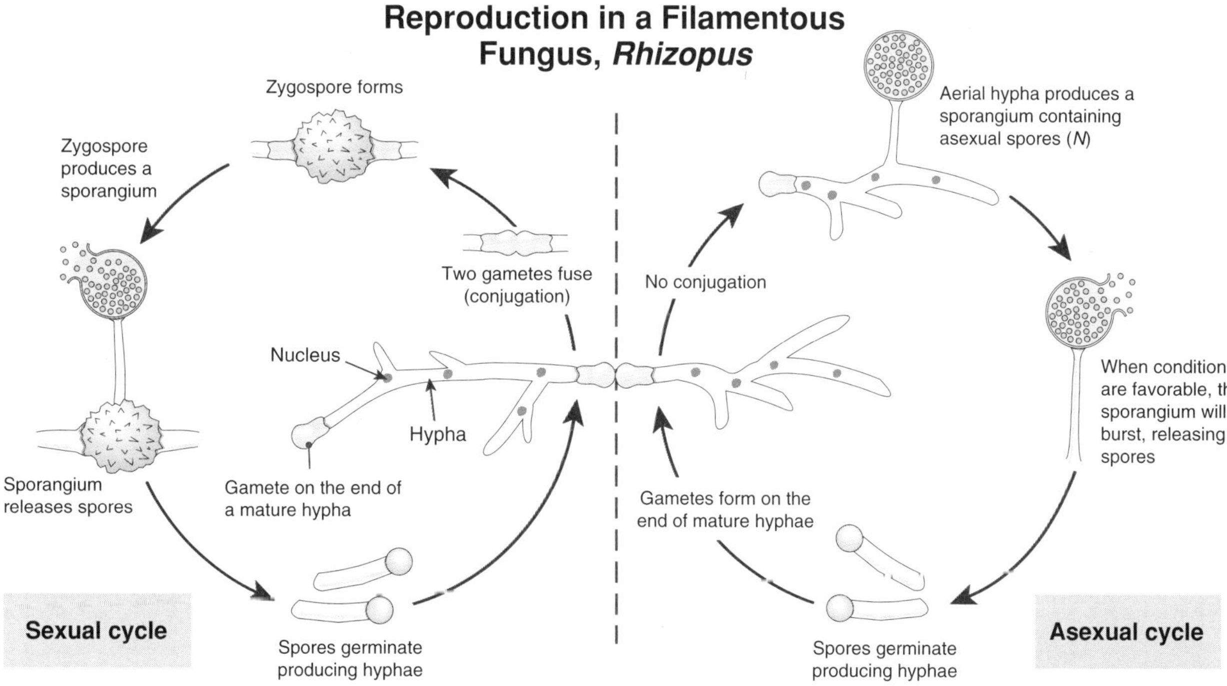

Zygospore forms
Zygospore produces a sporangium
Two gametes fuse (conjugation)
No conjugation
Aerial hypha produces a sporangium containing asexual spores (N)
Nucleus
Hypha
When conditions are favorable, the sporangium will burst, releasing spores
Sporangium releases spores
Gamete on the end of a mature hypha
Gametes form on the end of mature hyphae
Sexual cycle
Spores germinate producing hyphae
Spores germinate producing hyphae
Asexual cycle

1. List three distinguishing features of fungi: ____________________

2. Outline the key differences in the reproductive strategies of yeasts and molds: ____________________

3. Identify two commonly exploited fungal species and state how they are used:

   (a) ____________________

   (b) ____________________

ISBN: 978-1-927173-73-2

Plant Cells

Plant cells are eukaryotic cells. Eukaryotic cells have a similar basic structure, but may vary in size, shape, and function. Certain features are common to almost all eukaryotic cells, including their three main regions: a **nucleus** (usually located near the center of the cell), surrounded by a watery **cytoplasm**, which is itself enclosed by the **plasma membrane**. Plant cells share many structures and organelles in common with animal cells, but also have several unique features. Plant cells are enclosed in a cellulose cell wall, which gives them a regular and uniform appearance. The cell wall protects the cell, maintains its shape, and prevents excessive water uptake. It provides rigidity to plant structures but permits the free passage of materials into and out of the cell.

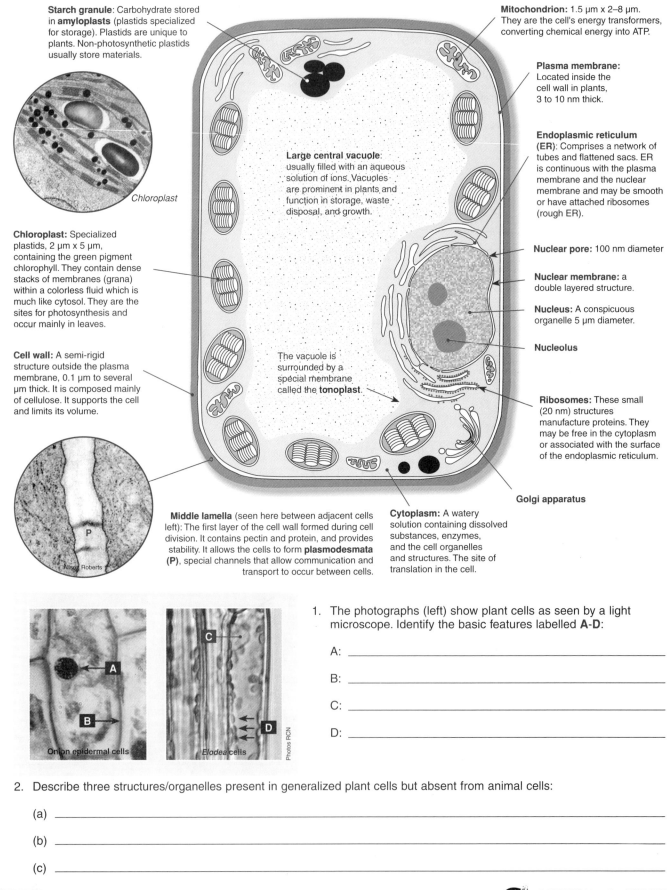

Starch granule: Carbohydrate stored in **amyloplasts** (plastids specialized for storage). Plastids are unique to plants. Non-photosynthetic plastids usually store materials.

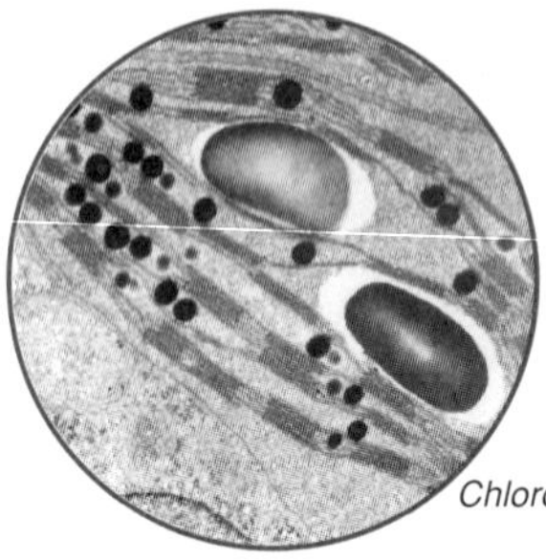

Chloroplast

Chloroplast: Specialized plastids, 2 μm x 5 μm, containing the green pigment chlorophyll. They contain dense stacks of membranes (grana) within a colorless fluid which is much like cytosol. They are the sites for photosynthesis and occur mainly in leaves.

Cell wall: A semi-rigid structure outside the plasma membrane, 0.1 μm to several μm thick. It is composed mainly of cellulose. It supports the cell and limits its volume.

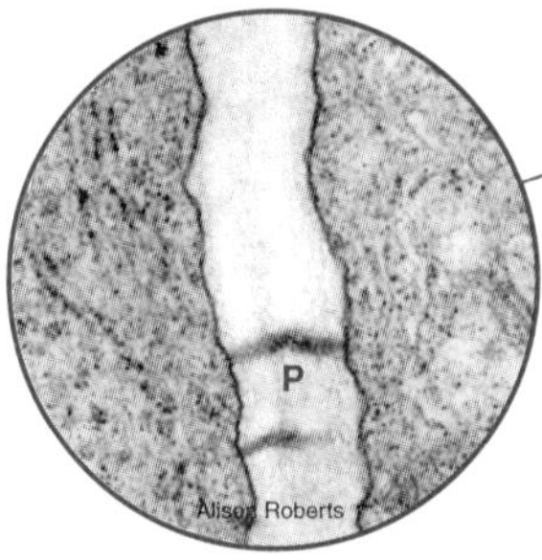
P
Alison Roberts

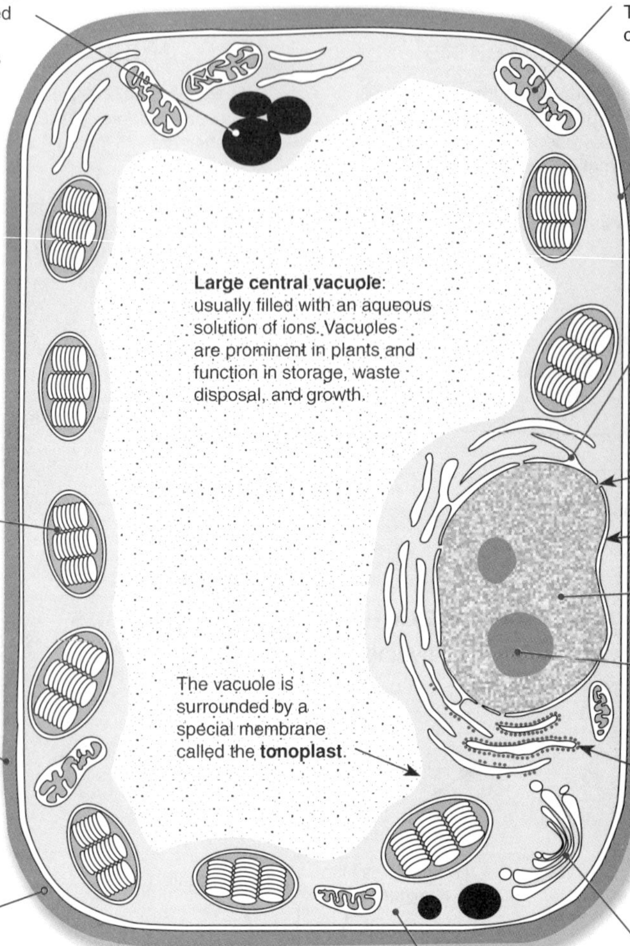
Large central vacuole: usually filled with an aqueous solution of ions. Vacuoles are prominent in plants and function in storage, waste disposal, and growth.
The vacuole is surrounded by a special membrane called the **tonoplast**.

Mitochondrion: 1.5 μm x 2–8 μm. They are the cell's energy transformers, converting chemical energy into ATP.

Plasma membrane: Located inside the cell wall in plants, 3 to 10 nm thick.

Endoplasmic reticulum (ER): Comprises a network of tubes and flattened sacs. ER is continuous with the plasma membrane and the nuclear membrane and may be smooth or have attached ribosomes (rough ER).

Nuclear pore: 100 nm diameter

Nuclear membrane: a double layered structure.

Nucleus: A conspicuous organelle 5 μm diameter.

Nucleolus

Ribosomes: These small (20 nm) structures manufacture proteins. They may be free in the cytoplasm or associated with the surface of the endoplasmic reticulum.

Golgi apparatus

Middle lamella (seen here between adjacent cells left): The first layer of the cell wall formed during cell division. It contains pectin and protein, and provides stability. It allows the cells to form **plasmodesmata (P)**, special channels that allow communication and transport to occur between cells.

Cytoplasm: A watery solution containing dissolved substances, enzymes, and the cell organelles and structures. The site of translation in the cell.

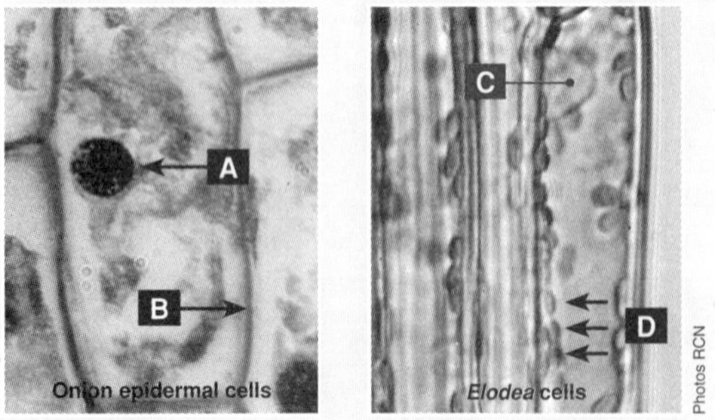
A
B
Onion epidermal cells
C
D
Elodea cells
Photos RCN

1. The photographs (left) show plant cells as seen by a light microscope. Identify the basic features labelled **A-D**:

   A: ______________________

   B: ______________________

   C: ______________________

   D: ______________________

2. Describe three structures/organelles present in generalized plant cells but absent from animal cells:

   (a) ______________________

   (b) ______________________

   (c) ______________________

ISBN: 978-1-927173-73-2

Animal Cells

Animal cells are eukaryotic cells. Unlike plant cells, animal cells do not have a regular shape. In fact, some animal cells (such as phagocytes) are able to alter their shape for various purposes (e.g. engulfment of foreign material). The diagram below shows the structure and function of a typical animal cell and its organelles. Note the differences between this cell and the generalized plant cell. Also see the previous page for further information on the organelles listed here but not described.

Generalized Animal Cell

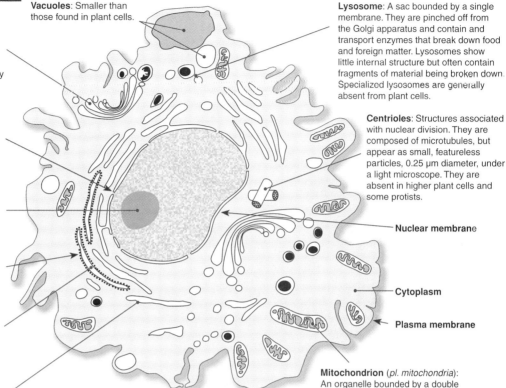

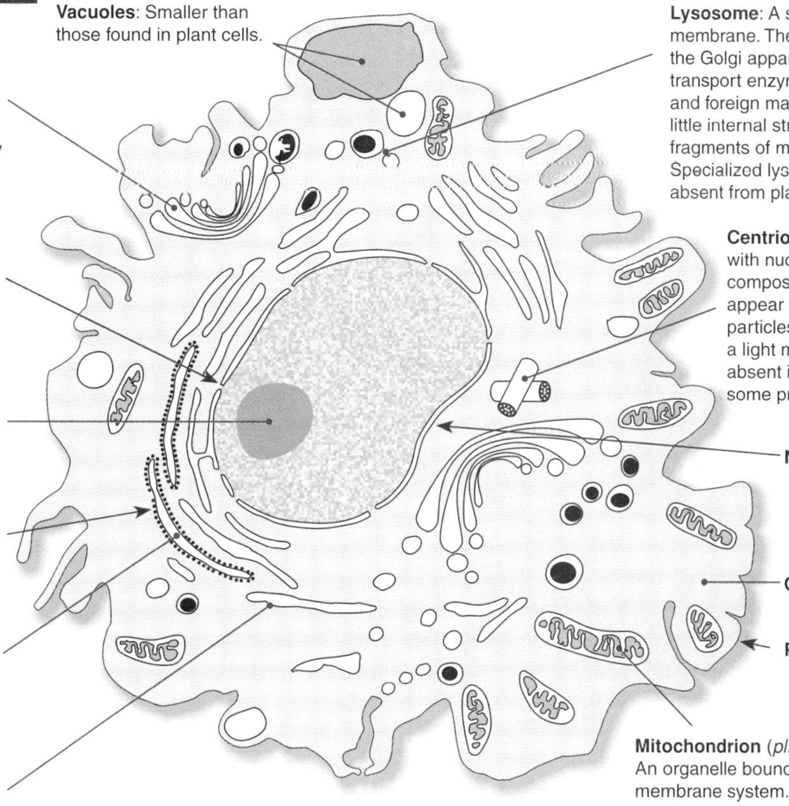
Golgi apparatus: A series of flattened, disc-shaped sacs, stacked one on top of the other and connected with the ER. The Golgi stores, modifies, and packages proteins. It 'tags' proteins so that they go to their correct destination.
Vacuoles: Smaller than those found in plant cells.
Lysosome: A sac bounded by a single membrane. They are pinched off from the Golgi apparatus and contain and transport enzymes that break down food and foreign matter. Lysosomes show little internal structure but often contain fragments of material being broken down. Specialized lysosomes are generally absent from plant cells.
Nuclear pore: A hole in the nuclear membrane. It allows communication between the nucleus and the rest of the cell.
Centrioles: Structures associated with nuclear division. They are composed of microtubules, but appear as small, featureless particles, 0.25 µm diameter, under a light microscope. They are absent in higher plant cells and some protists.
Nucleolus: A dense, solid structure composed of crystalline protein and nucleic acid. They are involved in ribosome synthesis.
Nuclear membrane
Ribosomes: These small structures may be free in the cytoplasm or associated with the endoplasmic reticulum (ER).
Cytoplasm
Plasma membrane
Rough endoplasmic reticulum: A site of protein synthesis.
Smooth endoplasmic reticulum: ER without ribosomes. It is a site for lipid and carbohydrate metabolism, including hormone synthesis.
Mitochondrion (*pl. mitochondria*): An organelle bounded by a double membrane system. The number in a cell depends on its metabolic activity.

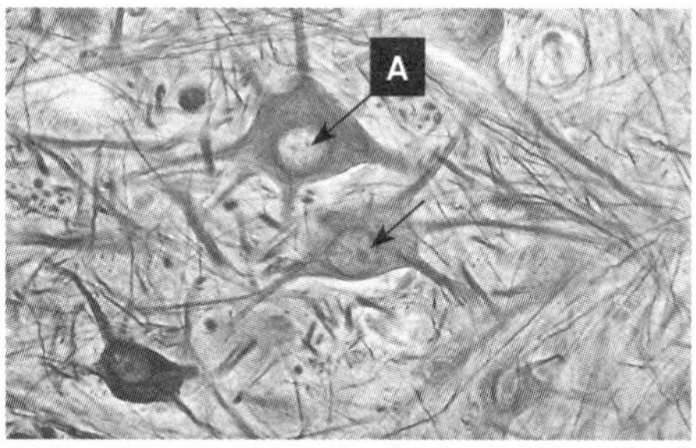
A

Neurons (nerve cells) in the spinal cord

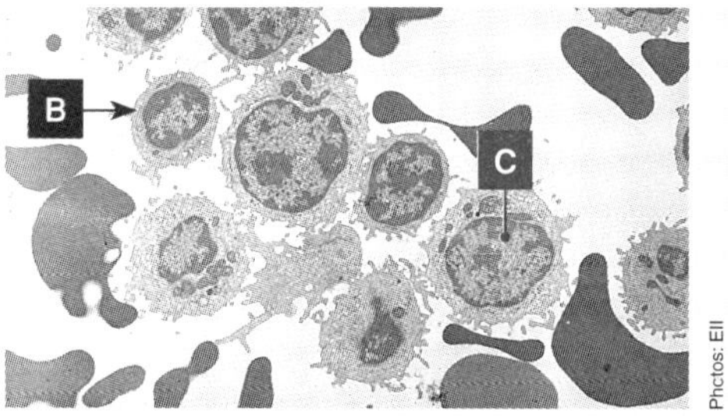
B
C
Photos: EII

White blood cells and red blood cells (blood smear)

1. The two photomicrographs (left) show several types of animal cells. Identify the features indicated by the letters A-C:

   A: ______________________________

   B: ______________________________

   C: ______________________________

2. White blood cells are mobile, phagocytic cells, whereas red blood cells are smaller than white blood cells and, in humans, lack a nucleus.

   (a) In the photomicrograph (below, left), circle a white blood cell and a red blood cell:

   (b) With respect to the features that you can see, explain how you made your decision.

   ____

   ____

   ____

   ____

3. Name and describe one structure or organelle present in generalized animal cells but absent from plant cells:

____

____

ISBN: 978-1-927173-73-2

Identifying Structures in an Animal Cell

Our current knowledge of cell ultrastructure has been made possible by the advent of electron microscopy. Transmission electron microscopy is the most frequently used technique for viewing cellular organelles. When viewing TEMs, the cellular organelles may appear to be quite different depending on whether they are in transverse or longitudinal section.

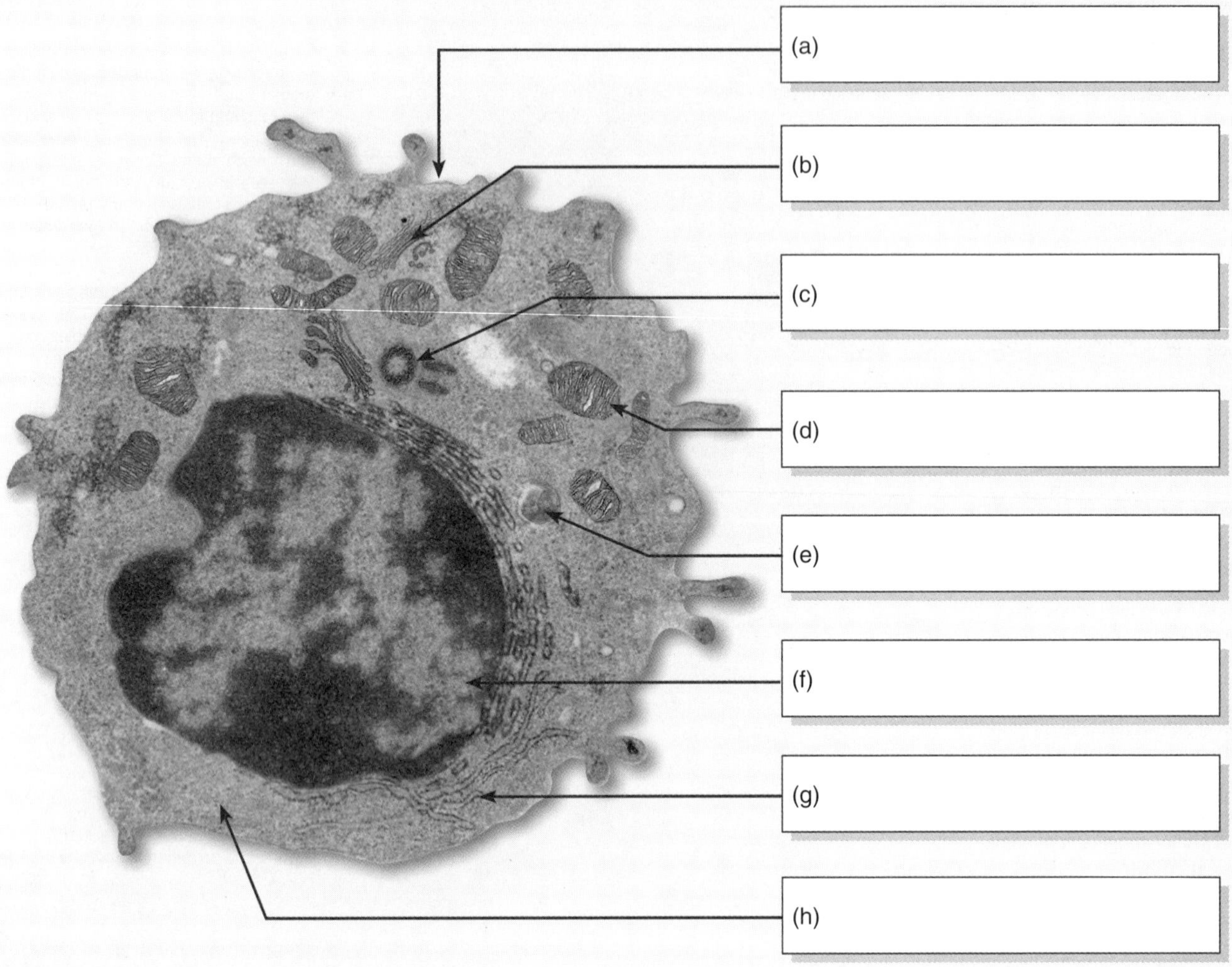
(a)
(b)
(c)
(d)
(e)
(f)
(g)
(h)

1. Identify and label the structures in the cell above using the following list of terms: *cytoplasm, plasma membrane, rough endoplasmic reticulum, mitochondrion, nucleus, centriole, Golgi apparatus, lysosome*

2. Which of the organelles in the EM above are shown in both transverse and longitudinal section?

3. Why do plants lack any of the mobile phagocytic cells typical of animals?

4. The animal pictured above is a lymphocyte. Describe the features that suggest to you that:

   (a) It has a role in producing and secreting proteins:

   (b) It is metabolically very active:

5. What features of the lymphocyte cell above identify it as eukaryotic?

ISBN: 978-1-927173-73-2

Identifying Structures in a Plant Cell

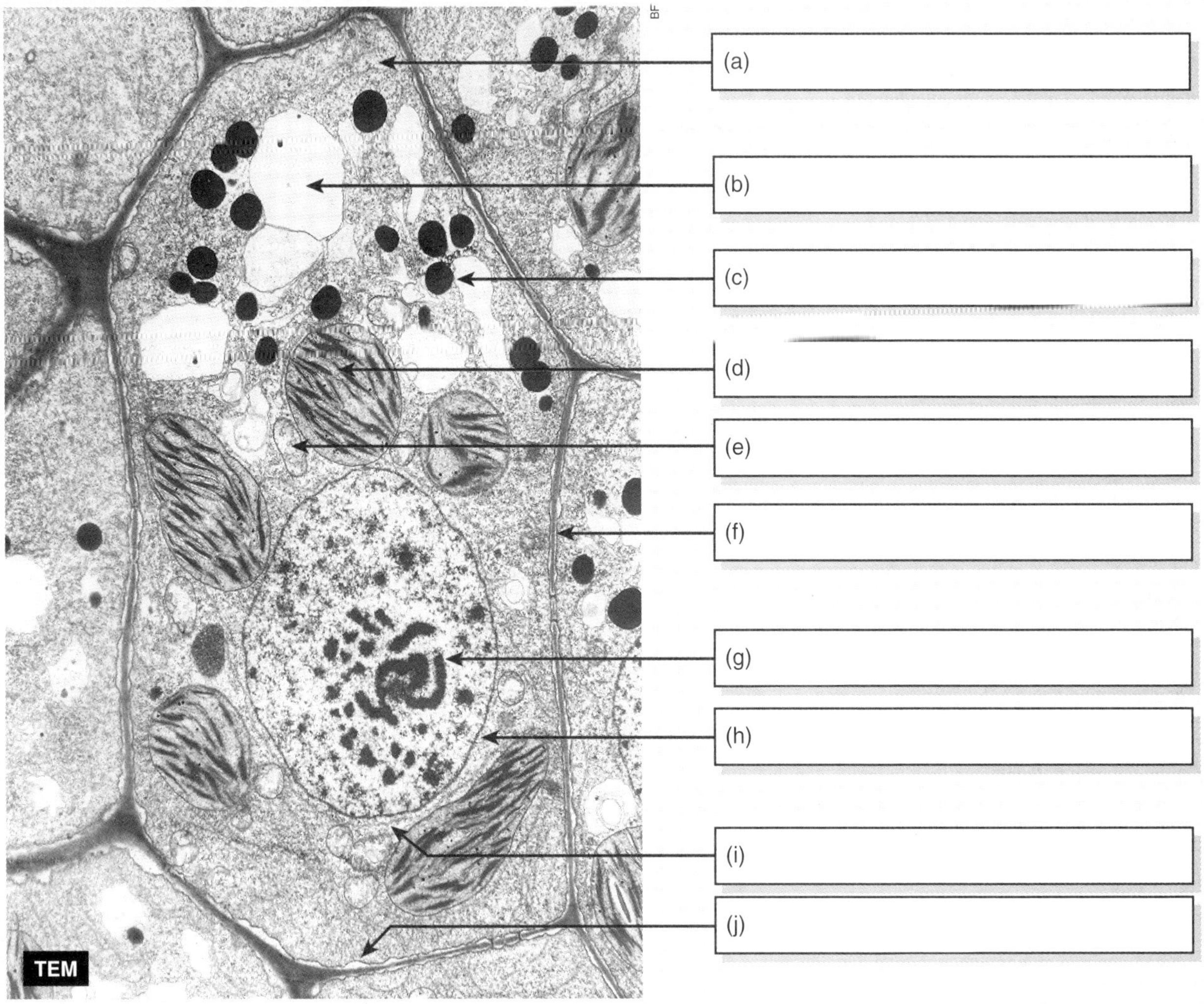
BF
(a)
(b)
(c)
(d)
(e)
(f)
(g)
(h)
(i)
(j)
TEM

1. Study the diagrams on the other pages in this chapter to familiarize yourself with the structures found in eukaryotic cells. Identify and label the ten structures in the cell above using the following list of terms: *nuclear membrane, cytoplasm, endoplasmic reticulum, mitochondrion, starch granules, chromosome, vacuole, plasma membrane, cell wall, chloroplast*

2. State how many cells, or parts of cells, are visible in the electron micrograph above: ______________________

3. Describe the features that identify this cell as a plant cell: ______________________

____

____

4. (a) Explain where cytoplasm is found in the cell: ______________________

____

(b) Describe what cytoplasm is made up of: ______________________

____

5. Describe two structures, pictured in the cell above, that are associated with storage:

(a) ____

____

(b) ____

____

ISBN: 978-1-927173-73-2

Types of Cells

Cells come in a wide range of types and forms. The diagram below shows a selection of cell types from the five kingdoms. The variety that results from cell specialization is enormous. In the following exercise, identify which of the cell types belongs to each of the kingdoms and list the major distinguishing characteristics of their cells.

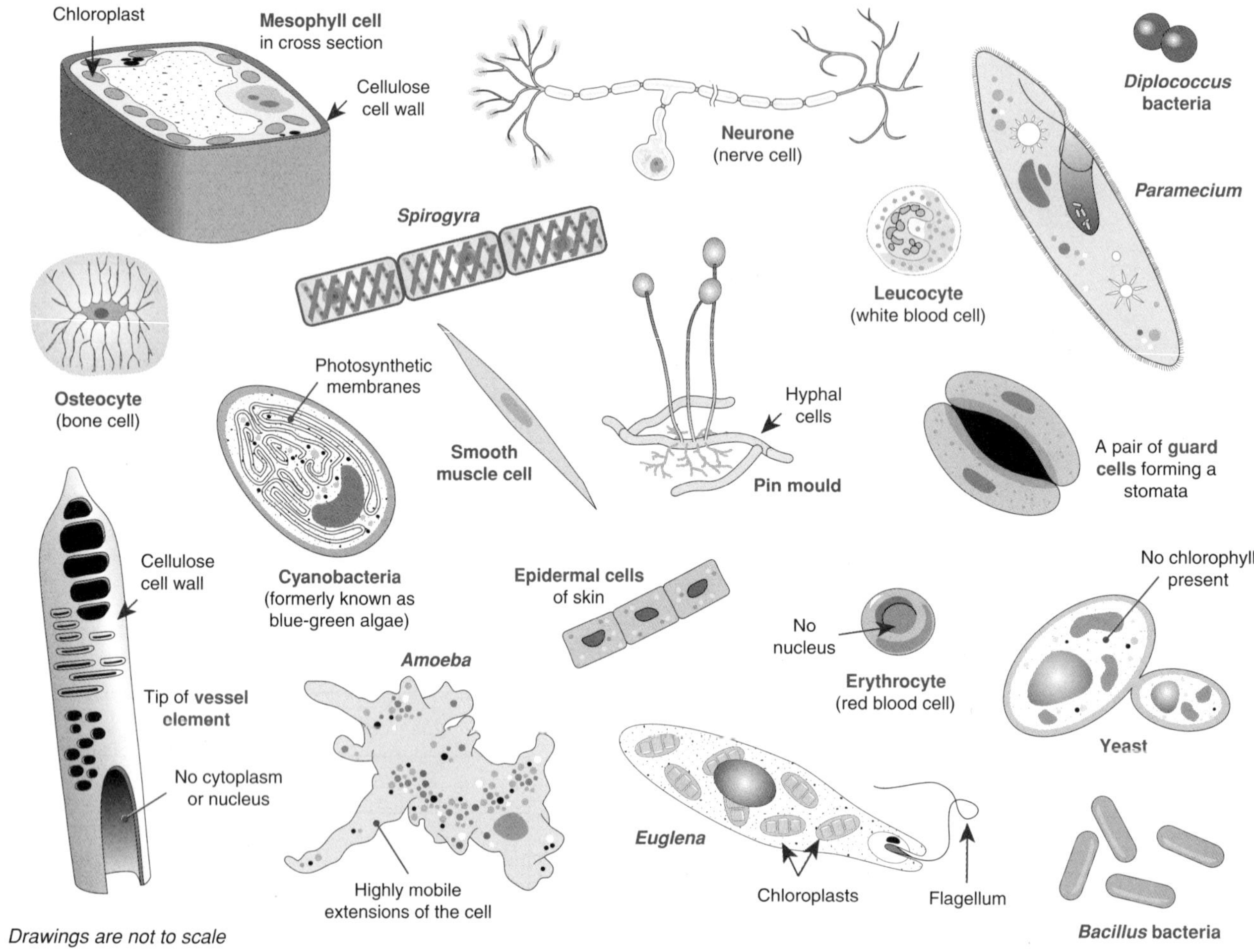

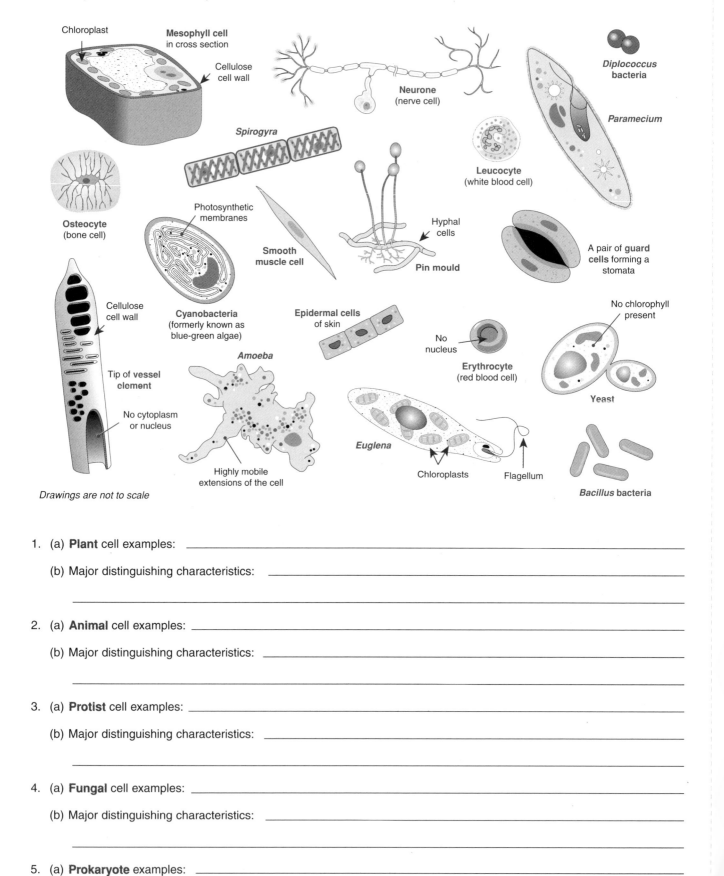

Chloroplast
Mesophyll cell in cross section
Cellulose cell wall
Neurone (nerve cell)
Diplococcus bacteria
Paramecium
Spirogyra
Leucocyte (white blood cell)
Osteocyte (bone cell)
Photosynthetic membranes
Smooth muscle cell
Hyphal cells
Pin mould
A pair of guard cells forming a stomata
Cellulose cell wall
Cyanobacteria (formerly known as blue-green algae)
Epidermal cells of skin
No chlorophyll present
No nucleus
Erythrocyte (red blood cell)
Amoeba
Tip of vessel element
Yeast
No cytoplasm or nucleus
Euglena
Highly mobile extensions of the cell
Chloroplasts
Flagellum
Bacillus bacteria

Drawings are not to scale

1. (a) **Plant** cell examples: ______

   (b) Major distinguishing characteristics: ______

2. (a) **Animal** cell examples: ______

   (b) Major distinguishing characteristics: ______

3. (a) **Protist** cell examples: ______

   (b) Major distinguishing characteristics: ______

4. (a) **Fungal** cell examples: ______

   (b) Major distinguishing characteristics: ______

5. (a) **Prokaryote** examples: ______

   (b) Major distinguishing characteristics: ______

Related activities: *Plant Cells, Animal Cells, Unicellular Eukaryotes*

ISBN: 978-1-927173-73-2

Review of Eukaryotic Cells

The diagrams below show the organelles and structures that are associated with plant and animal cells. From the word lists, revise previous material and use other references to identify and label the organelles depicted in the diagrams of the cells below.

Generalized Plant Cell

WORD LIST
Vacuole, mitochondrion, cell wall, plasma membrane, nucleus, nucleolus, nuclear membrane, Golgi apparatus, endoplasmic reticulum, cytoplasm, starch granule, ribosomes, chloroplast

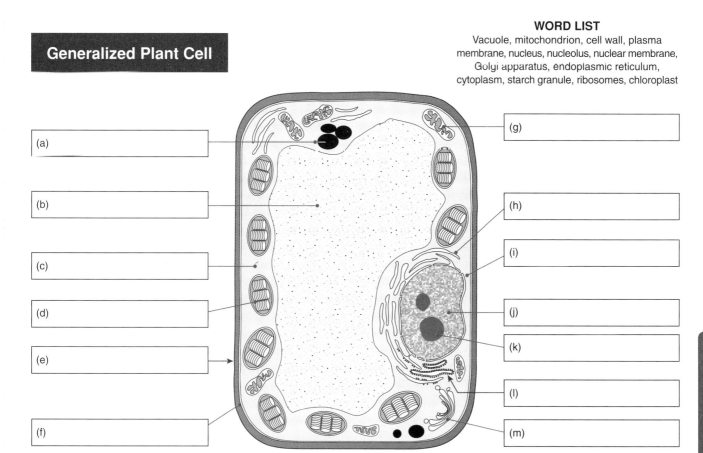

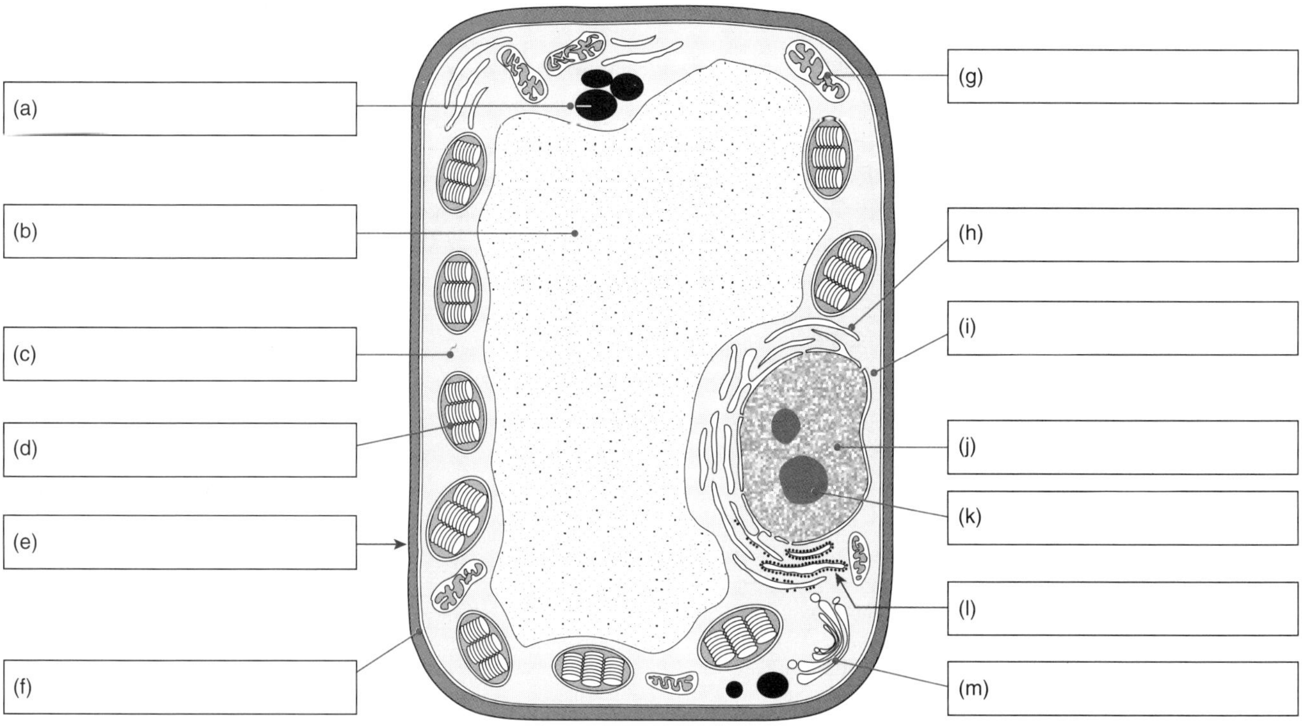
(a)
(b)
(c)
(d)
(e)
(f)
(g)
(h)
(i)
(j)
(k)
(l)
(m)

Generalized Animal Cell

WORD LIST
Lysosome, mitochondrion, plasma membrane, nucleus, nucleolus, nuclear membrane, nuclear pore, Golgi apparatus, endoplasmic reticulum, cytoplasm, centriole, ribosomes

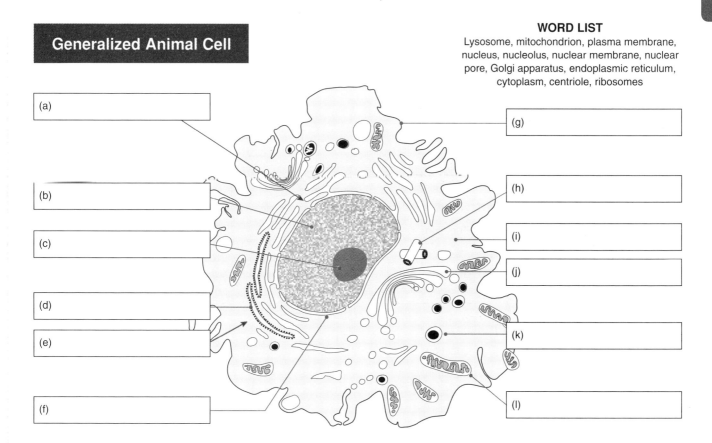

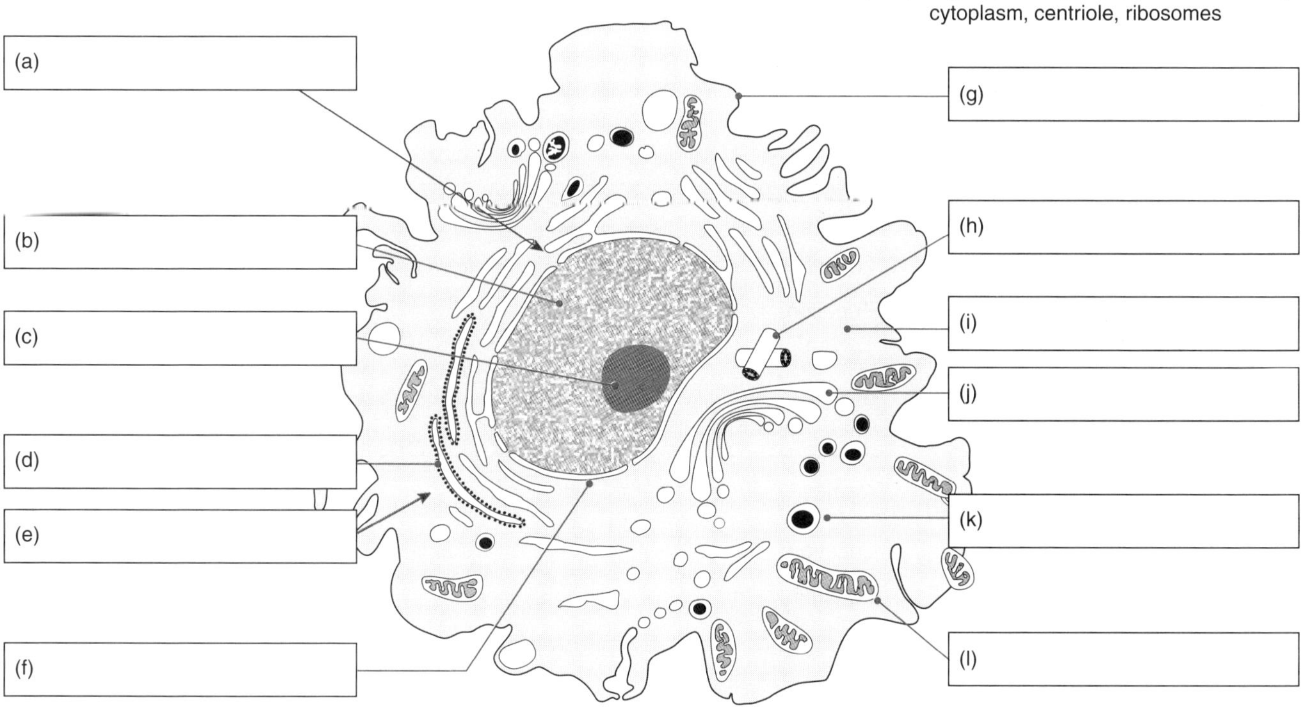
(a)
(b)
(c)
(d)
(e)
(f)
(g)
(h)
(i)
(j)
(k)
(l)

ISBN: 978-1-927173-73-2

Cell Structures and Organelles

The table below provides a format to summarize information about structures and organelles of typical eukaryotic cells. Complete the table using the list provided and by referring to a textbook and to other pages in this topic. Fill in the final three columns by writing either 'YES' or 'NO'. The first cell component has been completed for you as a guide and the log scale of measurements (top of next page) illustrates the relative sizes of some cellular structures. **List of structures and organelles**: *cell wall, mitochondrion, chloroplast, centrioles, ribosome, flagella, endoplasmic reticulum, Golgi apparatus, nucleus, flagella, lysosome, and vacuoles.*

Cell Component	Details	Present in: Plant cells	Present in: Animal cells	Visible under light microscope
(a) 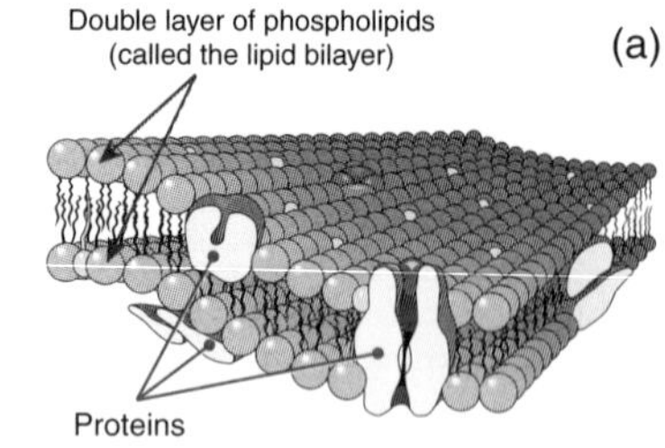 Double layer of phospholipids (called the lipid bilayer) Proteins	Name: Plasma (cell surface) membrane Location: Surrounding the cell Function: Gives the cell shape and protection. It also regulates the movement of substances into and out of the cell.	YES	YES	YES *(but not at the level of detail shown in diagram)*
(b) 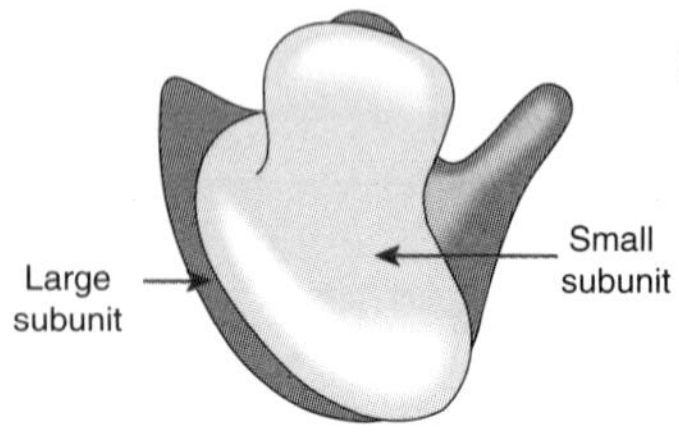 Large subunit Small subunit	Name: Location: Function:			
(c) 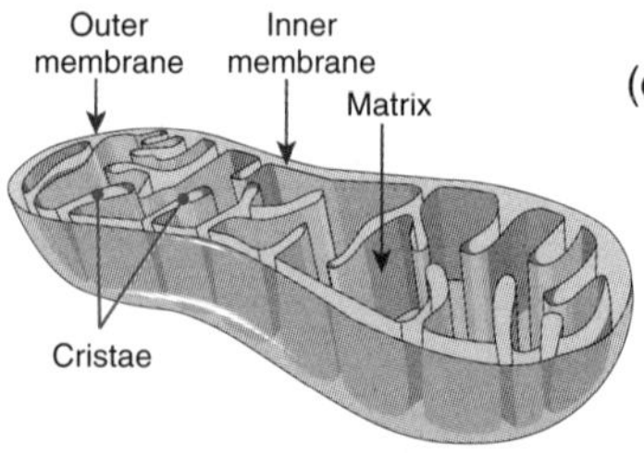 Outer membrane Inner membrane Matrix Cristae	Name: Location: Function:			
(d) 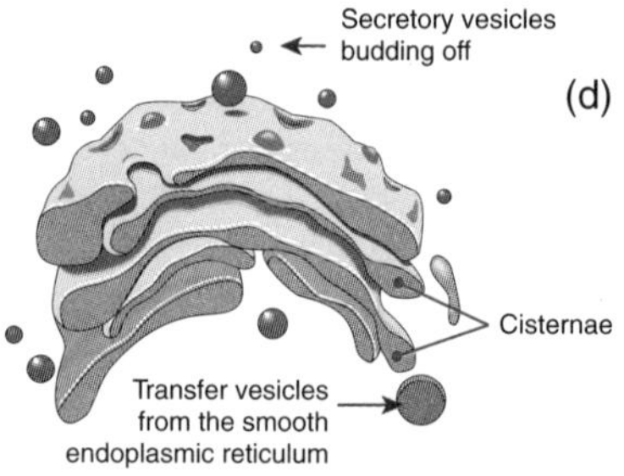 Secretory vesicles budding off Cisternae Transfer vesicles from the smooth endoplasmic reticulum	Name: Location: Function:			
(e) 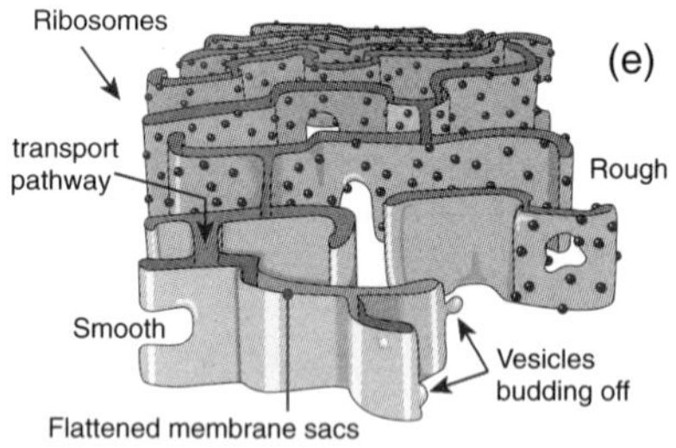 Ribosomes transport pathway Rough Smooth Vesicles budding off Flattened membrane sacs	Name: Location: Function:			
(f) 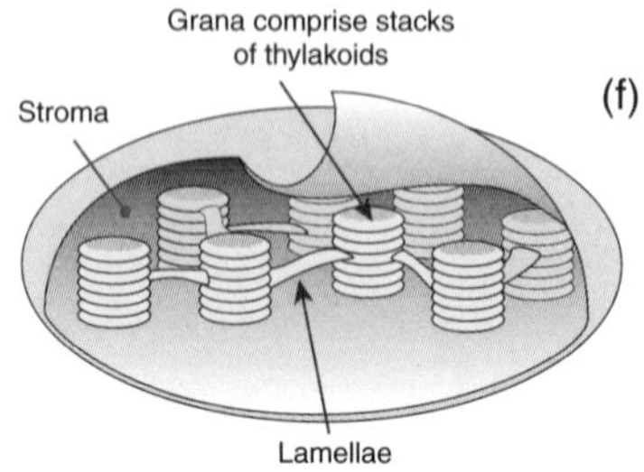 Grana comprise stacks of thylakoids Stroma Lamellae	Name: Location: Function:			

Related activities: *Animal Cells, Plant Cells*

ISBN: 978-1-927173-73-2

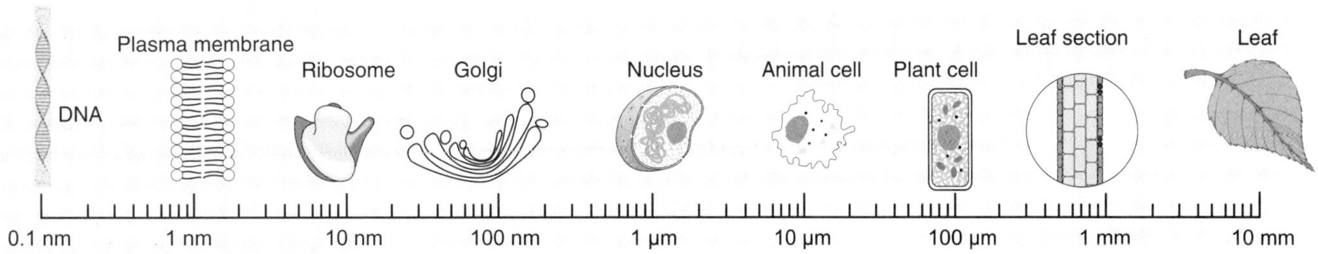
DNA
Plasma membrane
Ribosome
Golgi
Nucleus
Animal cell
Plant cell
Leaf section
Leaf
0.1 nm
1 nm
10 nm
100 nm
1 µm
10 µm
100 µm
1 mm
10 mm

Cell Component	Details	Present in		Visible under light microscope
		Plant cells	Animal cells	
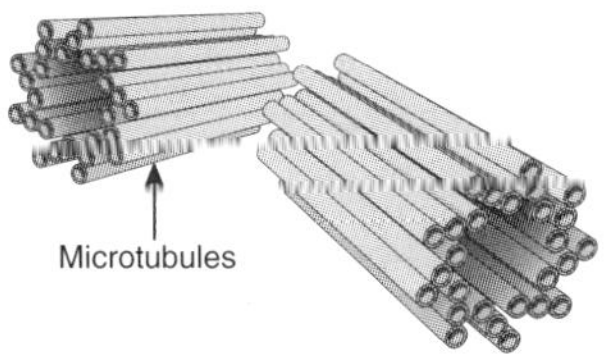 Microtubules (g)	Name: Location: Function:			
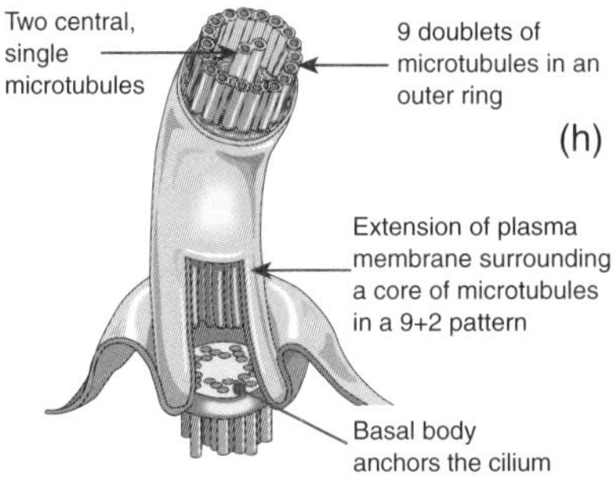 Two central, single microtubules 9 doublets of microtubules in an outer ring Extension of plasma membrane surrounding a core of microtubules in a 9+2 pattern Basal body anchors the cilium (h)	Name: Cilia and flagella (some eukaryotic cells) Location: Function:			
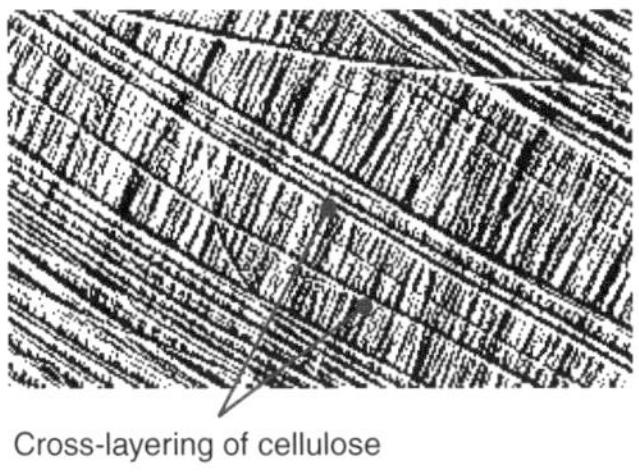 Cross-layering of cellulose (i)	Name: Location: Function:			
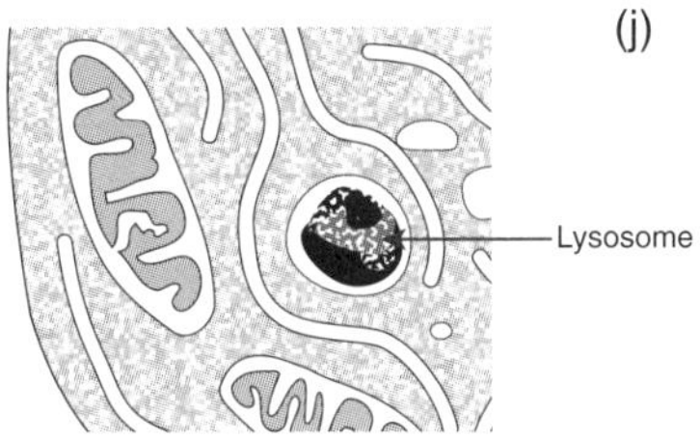 Lysosome (j)	Name: Lysosome Location: Function:			
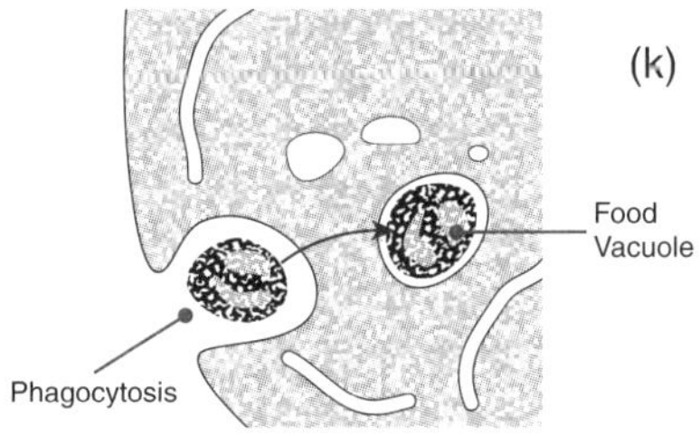 Food Vacuole Phagocytosis (k)	Name: Vacuole (a food vacuole is shown) Location: Function:			
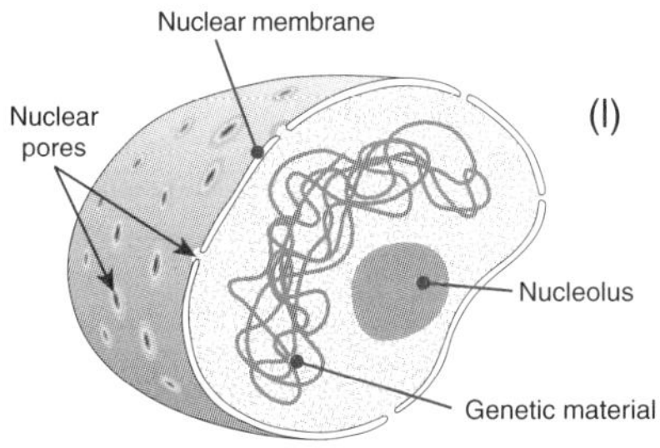 Nuclear membrane Nuclear pores Nucleolus Genetic material (l)	Name: Nucleus Location: Function:			

Cell Structure

ISBN: 978-1-927173-73-2

Interpreting Electron Micrographs

The photographs below were taken using a transmission electron microscope (TEM). They show some cell organelles in great detail. Remember that these photos are showing only **parts of cells, not whole cells**. Some of the photographs show more than one type of organelle. The questions refer to the main organelle in the center of the photo.

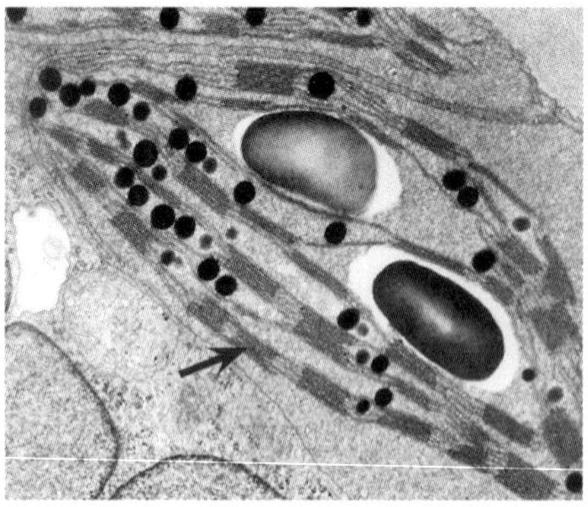

BF

1. (a) Name this organelle (arrowed): ______

   (b) State which kind of cell(s) this organelle would be found in:

   ______

   (c) Describe the function of this organelle: ______

   ______

   ______

   (d) Label two structures that can be seen inside this organelle.

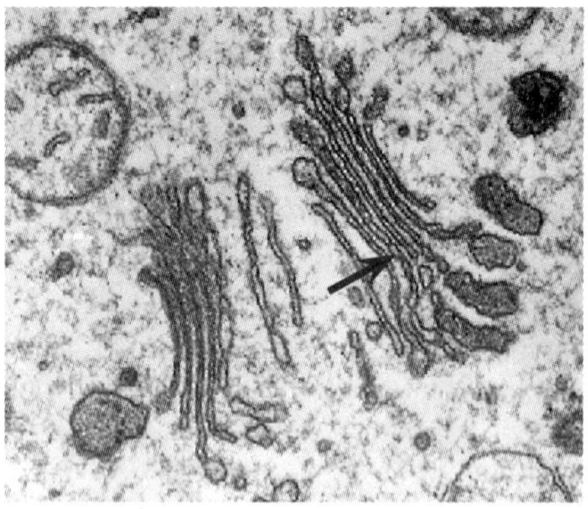

WMU

2. (a) Name this organelle (arrowed): ______

   (b) State which kind of cell(s) this organelle would be found in:

   ______

   (c) Describe the function of this organelle: ______

   ______

   ______

   ______

   ______

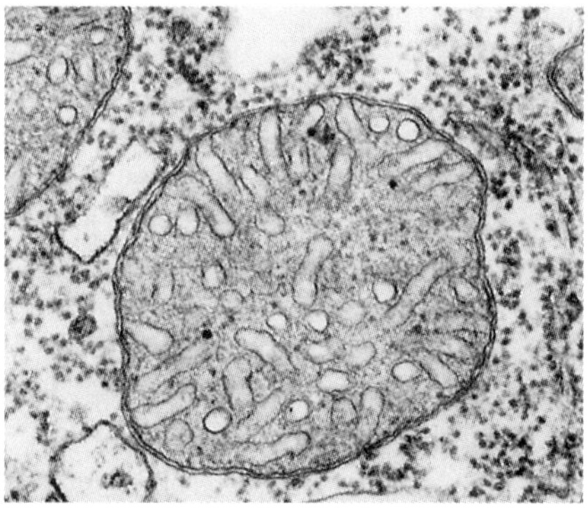

WMU

3. (a) Name the large, circular organelle: ______

   (b) State which kind of cell(s) this organelle would be found in:

   ______

   (c) Describe the function of this organelle: ______

   ______

   ______

   (d) Label two regions that can be seen inside this organelle.

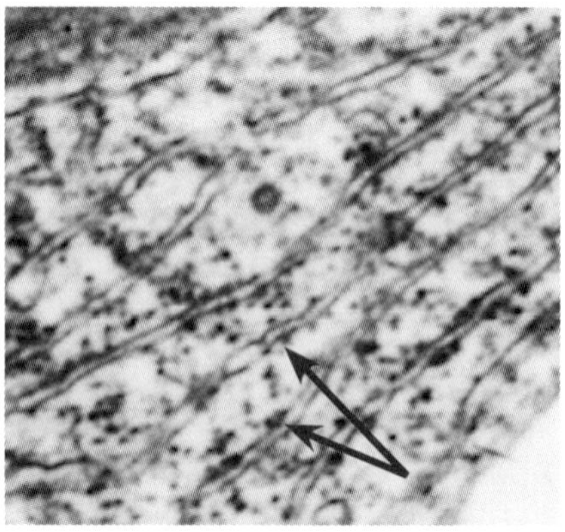

WMU

4. (a) Name and label the ribbon-like organelle in this photograph (arrowed):

   ______

   (b) State which kind of cell(s) this organelle is found in:

   ______

   (c) Describe the function of this organelle: ______

   ______

   ______

   (d) Name the dark 'blobs' attached to the organelle you have labeled:

   ______

Related activities: *Electron Microscopes, Plant Cells, Animal Cells, Cell Structures and Organelles*

ISBN: 978-1-927173-73-2

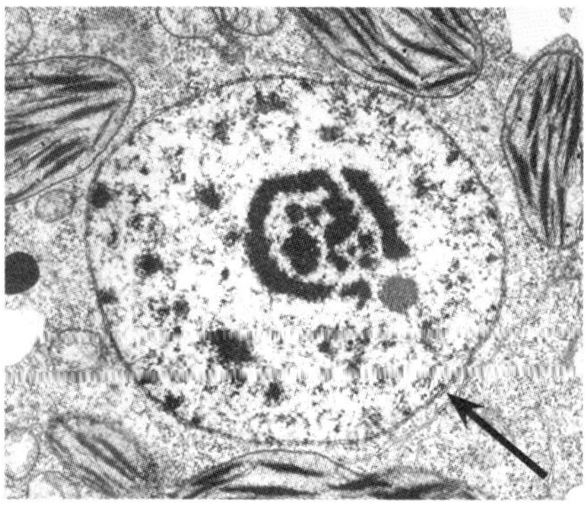

BF

5. (a) Name this large circular structure (arrowed): ______________________

(b) State which kind of cell(s) this structure would be found in:

____

(c) Describe the function of this structure: ______________________

____

____

(d) Label three features relating to this structure in the photograph.

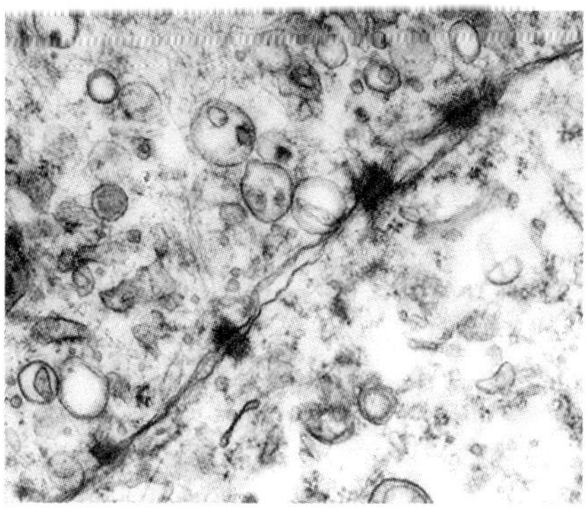

WMU

6. The four dark structures shown in this photograph are called **desmosomes**. They cause the plasma membranes of neighboring cells to stick together. Without desmosomes, animal cells would not combine together to form tissues.

(a) Describe the functions of the plasma membrane:

____

____

____

(b) Label the plasma membrane and the four desmosomes in the photograph.

7. In the space below, draw a simple, labeled diagram of a **generalized cell** to show the relative size and location of these six structures and organelles (simple outlines of the organelles will do):

ISBN: 978-1-927173-73-2

Plant Cell Specialization

Plants show a wide variety of cell types. The eight cell types illustrated below are representatives of these plant organ systems. Each has structural or physiological features that set it apart from the other cell types. The differentiation of cells enables each specialized type to fulfill a specific role in the plant.

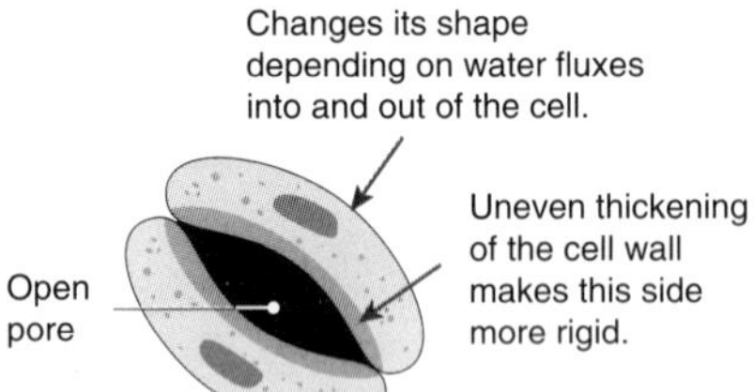
Changes its shape depending on water fluxes into and out of the cell.
Uneven thickening of the cell wall makes this side more rigid.
Open pore
A pair of **guard cells** forming a stoma

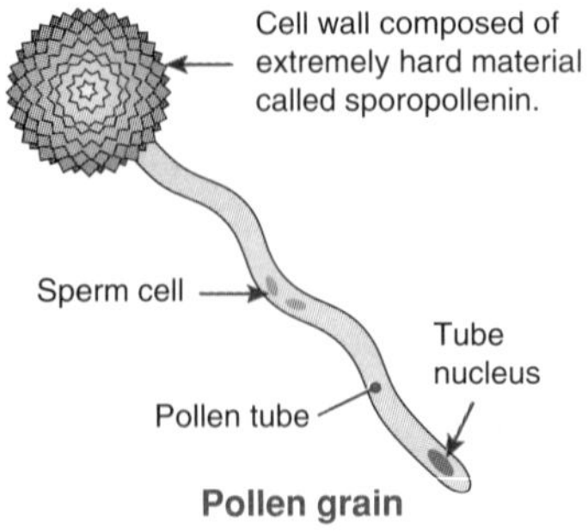
Cell wall composed of extremely hard material called sporopollenin.
Sperm cell
Tube nucleus
Pollen tube
Pollen grain

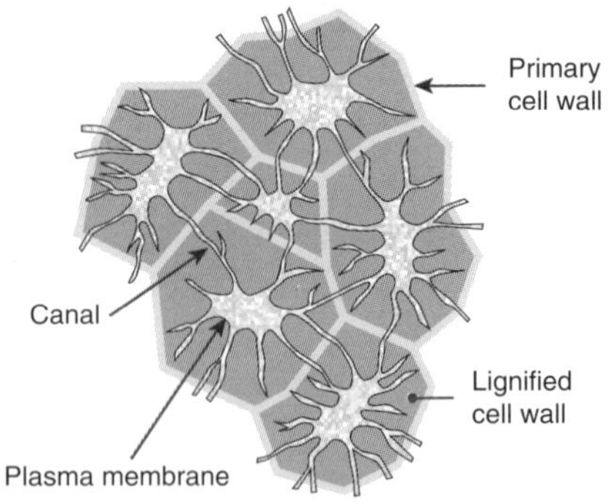
Primary cell wall
Canal
Lignified cell wall
Plasma membrane
Stone cells (sclereids) covering the seed in stone fruit

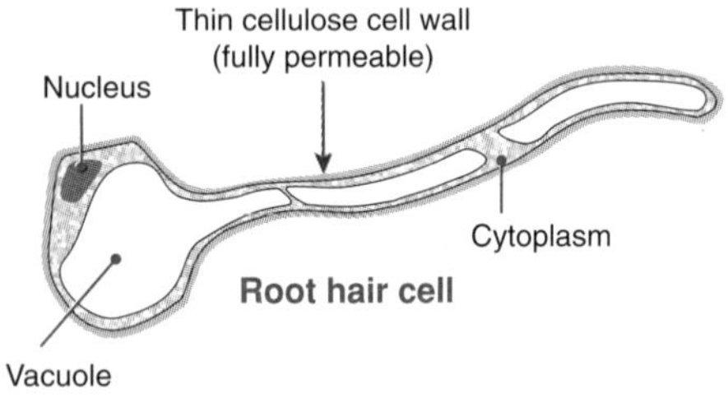
Thin cellulose cell wall (fully permeable)
Nucleus
Cytoplasm
Root hair cell
Vacuole

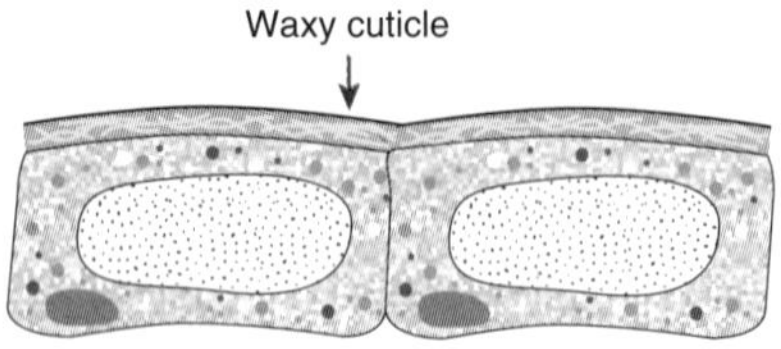
Waxy cuticle
Epidermal cells

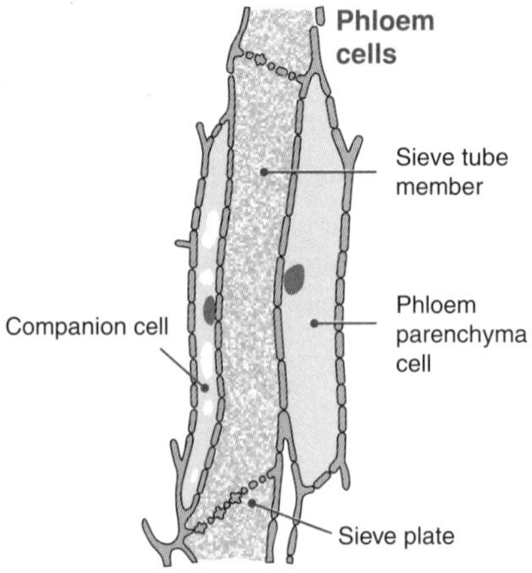
Phloem cells
Sieve tube member
Companion cell
Phloem parenchyma cell
Sieve plate

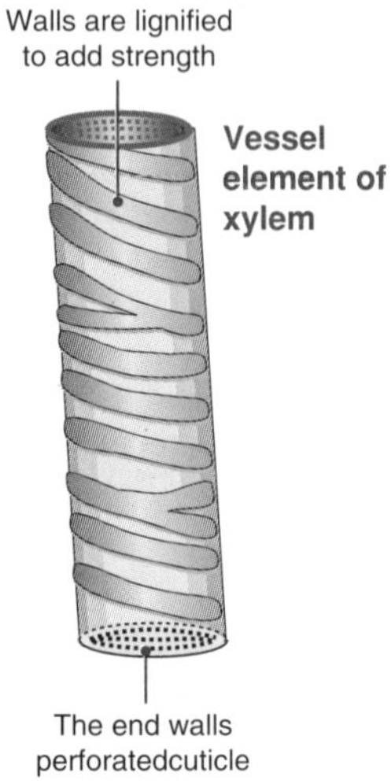
Walls are lignified to add strength
Vessel element of xylem
The end walls perforatedcuticle

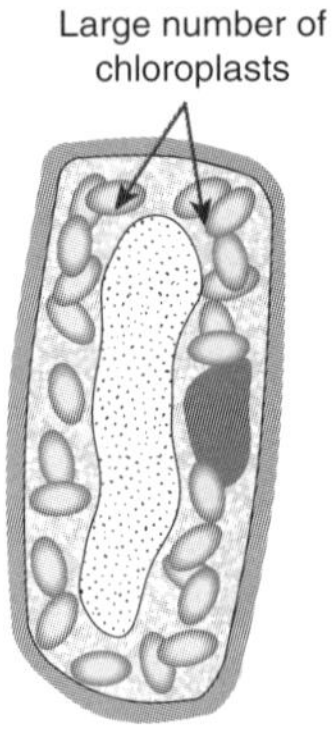
Large number of chloroplasts
Palisade parenchyma cell of the mesophyll

1. Using the information given above, describe the **specialized features** and **role** of each of the cell types (b)-(h) below:

   (a) **Guard cell**: Features: Curved, sausage shaped cell, unevenly thickened.

   Role in plant: Open or close the stoma.

   (b) **Pollen grain**: Features: ______

   Role in plant: ______

   (c) **Palisade parenchyma cell**: Features: ______

   Role in plant: ______

   (d) **Epidermal cell**: Features: ______

   Role in plant: ______

   (e) **Vessel element**: Features: ______

   Role in plant: ______

   (f) **Stone cell**: Features: ______

   Role in plant: ______

   (g) **Sieve tube member**: Features: ______

   Role in plant: ______

   (h) **Root hair cell**: Features: ______

   Role in plant: ______

ISBN: 978-1-927173-73-2

Human Cell Specialization

Animal cells are often specialized to perform particular functions. The eight specialized cell types shown below are representative of the 230 different cell types in humans. Each has specialized features that suit it to performing a specific role.

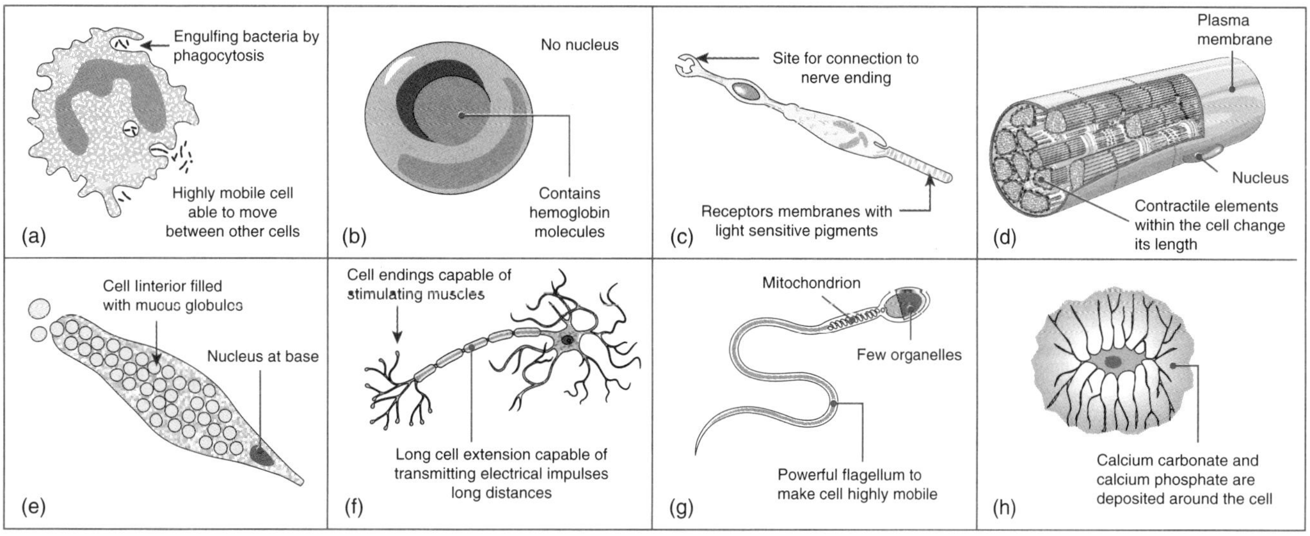

Engulfing bacteria by phagocytosis
Highly mobile cell able to move between other cells
(a)
No nucleus
Contains hemoglobin molecules
(b)
Site for connection to nerve ending
Receptors membranes with light sensitive pigments
(c)
Plasma membrane
Nucleus
Contractile elements within the cell change its length
(d)
Cell linterior filled with mucus globules
Nucleus at base
(e)
Cell endings capable of stimulating muscles
Long cell extension capable of transmitting electrical impulses long distances
(f)
Mitochondrion
Few organelles
Powerful flagellum to make cell highly mobile
(g)
Calcium carbonate and calcium phosphate are deposited around the cell
(h)

1. Identify each of the cells (b) to (h) pictured above, and describe their **specialized features** and **role** in the body:

(a) Type of cell: Phagocytic white blood cell (neutrophil)

Specialized features: Engulfs bacteria and other foreign material by phagocytosis

Role of cell within body: Destroys pathogens and other foreign material as well as cellular debris

(b) Type of cell: ______

Specialized features: ______

Role of cell within body: ______

(c) Type of cell: ______

Specialized features: ______

Role of cell within body: ______

(d) Type of cell: ______

Specialized features: ______

Role of cell within body: ______

(e) Type of cell: ______

Specialized features: ______

Role of cell within body: ______

(f) Type of cell: ______

Specialized features: ______

Role of cell within body: ______

(g) Type of cell: ______

Specialized features: ______

Role of cell within body: ______

(h) Type of cell: ______

Specialized features: ______

Role of cell within body: ______

ISBN: 978-1-927173-73-2

Levels of Organization

Organisms are organized according to a hierarchy of structural levels (below), each level building on the one below it. At each level, novel properties emerge that were not present at the simpler level. Hierarchical organization allows specialized cells to group together into tissues and organs to perform a particular function. This improves efficiency of function in the organism.

In the spaces provided for each question below, assign each of the examples listed to one of the levels of organization as indicated.

1. **Animals**: *epinephrine, blood, bone, brain, cardiac muscle, cartilage, collagen, DNA, heart, leukocyte, lysosome, mast cell, nervous system, neuron, phospholipid, reproductive system, ribosomes, Schwann cell, spleen, squamous epithelium.*

   (a) Molecular level: ______________________

   (b) Organelles: ______________________

   (c) Cells: ______________________

   (d) Tissues: ______________________

   (e) Organs: ______________________

   (f) Organ system: ______________________

2. **Plants**: *cellulose, chloroplasts, collenchyma, companion cells, DNA, epidermal cell, fibers, flowers, leaf, mesophyll, parenchyma, pectin, phloem, phospholipid, ribosomes, roots, sclerenchyma, tracheid.*

   (a) Molecular level: ______________________

   (b) Organelles: ______________________

   (c) Cells: ______________________

   (d) Tissues: ______________________

   (e) Organs: ______________________

MOLECULAR LEVEL

Atoms and molecules form the most basic level of organization. This level includes all the chemicals essential for maintaining life, e.g. water, ions, fats, carbohydrates, amino acids, proteins, and nucleic acids.

ORGANELLE LEVEL

Many diverse molecules may associate together to form complex, specialized cellular organelles, where metabolic reactions may be compartmentalized, e.g. mitochondria, Golgi apparatus, endoplasmic reticulum, chloroplasts.

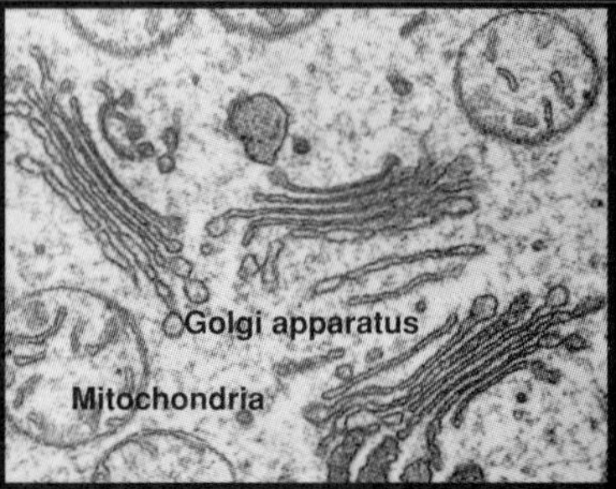
Golgi apparatus
Mitochondria
WMU

CELLULAR LEVEL

Cells are the basic structural and functional units of an organism. Each specialized cell type has a different structure and role as a result of cellular differentiation during development.
***Animal examples** include: epithelial cells, osteoblasts, muscle fibers.*
***Plant examples** include: sclereids, xylem vessels, sieve tubes.*

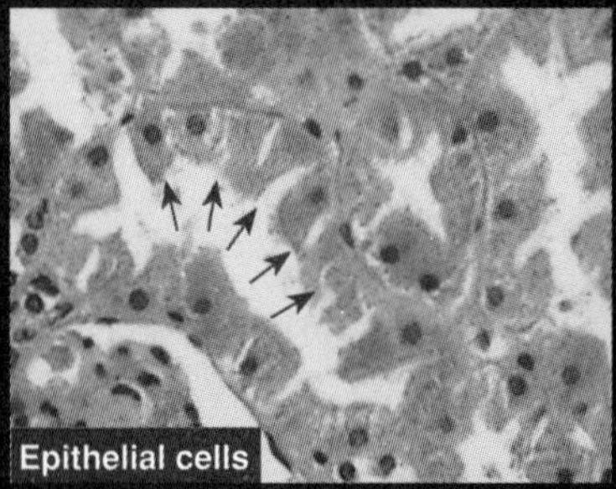
EII
Epithelial cells

TISSUE LEVEL

Tissues are collections of specialized cells of the same origin that together carry out a specific function.
***Animal examples** include: epithelial tissue, bone, muscle.*
***Plant examples** include: phloem, chlorenchyma, endodermis, xylem.*

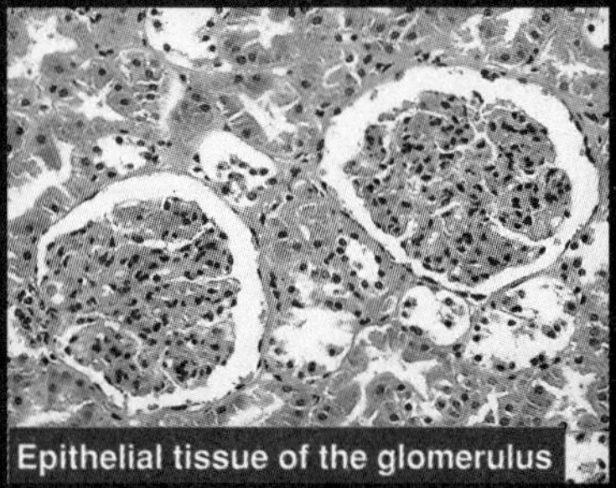
Epithelial tissue of the glomerulus

ORGAN LEVEL

Organs are formed by the functional grouping together of multiple tissues. They have a definite form and structure.
***Animal examples** include: stomach, heart, lungs, brain, kidney.*
***Plant examples** include: leaves, roots, storage organs, ovary.*

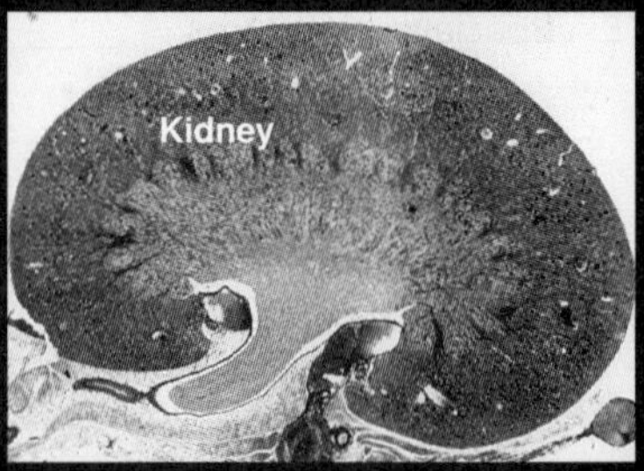
RCN
Kidney

ORGAN SYSTEM LEVEL

In animals, organs form parts of larger units called **organ systems**. An organ system is an association of organs with a common function, e.g. digestive system, cardiovascular system, urinary system. In all, eleven organ systems make up a mammalian **organism.**

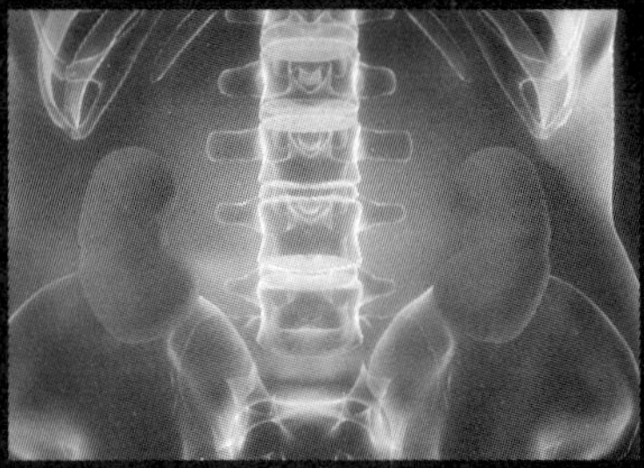

ISBN: 978-1-927173-73-2

Animal Tissues

The study of tissues (plant or animal) is called **histology**. The cells of a tissue, and their associated extracellular substances, e.g. collagen, are grouped together to perform particular functions. Tissues improve the efficiency of operation because they enable tasks to be shared amongst various specialized cells. **Animal tissues** can be divided into four broad groups: **epithelial tissues**, **connective tissues**, **muscle**, and **nervous tissues**. Organs usually consist of several types of tissue. For example, the heart mostly consists of cardiac muscle tissue, but also has epithelial tissue, which lines the heart chambers to prevent leaking, connective tissue for strength and elasticity, and nervous tissue, which directs the contractions of the cardiac muscle. The features of some animal tissues are described below.

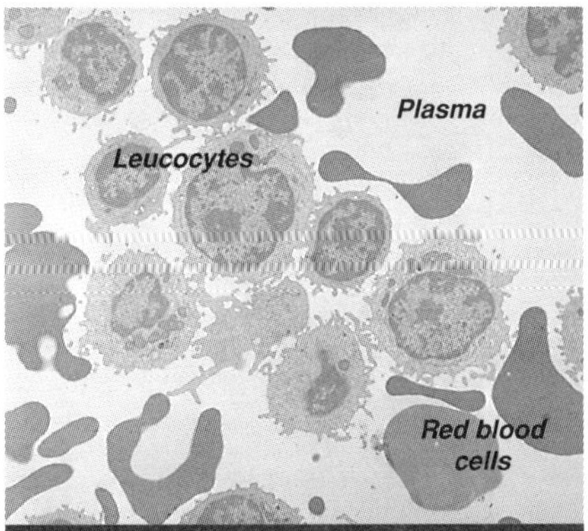
Plasma
Leucocytes
Red blood cells
Blood

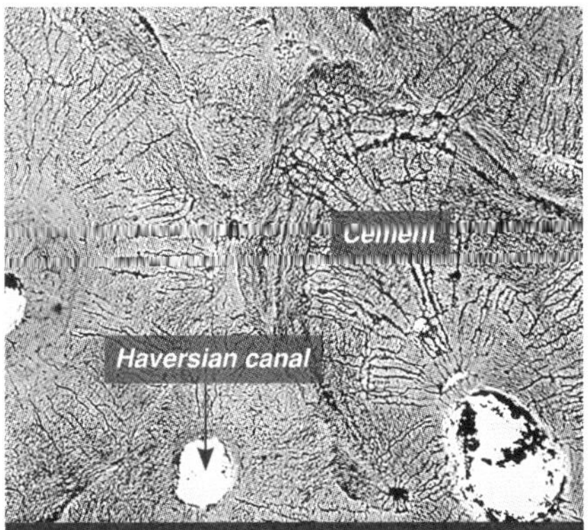
Cement
Haversian canal
Dense bone tissue

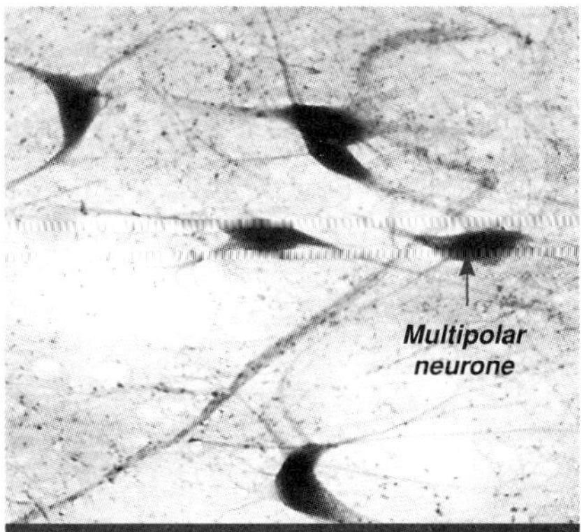
Multipolar neurone
Nervous tissue

Connective tissue is the major supporting tissue of the animal body. It comprises cells, widely dispersed in a semi-fluid matrix. Connective tissues bind other structures together and provide support, and protection against damage, infection, or heat loss. Connective tissues include dentine (teeth), adipose (fat) tissue, bone (above) and cartilage, and the tissues around the body's organs and blood vessels. Blood (above, left) is a special type of liquid tissue, comprising cells floating in a liquid matrix.

Nervous tissue contains densely packed nerve cells (neurons) which are specialized for the transmission of nerve impulses. Associated with the neurons there may also be supporting cells and connective tissue containing blood vessels.

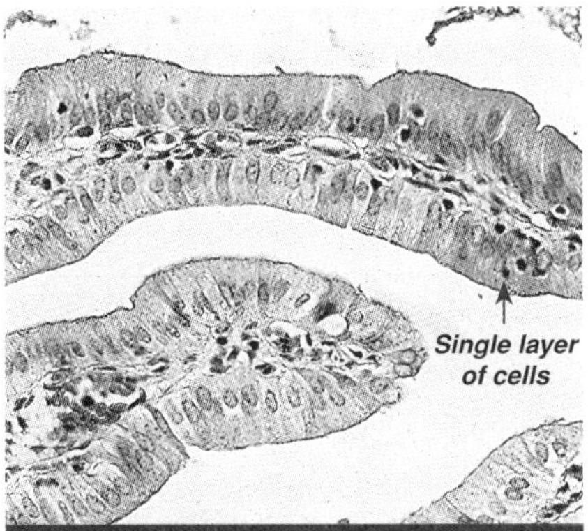
Single layer of cells
Simple columnar epithelium: gall bladder

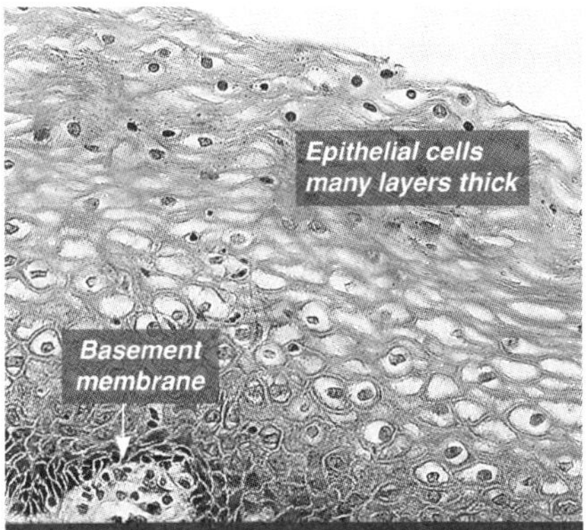
Epithelial cells many layers thick
Basement membrane
Compound stratified epithelium: vagina

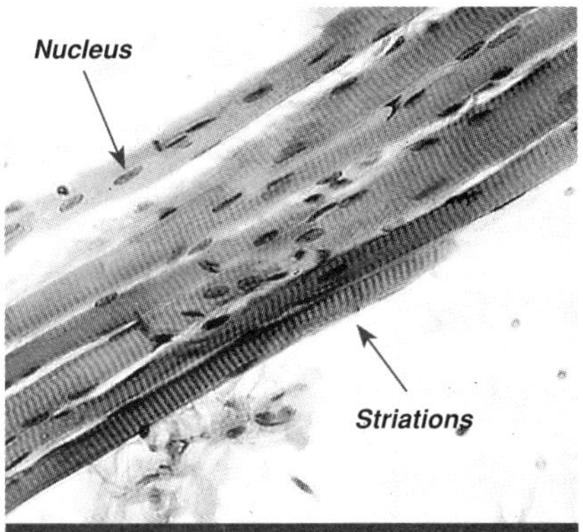
Nucleus
Striations
Skeletal (striated) muscle fibres

Epithelial tissue is organized into single (above, left) or layered (above) sheets. It lines internal and external surfaces (e.g. blood vessels, ducts, gut lining) and protects the underlying structures from wear, infection, and pressure. Epithelial cells rest on a basement membrane of fibers and collagen and are held together by a carbohydrate-based glue. The cells may also be specialized for absorption, secretion, or excretion. Examples: stratified (compound) epithelium of vagina, ciliated epithelium of respiratory tract, cuboidal epithelium of kidney ducts, and the columnar epithelium of the intestine.

Muscle tissue consists of very highly specialized cells called fibers, held together by connective tissue. There are three types of muscle in the body: cardiac muscle, skeletal muscle (above), and smooth muscle. Muscles bring about both voluntary and involuntary body movements.

1. Explain how the development of tissues improves functional efficiency: ____________________

2. Describe the general functional role of each of the following broad tissue types:

(a) Epithelial tissue: ____________________ (c) Muscle tissue: ____________________

(b) Nervous tissue: ____________________ (d) Connective tissue: ____________________

3. Identify the particular features that contribute to the particular functional role of each of the following tissue types:

(a) Muscle tissue: ____________________

(b) Nervous tissue: ____________________

ISBN: 978-1-927173-73-2

Plant Tissues

Plant tissues are divided into two groups: simple and complex. **Simple tissues** contain only one or two cell types and form packing and support tissues. **Complex tissues** contain more than one cell type and form the conducting and support tissues of plants. Tissues are in turn grouped into tissue systems which make up the plant body. Vascular plants have three systems; the dermal, vascular, and ground tissue systems. The **dermal system** is the outer covering of the plant providing protection and reducing water loss. **Vascular tissue** provides the transport system by which water and nutrients are moved through the plant. The **ground tissue** system, which makes up the bulk of a plant, is made up mainly of simple tissues such as parenchyma, and carries out a wide variety of roles within the plant including photosynthesis, storage, and support.

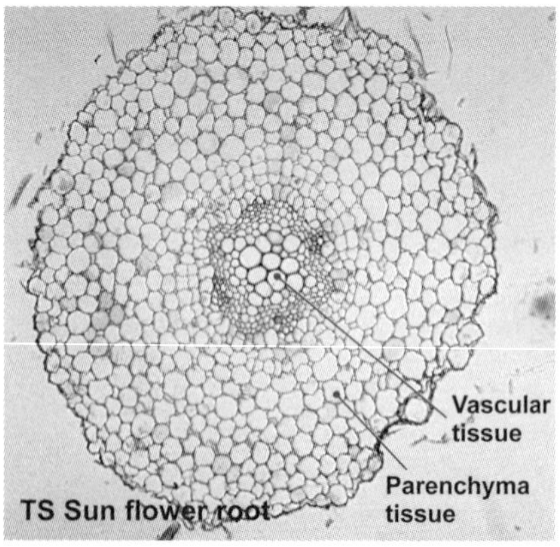
Vascular tissue
Parenchyma tissue
TS Sun flower root
EII

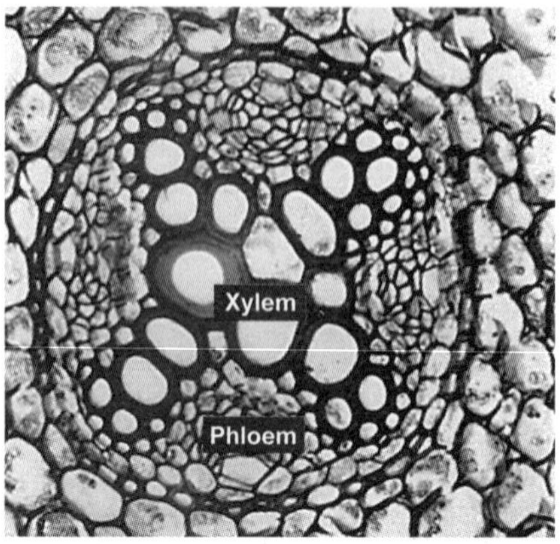
Xylem
Phloem
RCN

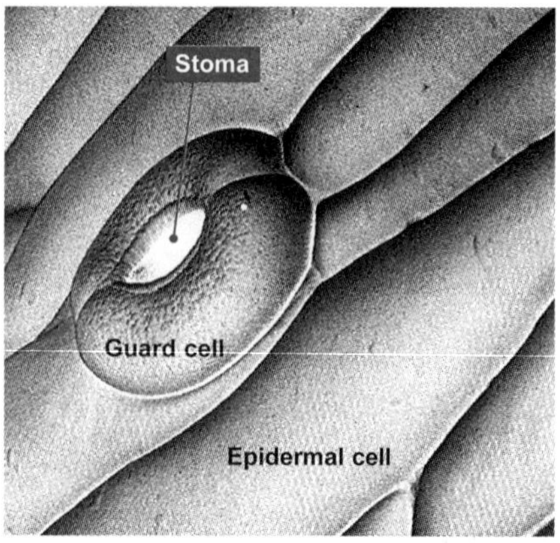
Stoma
Guard cell
Epidermal cell
EII

Simple Tissues

Simple tissues consists of only one or two cell types. **Parenchyma tissue** is the most common and involved in storage, photosynthesis, and secretion. **Collenchyma tissue** comprises thick-walled collenchyma cells alternating with layers of intracellular substances (pectin and cellulose) to provide flexible support. The cells of **sclerenchyma** tissue (fibers and sclereids) have rigid cell walls which provide support.

Complex Tissues

Xylem and phloem tissue (above left), which together make up the plant **vascular tissue** system, are complex tissues. Each is made up of several cell types including tracheids, vessel members, parenchyma and fibers in xylem, and sieve tube members, companion cells, parenchyma and sclerenchyma in phloem. **Dermal tissue** is also complex tissue and covers the outside of the plant. The composition of dermal tissue varies depending upon its location on the plant. Root epidermal tissue consist of epidermal cells which extend to root hairs (**trichomes**) for increasing surface area. In contrast, the epidermal tissue of leaves (above right) are covered by a waxy cuticle to reduce water loss, and specialized guard cells regulate water intake via the stomata (pores in the leaf through which gases enter and leave the leaf tissue).

1. The table below lists the major types of simple and complex plant tissue. Complete the table by filling in the role each of the tissue types plays within the plant. The first example has been completed for you.

Simple Tissue	Cell Type(s)	Role within the Plant
Parenchyma	Parenchyma cells	Involved in respiration, photosynthesis, storage and secretion.
Collenchyma		
Sclerenchyma		
Root endodermis	Endodermal cells	
Pericycle		
Complex Tissue		
Leaf mesophyll	Spongy mesophyll cells, palisade mesophyll cells	
Xylem		
Phloem		
Epidermis		

ISBN: 978-1-927173-73-2

Differential Centrifugation

Differential centrifugation (also called **cell fractionation**) is a technique used to extract organelles from cells so that they can be studied. The aim is to extract undamaged intact organelles. Samples must be kept very cool so that metabolism is slowed and self digestion of the organelles is prevented. The samples must also be kept in a buffered, isotonic solution so that the organelles do not change volume and the enzymes are not denatured by changes in pH.

Differontial Contrifugation

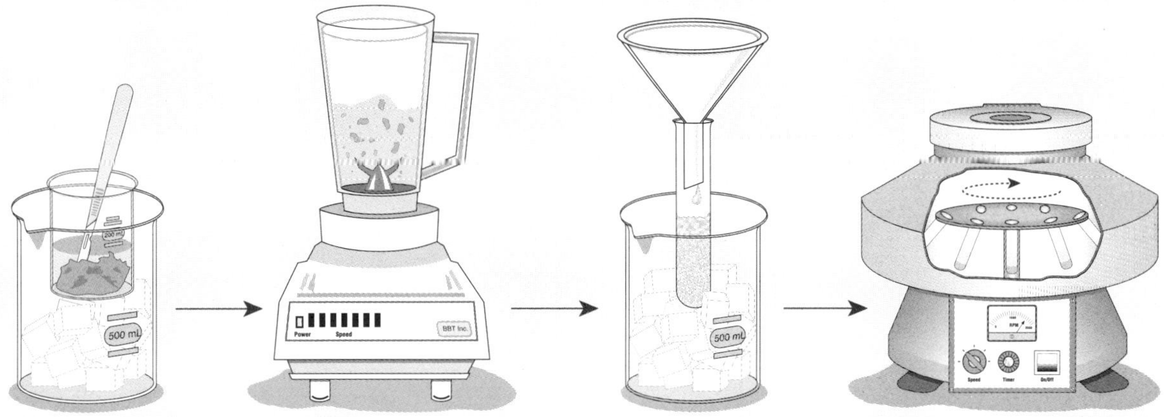
200 mL
500 mL
Power
Speed
BBT Inc.
500 mL
RPM
Speed
Timer
On/Off

1. The sample is chilled over ice and cut into small pieces in a cold, buffered, isotonic solution.
2. The sample is homogenized by breaking down the cells' outer membranes. The cell organelles remain intact.
3. The homogenized suspension is filtered to remove cellular debris. It is kept cool throughout.
4. The filtrate is centrifuged at low speed to remove partially opened cells and small pieces of debris.

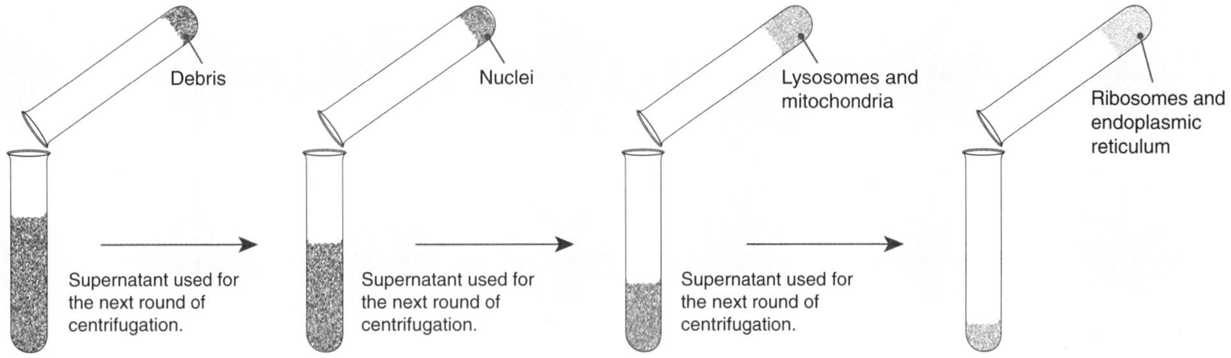
Debris
Nuclei
Lysosomes and mitochondria
Ribosomes and endoplasmic reticulum
Supernatant used for the next round of centrifugation.
Supernatant used for the next round of centrifugation.
Supernatant used for the next round of centrifugation.

5. The supernatant containing the organelles is carefully decanted off.
6. The sample is centrifuged at 500-600 *g* for 5-10 minutes then decanted.
7. The sample is centrifuged at 10 000-20 000 *g* for 15-20 minutes then decanted.
8. The sample is centrifuged at 100 000 *g* for 60 minutes then decanted.

NOTE: In centrifugation, the relative centrifugal force (RCF) is expressed as g , where g represents the gravitational field strength.

1. Explain why it is possible to separate cell organelles using centrifugation: ____________________

2. Suggest why the sample is homogenized before centrifugation: ____________________

3. Explain why the sample must be kept in a solution that is:

   (a) Isotonic: ____________________

   (b) Cool: ____________________

   (c) Buffered: ____________________

4. **Density gradient centrifugation** (right) is another method of cell fractionation. Sucrose is added to a sample, which is then centrifuged at high speed. The organelles will form layers according to their specific densities. Using the information above, label the centrifuge tube on the right with the organelles you would find in each layer.

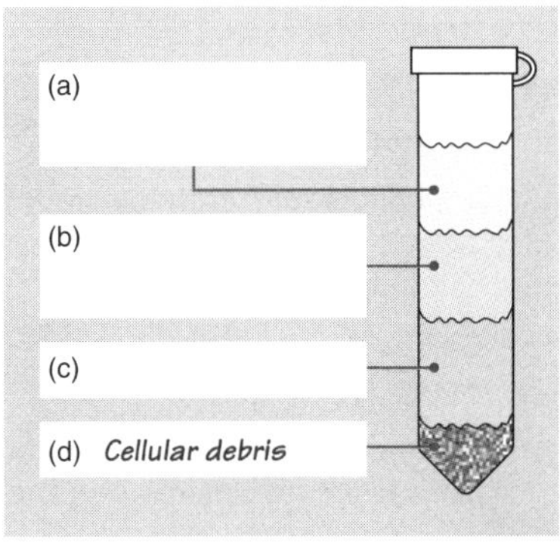
(a)
(b)
(c)
(d) Cellular debris

Cell Structure

KEY TERMS: Crossword

Complete the crossword below, which will test your understanding of key terms in this chapter and their meanings.

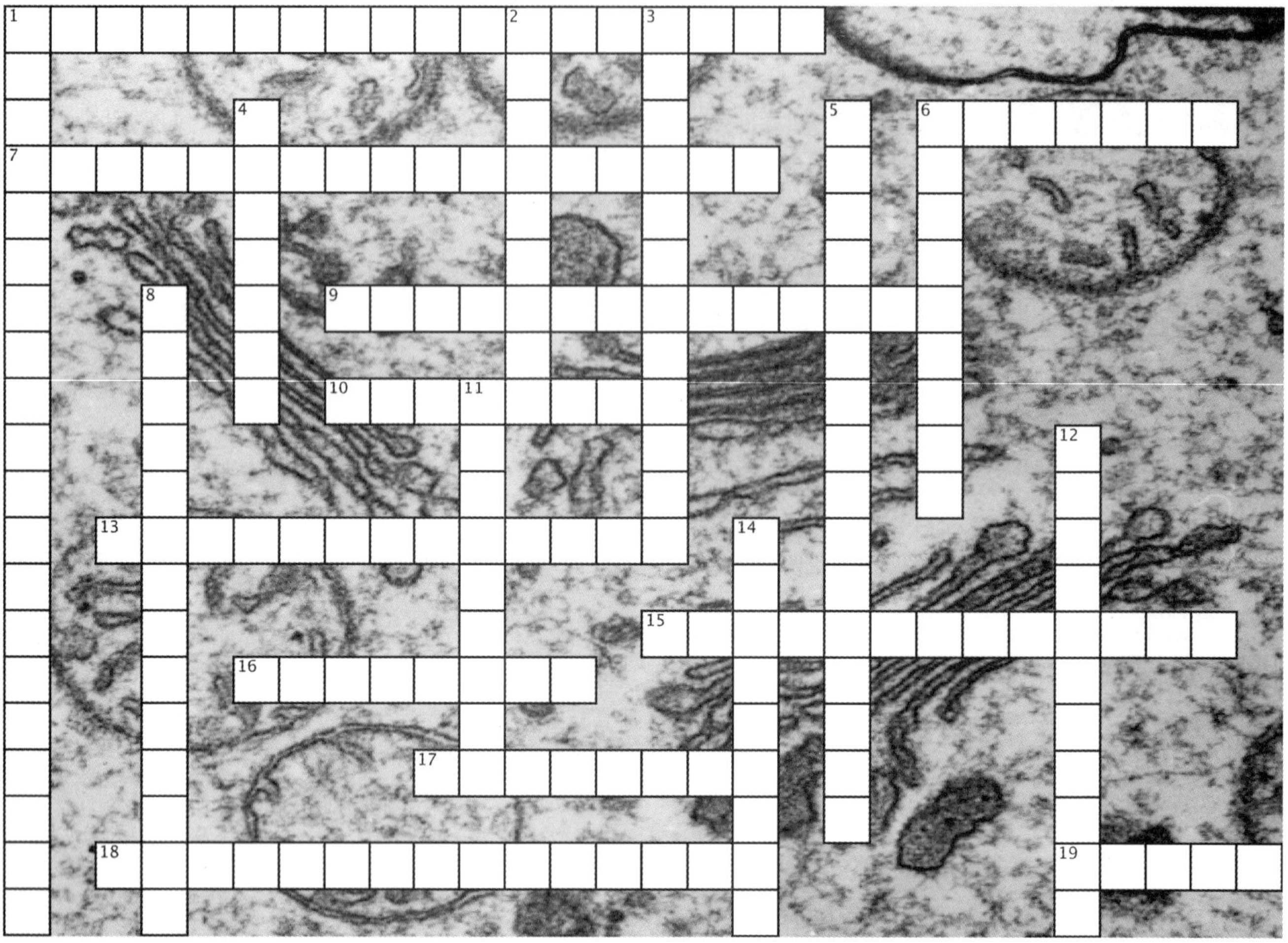

Clues Across

1. An advanced microscope that uses electron beams to produce high resolution images (2 words: 8, 10).
6. Membrane-bound area within a eukaryotic cell where the chromosomes are found.
7. A type of microscope in which lenses use light to magnify objects (2 words: 7, 10)
9. Lipid bilayer membrane surrounding the cell. Proteins are embedded in it and are responsible for the passage of material into and out of the cell (2 words: 6, 8)
10. Membrane-bound vacuolar organelle that contains enzymes that form part of the intracellular digestive system.
13. How many times larger an image is than the original object.
15. Organelle responsible for producing the cell's energy. It appears oval in shape with an outer double membrane and a convoluted interior membrane. It has its own circular DNA.
16. Long, filamentous appendages in bacteria used for locomotion.
17. A structure, present in plants and bacteria, which is found outside the plasma membrane and gives rigidity to the cell (2 words: 4, 4)
18. Cells with a membrane bound nucleus and organelles.(2 words:10,5)
19. A chemical that binds to parts of the cell and allows those parts to be seen more easily under a microscope.

Clues Down

1. An organelle comprising a convoluted membranous stack and divided into rough and smooth regions. It plays a part in protein and membrane synthesis. (2 words: 11, 9)
2. Small structures comprising RNA and protein that are found in all cells. They function in translation of the genetic code (mRNA into proteins).
3. A network of actin filaments and microtubules within the cytosol that provide structure and assist the movement of materials within the cell.
4. A membrane-bound cavity in the cytoplasm of eukaryotic cells, usually filled with an aqueous solution of ions. They are much larger in plant cells than in animal cells.
5. Cells that lack a membrane-bound nucleus or organelles. (2 words:10, 5)
6. An organelle found within the nucleus that contains ribosomal RNA and is associated with the part of the chromosome that codes for rRNA.
8. Organelle that resembles a series of flattened stacks. It modifies and packages proteins and also performs a secretory function by budding off vesicles (2 words: 5, 9)
11. A structural and functional part of the cell usually bound within its own membrane. Examples include the mitochondria and lysosomes.
12. An organelle found in photosynthetic organisms such as plants, which contains chlorophyll and in which the reactions of photosynthesis take place.
14. The watery contents of the cell within the plasma membrane, but excluding the contents of the nucleus.

ISBN: 978-1-927173-73-2

Chapter 3

Cell **Membranes and Transport**

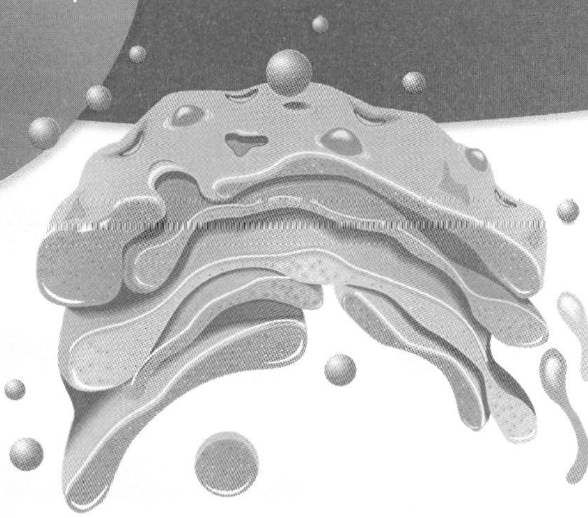

Key concepts

- Cellular metabolism depends on the transport of substances across cellular membranes.
- The plasma membrane forms a selectively permeable barrier to entry and exit of substances into the cell.
- The fluid mosaic model satisfies the observed properties of cellular membranes.
- Substances in cells move by passive or active transport.

Key terms

active transport
amphipathic
aquaporin
carrier protein
cell wall
channel protein
concentration gradient
diffusion
endocytosis
exocytosis
facilitated diffusion
fluid mosaic model
glycolipid
glycoprotein
hypertonic
hypotonic
ion pump
isotonic
osmosis
passive transport
phagocytosis
phospholipid
pinocytosis
plasma membrane
plasmolysis
selectively permeable
surface area: volume ratio
transmembrane protein
turgor

Learning Objectives

☐ 1. Use the **KEY TERMS** to compile a glossary for this topic.

The Structure of Cellular Membranes pages 66-69

☐ 2. Describe the role of the **plasma membrane** in separating the internal environment of the cell from the external environment.

☐ 3. Describe the **fluid mosaic model** of the plasma membrane, including the significance of the **amphipathic** character of the phospholipids that make up the structural framework of the membrane and the role of **transmembrane proteins**, **glycoproteins**, and **glycolipids**.

☐ 4. Explain how the properties of the embedded proteins contribute to the selectively permeable nature of the membrane. Include reference to **aquaporins**, and embedded **channel proteins** and **carrier proteins**.

Transport Across Membranes pages 70-78

☐ 5. Distinguish between passive transport and **active transport**, identifying the involvement of membrane proteins and **ATP** in active transport processes.

☐ 6. Explain **passive transport** across membranes by **diffusion** and **osmosis**. If required, use **water potential** to explain net movement of water by osmosis.

☐ 7. Explain **turgor** and **plasmolysis** in plant cells. With respect to solutions of differing solute concentration, explain **hypotonic**, **isotonic**, and **hypertonic**.

☐ 8. Using examples, describe and explain the role of **ion pumps** in the active transport of materials in and out of cells.

☐ 9. Recognize that **endocytosis**, and **exocytosis are** active transport processes that move material into and out of the cell.

☐ 10. Explain how vesicles are used to transport materials within the cell between the rough endoplasmic reticulum, Golgi, and plasma membrane.

☐ 11. Explain the role of **surface area: volume ratio** in limiting the size of cells. Describe factors affecting the rates of transport processes in cells.

Weblinks:
www.thebiozone.com/weblink/Cellbio-3732/

BIOZONE APP:
Student Review Series
Cell Membranes and Transport

Cell Processes

All of the organelles and other structures in the cell have functions. The cell can be compared to a factory with an assembly line. Organelles in the cell provide the equivalent of the power supply, assembly line, packaging department, repair and maintenance, transport system, and the control center.

The sum total of all the processes occurring in a cell is known as **metabolism**. Some of these processes store energy in molecules (**anabolism**) while others release that stored energy (**catabolism**). Below is a summary of the major processes that take place in an animal cell.

Autolysis

Lysosomes contain powerful digestive enzymes that destroy unwanted cell organelles and foreign objects brought into the cell.

Transport in and out of the cell

Simple diffusion and active transport move substances into and out of the cell across the plasma (cell surface) membrane.

Protein synthesis

Chromosomes in the nucleus store genetic instructions for the production of specific proteins. These proteins are put together by ribosomes in the cytoplasm and on the endoplasmic reticulum.

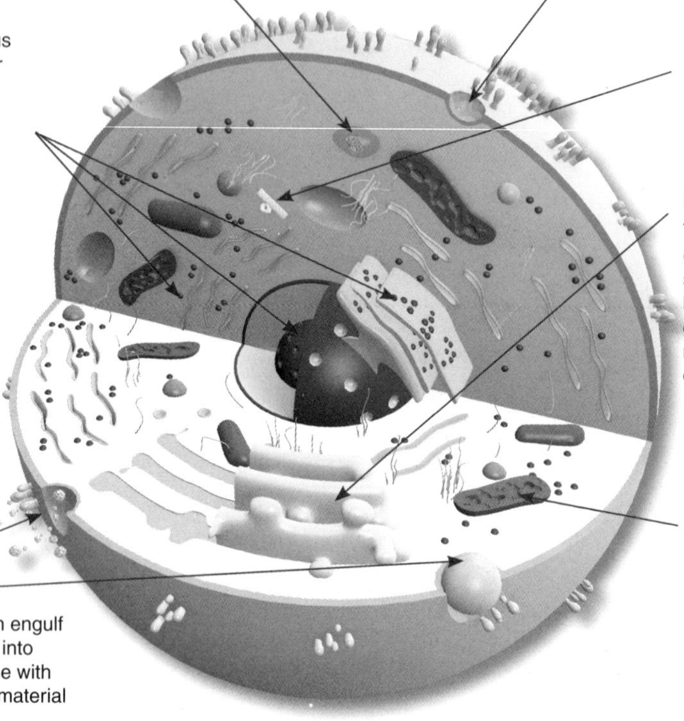

Cell division

Centrioles control the movement of chromosomes during cell division.

Secretion

The Golgi apparatus is the packaging department of the cell. It produces secretory vesicles (small membrane-bound sacs) that are used to store useful chemicals, prepare substances for movement out of the cell (e.g. hormones), or to package digestive enzymes.

Cellular respiration

The breakdown of glucose is a complex process which starts with glycolysis in the cytoplasm and is completed with cellular respiration in the mitochondria. This process supplies the cell with energy to carry out the many other chemical reactions of metabolism.

Cytosis

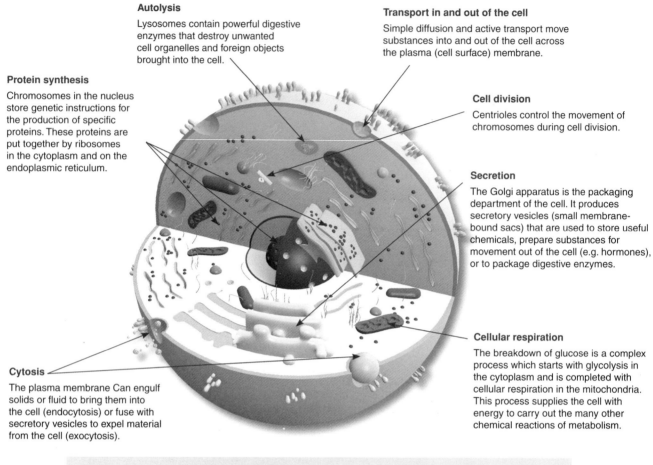

The plasma membrane Can engulf solids or fluid to bring them into the cell (endocytosis) or fuse with secretory vesicles to expel material from the cell (exocytosis).

Plant cells carry out photosynthesis

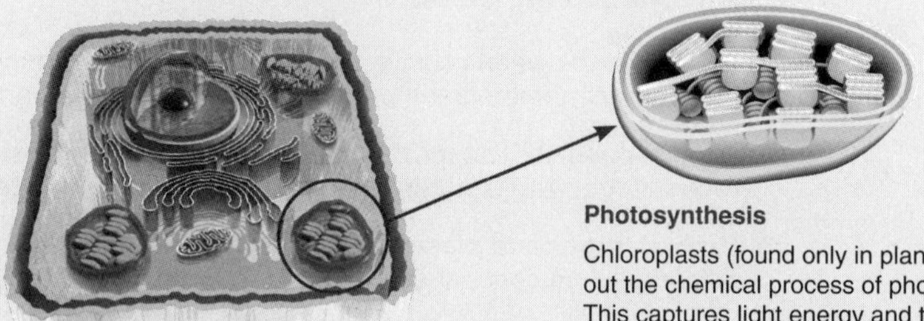

Photosynthesis

Chloroplasts (found only in plant cells) carry out the chemical process of photosynthesis. This captures light energy and transfers it into useful chemical energy.

1. For each of the processes listed below, identify the organelles or structures associated with that process (there may be more than one associated with a process):

(a) Secretion: ____________________ (f) Photosynthesis: ____________________

(b) Respiration: ____________________ (g) Cell division: ____________________

(c) Endocytosis: ____________________ (h) Autolysis: ____________________

(d) Protein synthesis: ____________________ (i) Transport in/out of cell: ____________________

2. Explain what is meant by **metabolism** and describe an example of a metabolic process: ____________________

____

____

Related activities: *Animal Cells, Plant Cells*

ISBN: 978-1-927173-73-2

The Structure of Membranes

All cells have a plasma membrane that forms the outer limit of the cell. Bacteria, fungi, and plant cells have a cell wall outside this, but it is quite distinct and outside the plasma membrane. Membranes are also found inside eukaryotic cells as part of membranous **organelles**. Current knowledge of membrane structure has been built up from many observations and experiments. The original model of membrane structure, proposed by Davson and Danielli, was the unit membrane (a lipid bilayer coated with protein). This model was later modified after the discovery that the protein molecules were embedded *within* the bilayer rather than coating the outside. The now-accepted model of membrane structure is the **fluid mosaic model** described below.

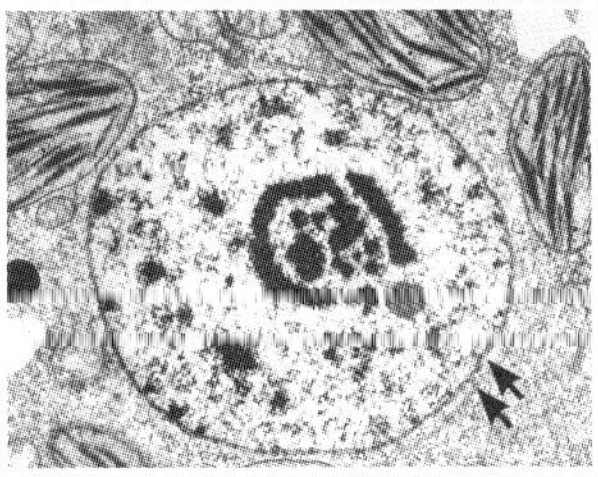
BF

The **nuclear membrane** that surrounds the nucleus helps to control the passage of genetic information to the cytoplasm. It may also serve to protect the DNA.

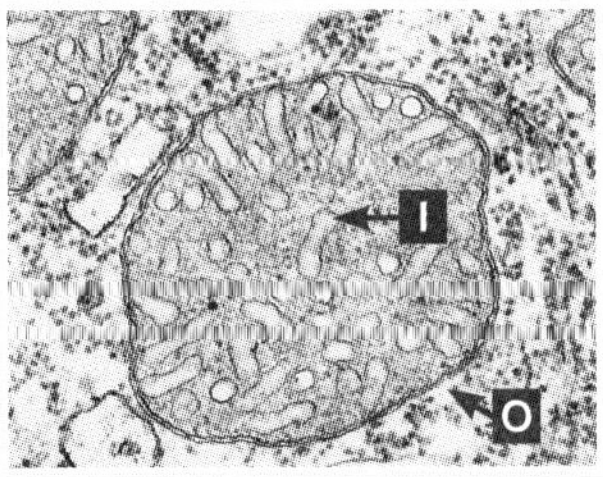
I
O
WMU

Mitochondria have an outer membrane (**O**) which controls the entry and exit of materials involved in aerobic respiration. Inner membranes (**I**) provide attachment sites for enzyme activity.

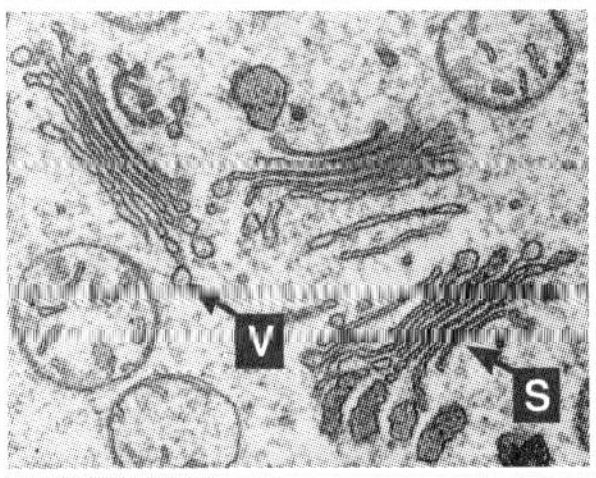
V
S
WMU

The **Golgi apparatus** comprises stacks of membrane-bound sacs (**S**). It is involved in packaging materials for transport or export from the cell as secretory vesicles (**V**).

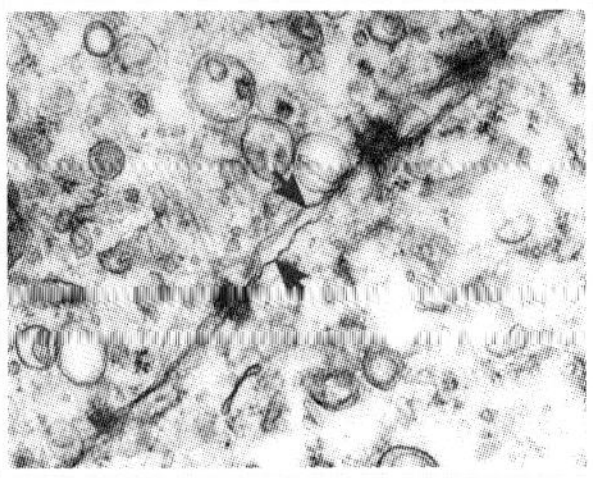
WMU

The cell is surrounded by a **plasma membrane** which controls the movement of most substances into and out of the cell. This photo shows the plasma membranes of two neighboring cells (arrows).

The Fluid Mosaic Model of Membrane Structure

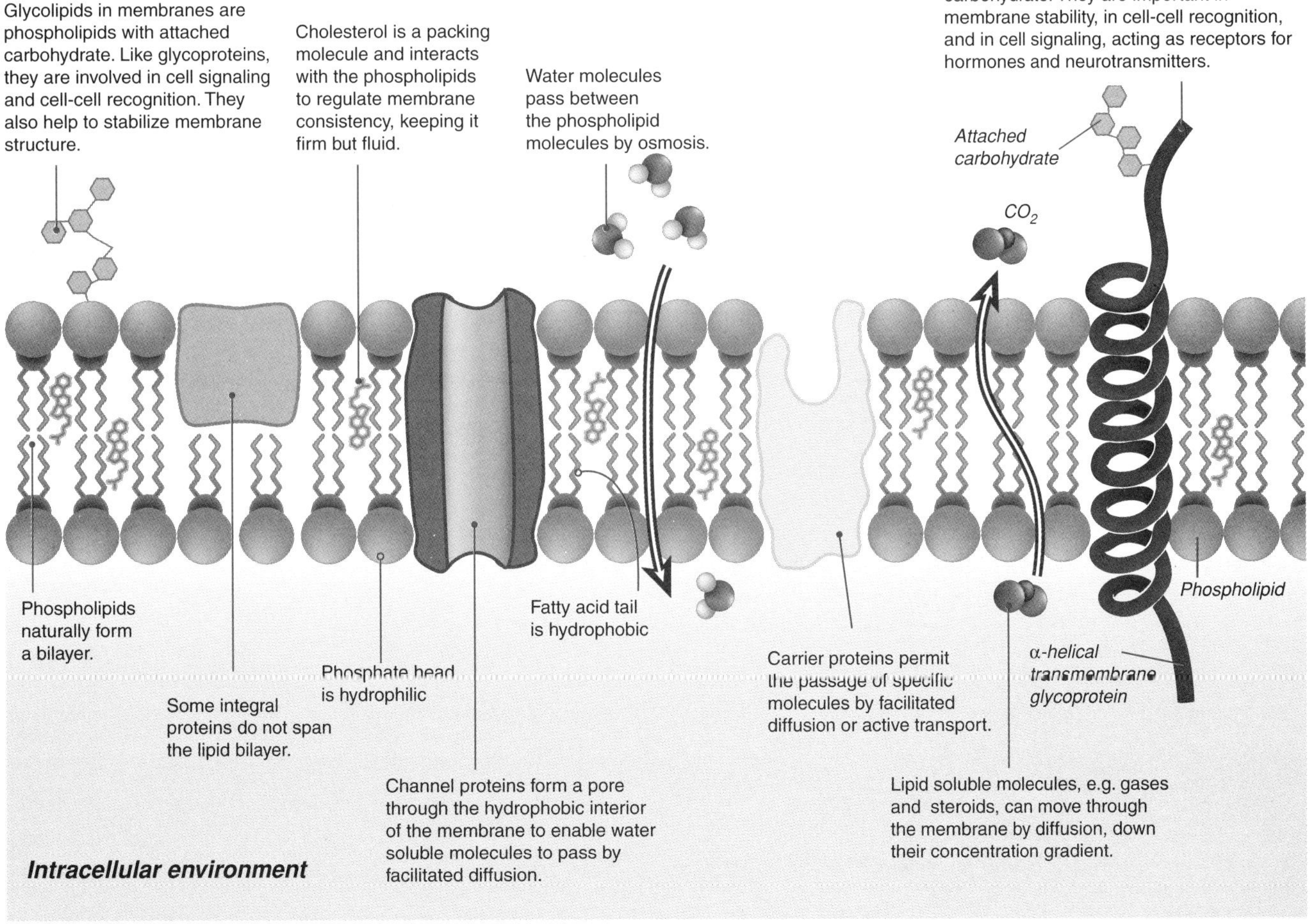
Glycolipids in membranes are phospholipids with attached carbohydrate. Like glycoproteins, they are involved in cell signaling and cell-cell recognition. They also help to stabilize membrane structure.
Cholesterol is a packing molecule and interacts with the phospholipids to regulate membrane consistency, keeping it firm but fluid.
Water molecules pass between the phospholipid molecules by osmosis.
Glycoproteins are proteins with attached carbohydrate. They are important in membrane stability, in cell-cell recognition, and in cell signaling, acting as receptors for hormones and neurotransmitters.
Attached carbohydrate
CO_2
Phospholipids naturally form a bilayer.
Some integral proteins do not span the lipid bilayer.
Phosphate head is hydrophilic
Fatty acid tail is hydrophobic
Channel proteins form a pore through the hydrophobic interior of the membrane to enable water soluble molecules to pass by facilitated diffusion.
Carrier proteins permit the passage of specific molecules by facilitated diffusion or active transport.
α-helical transmembrane glycoprotein
Phospholipid
Lipid soluble molecules, e.g. gases and steroids, can move through the membrane by diffusion, down their concentration gradient.
Intracellular environment

Based on a diagram in Biol. Sci. Review, Nov. 2009, pp. 20-21

1. Identify the component(s) of the plasma membrane involved in:

   (a) Facilitated diffusion: ______________________

   (b) Active transport: ______________________

   (c) Cell signaling: ______________________

   (d) Regulating membrane fluidity: ______________________

2. How do the properties of phospholipids contribute to their role in forming the structural framework of membranes?

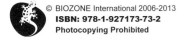

____

____

ISBN: 978-1-927173-73-2

3. (a) Describe the modern fluid mosaic model of membrane structure: ______________________________

____

____

(b) Explain how the fluid mosaic model accounts for the observed properties of cellular membranes: ______________

____

____

____

____

4. Discuss the various functional roles of membranes in cells: ______________________________

____

____

____

5. (a) Name a cellular organelle that possesses a membrane: ______________________________

(b) Describe the membrane's purpose in this organelle: ______________________________

____

____

____

6. Describe the purpose of cholesterol in plasma membranes: ______________________________

____

____

7. List three substances that need to be transported **into** all kinds of animal cells, in order for them to survive:

(a) ______________ (b) ______________ (c) ______________

8. List two substances that need to be transported **out** of all kinds of animal cells, in order for them to survive:

(a) ______________ (b) ______________

9. Use the symbol for a phospholipid molecule (below) to draw a **simple labeled diagram** to show the structure of a plasma membrane (include features such as lipid bilayer and various kinds of proteins):

The Role of Membranes in Cells

Many of the important structures and organelles in cells are composed of, or are enclosed by, membranes. These include: the endoplasmic reticulum, mitochondria, nucleus, Golgi apparatus, chloroplasts, lysosomes, vesicles and the cell plasma membrane itself. All membranes within eukaryotic cells share the same basic structure as the plasma membrane that encloses the entire cell. They perform a number of critical functions in the cell: compartmentalizing regions of different function within the cell, controlling the entry and exit of substances, and fulfilling a role in recognition and communication between cells. Some of these roles are described below and electron micrographs of the organelles involved are on the following page.

Isolation of enzymes
Membrane-bound lysosomes contain enzymes for the destruction of wastes and foreign material. Peroxisomes are the site for destruction of the toxic and reactive molecule, hydrogen peroxide (formed as a result of some cellular reactions).

Role in lipid synthesis
The smooth ER is the site of lipid and steroid synthesis.

Containment of DNA
The nucleus is surrounded by a nuclear envelope of two membranes, forming a separate compartment for the cell's genetic material.

Role in protein and membrane synthesis
Some protein synthesis occurs on free ribosomes, but much occurs on membrane-bound ribosomes on the rough endoplasmic reticulum. Here, the protein is synthesized directly into the space within the ER membranes. The rough ER is also involved in membrane synthesis, growing in place by adding proteins and phospholipids.

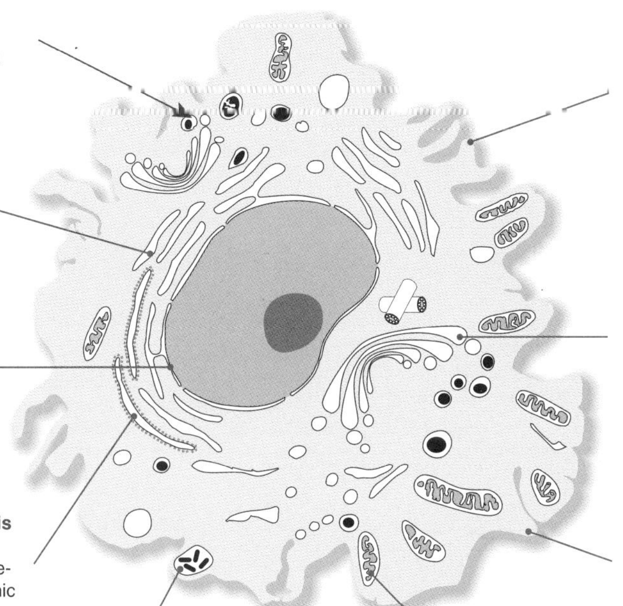

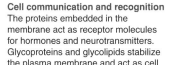

Cell communication and recognition
The proteins embedded in the membrane act as receptor molecules for hormones and neurotransmitters. Glycoproteins and glycolipids stabilize the plasma membrane and act as cell identity markers, helping cells to organize themselves into tissues, and enabling foreign cells to be recognized.

Packaging and secretion
The Golgi apparatus is a specialized membrane-bound organelle which produces lysosomes and compartmentalizes the modification, packaging and secretion of substances such as proteins and hormones.

Transport processes
Channel and carrier proteins are involved in selective transport across the plasma membrane. The level of cholesterol in the membrane influences permeability and transport functions.

Entry and export of substances
The plasma membrane may take up fluid or solid material and form membrane-bound vesicles (or larger vacuoles) within the cell. Membrane-bound transport vesicles move substances to the inner surface of the cell where they can be exported from the cell by exocytosis.

Energy transfer
The reactions of cellular respiration (and photosynthesis in plants) take place in the membrane-bound energy transfer systems occurring in mitochondria and chloroplasts respectively. See the example explained below.

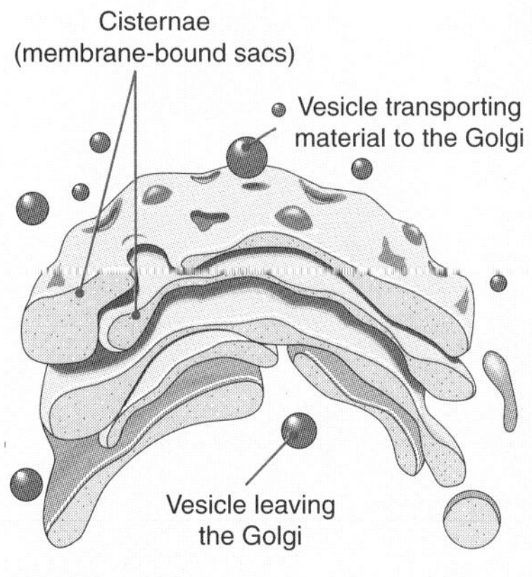
Cisternae
(membrane-bound sacs)
Vesicle transporting material to the Golgi
Vesicle leaving the Golgi

Compartmentation within Membranes

Membranes play an important role in separating regions within the cell (and within organelles) where particular reactions occur. Specific enzymes are therefore often located in particular organelles. The reaction rate is controlled by controlling the rate at which substrates enter the organelle and therefore the availability of the raw materials required for the reactions.

The Golgi *(diagram left and TEM right) modifies, sorts, and packages macromolecules for cell secretion. Enzymes within the cisternae modify proteins by adding carbohydrates and phosphates. To do this, the Golgi imports the substances it needs from the cytosol.*

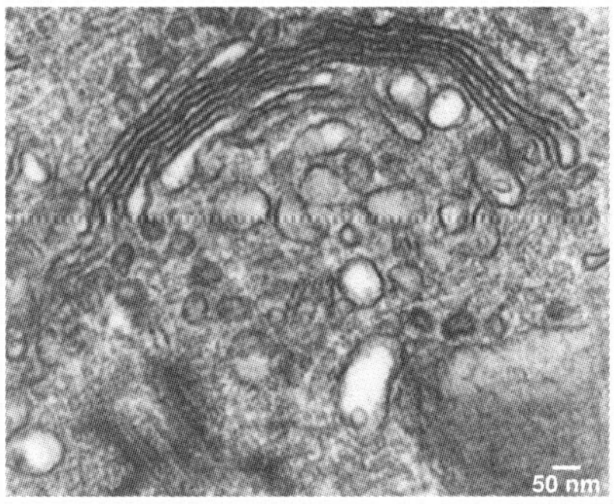
50 nm

Louisa Howard-Dartmouth College PD

1. Discuss the importance of membrane systems and organelles in providing compartments within the cell:

____

____

____

____

____

ISBN: 978-1-927173-73-2

Packaging Macromolecules

Cells produce a range of organic polymers made up of repeating units of smaller molecules. The synthesis, packaging and movement of these **macromolecules** inside the cell involves a number of membrane bound organelles, as indicated below. These organelles provide compartments where the enzyme systems involved can be isolated.

Golgi apparatus
The Golgi apparatus comprises stacks of flattened membranes in the shape of curved sacs. This organelle receives transport vesicles and the products they contain from smooth ER. They are modified, stored and eventually shipped to the surface of the cell or other destinations.

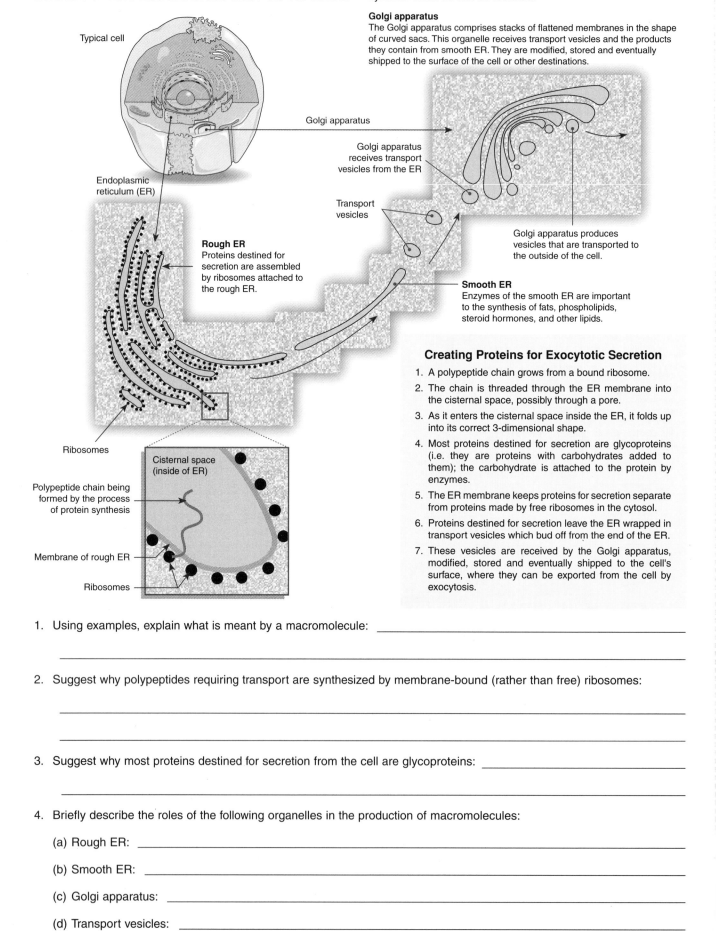

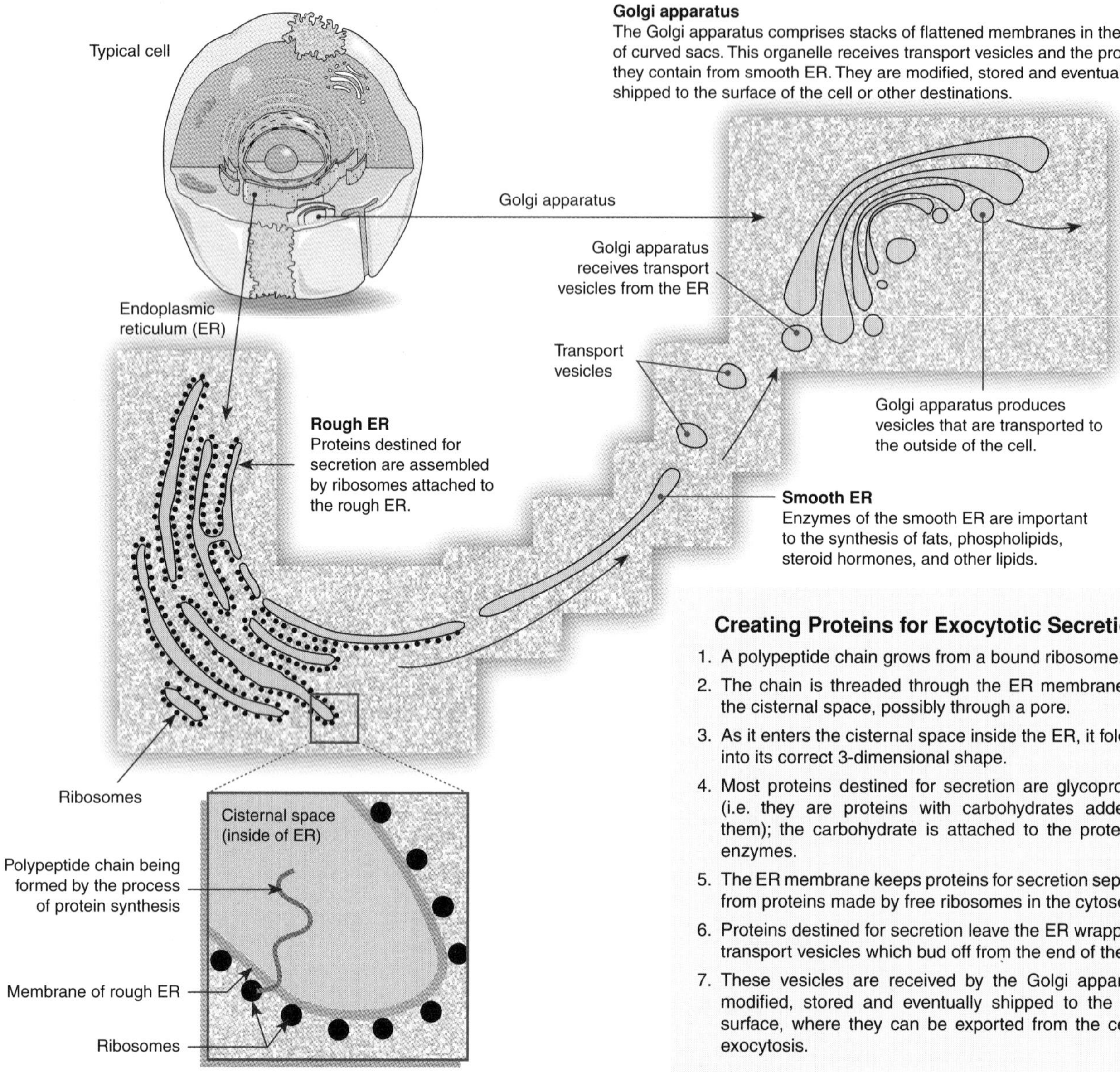
Typical cell
Golgi apparatus
Golgi apparatus receives transport vesicles from the ER
Endoplasmic reticulum (ER)
Transport vesicles
Golgi apparatus produces vesicles that are transported to the outside of the cell.
Rough ER
Proteins destined for secretion are assembled by ribosomes attached to the rough ER.
Smooth ER
Enzymes of the smooth ER are important to the synthesis of fats, phospholipids, steroid hormones, and other lipids.
Ribosomes
Cisternal space (inside of ER)
Polypeptide chain being formed by the process of protein synthesis
Membrane of rough ER
Ribosomes

Creating Proteins for Exocytotic Secretion

1. A polypeptide chain grows from a bound ribosome.
2. The chain is threaded through the ER membrane into the cisternal space, possibly through a pore.
3. As it enters the cisternal space inside the ER, it folds up into its correct 3-dimensional shape.
4. Most proteins destined for secretion are glycoproteins (i.e. they are proteins with carbohydrates added to them); the carbohydrate is attached to the protein by enzymes.
5. The ER membrane keeps proteins for secretion separate from proteins made by free ribosomes in the cytosol.
6. Proteins destined for secretion leave the ER wrapped in transport vesicles which bud off from the end of the ER.
7. These vesicles are received by the Golgi apparatus, modified, stored and eventually shipped to the cell's surface, where they can be exported from the cell by exocytosis.

1. Using examples, explain what is meant by a macromolecule: ______________________

____

2. Suggest why polypeptides requiring transport are synthesized by membrane-bound (rather than free) ribosomes:

____

____

3. Suggest why most proteins destined for secretion from the cell are glycoproteins: ______________________

____

4. Briefly describe the roles of the following organelles in the production of macromolecules:

(a) Rough ER: ______________________

(b) Smooth ER: ______________________

(c) Golgi apparatus: ______________________

(d) Transport vesicles: ______________________

ISBN: 978-1-927173-73-2

Passive Transport Processes

The molecules that make up substances are constantly moving about in a random way. This random motion causes molecules to disperse from areas of high to low concentration. This movement is called **diffusion**. The molecules move down a **concentration gradient**. Diffusion and **osmosis** (diffusion of water molecules across a partially permeable membrane) are **passive** processes, and use no energy. Diffusion occurs freely across membranes, as long as the membrane is permeable to that molecule (partially permeable membranes allow the passage of some molecules but not others). Each type of molecule diffuses down its own concentration gradient. Diffusion of molecules in one direction does not hinder the movement of other molecules. Diffusion is important in allowing exchanges with the environment and in the regulation of cell water content.

Diffusion is the movement of particles from regions of high to low concentration (down a **concentration gradient**), with the end result being that the molecules become evenly distributed. In biological systems, diffusion often occurs across selectively permeable membranes.

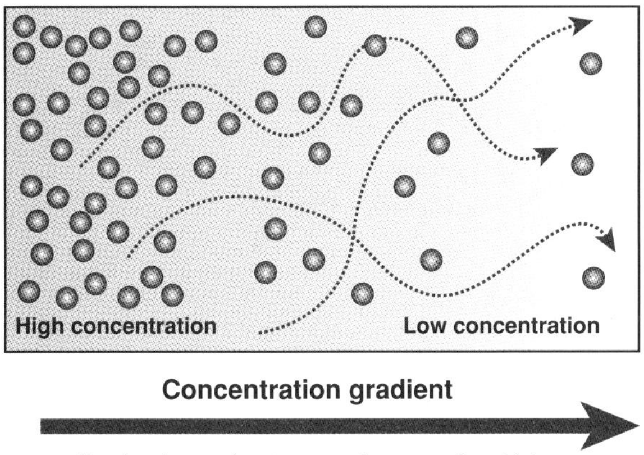
High concentration
Low concentration
Concentration gradient

If molecules are free to move, they move from high to low concentration until they are evenly dispersed.

Factors affecting rates of diffusion

Concentration gradient:	Diffusion rates will be higher when there is a greater difference in concentration between two regions.
The distance involved:	Diffusion over shorter distances occurs at a greater rate than diffusion over larger distances.
The area involved:	The larger the area across which diffusion occurs, the greater the rate of diffusion.
Barriers to diffusion:	Thicker barriers slow diffusion rate. Pores in a barrier enhance diffusion.

Fick's law

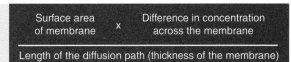

$$\frac{\text{Surface area of membrane} \times \text{Difference in concentration across the membrane}}{\text{Length of the diffusion path (thickness of the membrane)}}$$

These factors are expressed in Fick's law, which governs the rate of diffusion of substances within a system. Temperature also affects diffusion rates; at higher temperatures molecules have more energy and move more rapidly.

Diffusion Through Membranes

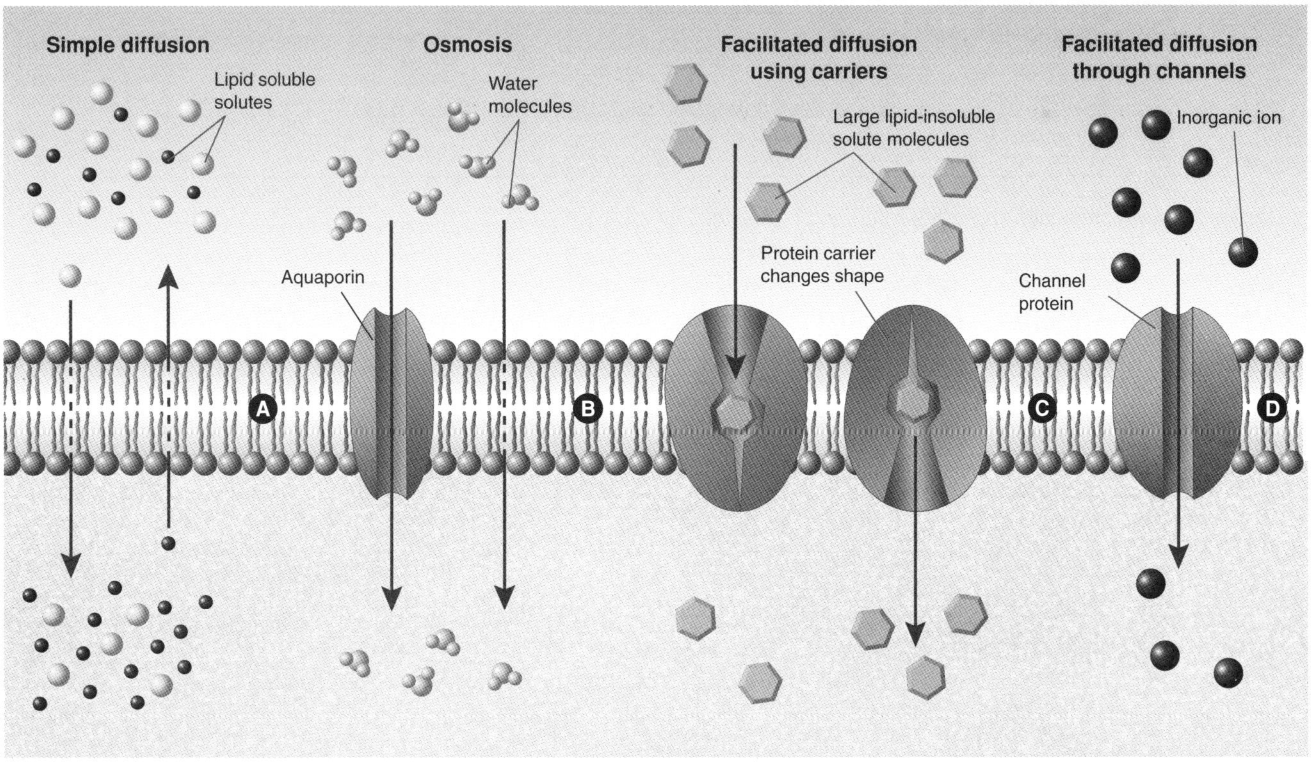
Simple diffusion
Lipid soluble solutes
Osmosis
Water molecules
Aquaporin
Facilitated diffusion using carriers
Large lipid-insoluble solute molecules
Protein carrier changes shape
Facilitated diffusion through channels
Inorganic ion
Channel protein
A
B
C
D

A: Some molecules (e.g. gases and lipid soluble molecules) diffuse directly across the plasma membrane. Two-way diffusion is common in biological systems, EXAMPLE: At the alveolar surface of the lung, oxygen diffuses into the blood and CO_2 diffuses out.

B: Osmosis is the diffusion of water across a selectively permeable membrane (in this case, the plasma membrane). Some water can diffuse directly through the lipid bilayer, but diffusion rate is increased by protein channels in the membrane called **aquaporins**.

C: A lipid-insoluble molecule is aided across the membrane by **carrier mediated facilitated diffusion**. This involves a trans-membrane carrier protein specific to the molecule being transported EXAMPLE: Glucose transport into red blood cells.

D: Small polar molecules and ions diffuse rapidly across the membrane by **channel-mediated facilitated diffusion**. Special channel proteins create hydrophilic pores that allow some solutes, usually inorganic ions, to pass through. EXAMPLE: Na^+ entering nerve cells.

ISBN: 978-1-927173-73-2

Osmotic Gradients and Water Movement

Osmosis is the diffusion of water molecules, across a selectively permeable membrane, from higher to lower concentration of water molecules (sometimes described as from lower to higher solute concentration).Water always diffuses in this direction. The cytoplasm contains dissolved substances (**solutes**). When cells are placed in a solution of different concentration, there is an **osmotic gradient** between the external environment and the inside of the cell. In plant cells, the rigid cell wall is also important. When a plant cell takes up water, it swells until the cell contents exert a pressure on the cell wall. The cell wall is rigid and the pressure from the cytoplasm is called the wall pressure or **turgor pressure**. Turgor is important in plant support.

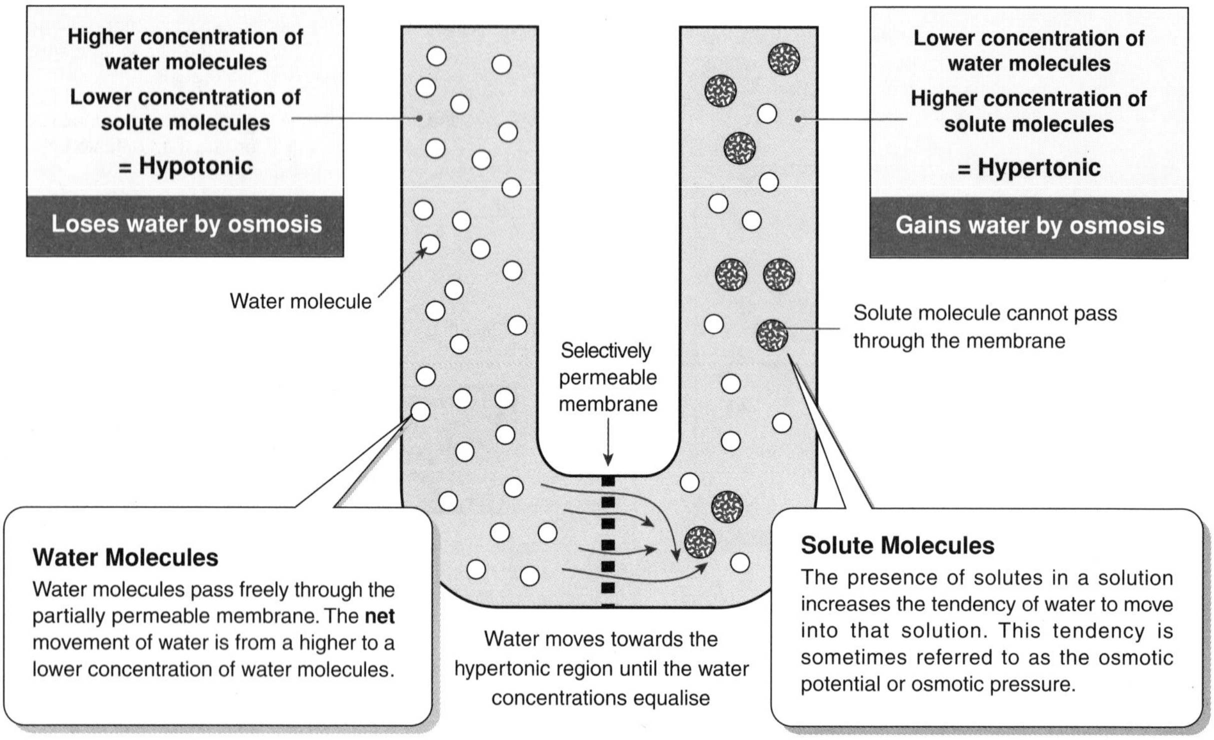
Higher concentration of water molecules
Lower concentration of solute molecules
= Hypotonic
Loses water by osmosis
Lower concentration of water molecules
Higher concentration of solute molecules
= Hypertonic
Gains water by osmosis
Water molecule
Solute molecule cannot pass through the membrane
Selectively permeable membrane
Water Molecules
Water molecules pass freely through the partially permeable membrane. The net movement of water is from a higher to a lower concentration of water molecules.
Water moves towards the hypertonic region until the water concentrations equalise
Solute Molecules
The presence of solutes in a solution increases the tendency of water to move into that solution. This tendency is sometimes referred to as the osmotic potential or osmotic pressure.

1. Describe two properties of an exchange surface that would facilitate rapid diffusion rates:

   (a) ______________________ (b) ______________________

2. Describe two biologically important features of diffusion:

   (a) ______________________

   (b) ______________________

3. Describe how facilitated diffusion is achieved for:

   (a) Small polar molecules and ions: ______________________

   (b) Glucose: ______________________

4. How are concentration gradients maintained across membranes? ______________________

5. Describe the role of aquaporins in the rapid movement of water through some cells: ______________________

6. (a) What happens if a cell takes up sucrose by active transport? ______________________

   (b) Describe a situation where this occurs in plants: ______________________

ISBN: 978-1-927173-73-2

Water Relations in Plant Cells

The plasma membrane of cells is a selectively permeable membrane and osmosis is the main way by which water enters and leaves the cell. When the external water concentration is the same as that of the cell there is no net movement of water. Two systems (cell and environment) with the same water concentration are termed isotonic. The diagram below illustrates two different situations: when the external water concentration is higher than the cell (**hypotonic**) and when it is lower than the cell (**hypertonic**).

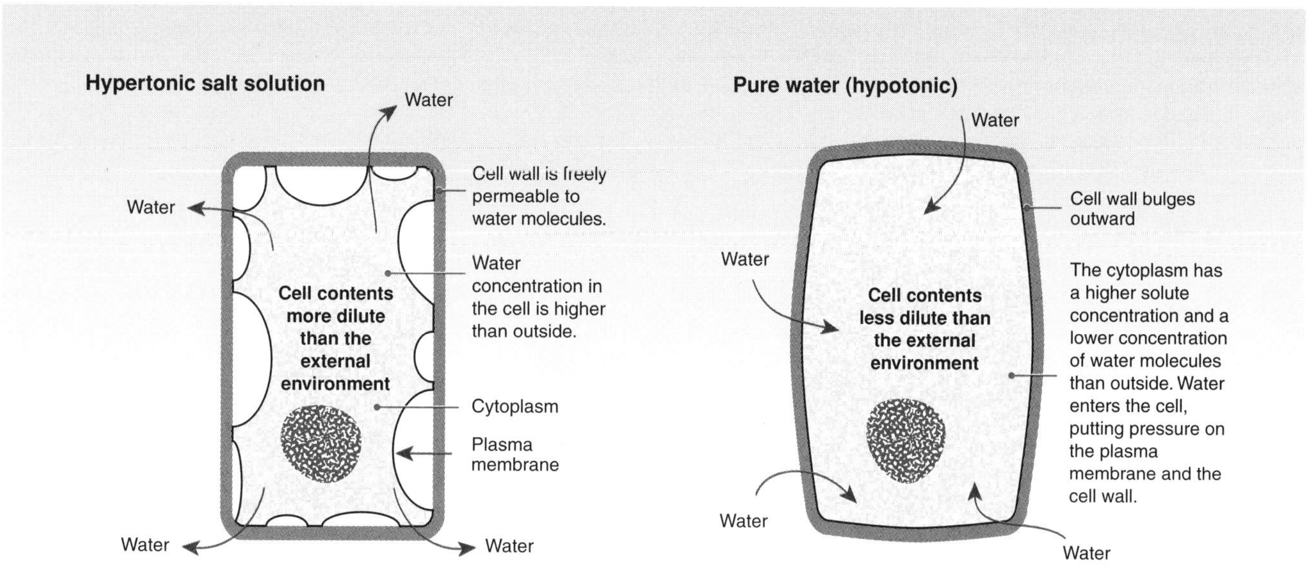
Hypertonic salt solution
Water
Water
Cell wall is freely permeable to water molecules.
Water concentration in the cell is higher than outside.
Cell contents more dilute than the external environment
Cytoplasm
Plasma membrane
Water
Water
Pure water (hypotonic)
Water
Cell wall bulges outward
Water
Cell contents less dilute than the external environment
The cytoplasm has a higher solute concentration and a lower concentration of water molecules than outside. Water enters the cell, putting pressure on the plasma membrane and the cell wall.
Water
Water

Plasmolysis in a plant cell

In a **hypertonic** solution, the external water concentration is lower than the water concentration of the cell. Water leaves the cell and, because the cell wall is rigid, the cell membrane shrinks away from the cell wall. This process is termed **plasmolysis** and the cell becomes **flaccid** (turgor pressure = 0). Complete plasmolysis is irreversible; the cell cannot recover by taking up water.

Turgor in a plant cell

In a **hypotonic** solution, the external water concentration is higher than the cell cytoplasm. Water enters the cell, causing it to swell tight. A wall (turgor) pressure is generated when enough water has been taken up to cause the cell contents to press against the cell wall. Turgor pressure rises until it offsets further net influx of water into the cell (the cell is turgid). The rigid cell wall prevents cell rupture.

7. Describe what would happen to an animal cell (e.g. a red blood cell) if it was placed into:

   (a) Pure water: ____________________

   (b) A hypertonic solution: ____________________

   (c) A hypotonic solution: ____________________

8. *Paramecium* is a freshwater protozoan. Describe the problem it has in controlling the amount of water inside the cell:

   ____

   ____

9. Fluid replacements are usually provided for heavily perspiring athletes after endurance events.

   (a) Identify the preferable tonicity of these replacement drinks (isotonic, hypertonic, or hypotonic): ____________________

   (b) Give a reason for your answer: ____________________

   ____

10. The malarial parasite lives in human blood. Relative to the tonicity of the blood, the parasite's cell contents would be hypertonic / isotonic / hypotonic (circle the correct answer).

11. (a) Explain the role of cell wall pressure in generating cell turgor in plants: ____________________

    ____

    (b) Discuss the role of cell turgor in plants: ____________________

    ____

    ____

    ____

ISBN: 978-1-927173-73-2

Ion Pumps

Diffusion alone cannot supply the cell's entire requirements for molecules (and ions). Some molecules (e.g. sucrose) are required by the cell in higher concentrations than occur outside the cell. Others (e.g. sodium) must be removed from the cell in order to maintain fluid balance. These molecules must be moved across the plasma membrane by **active transport** mechanisms, and this work is performed by membrane **ion pumps**. These are specific transport proteins in the membrane that utilize ATP to pump molecules from a low to a high concentration. The sodium-potassium pump is almost universal, and is often coupled to the cotransport of specific molecules such as glucose. Proton pumps can be utilized in the same way. The example below illustrates how plant cells use the gradient in hydrogen ion concentration to drive the active transport of sucrose. The transport protein couples the return of H^+ to the transport of sucrose into the phloem transfer cells (modified companion cells adjacent to the sieve tube cells). The sucrose rides with the H^+ as it diffuses down the concentration gradient maintained by the proton pump. From here, water follows by osmosis and generates a pressure-flow that moves plant sap by bulk flow in the phloem sieve tubes).

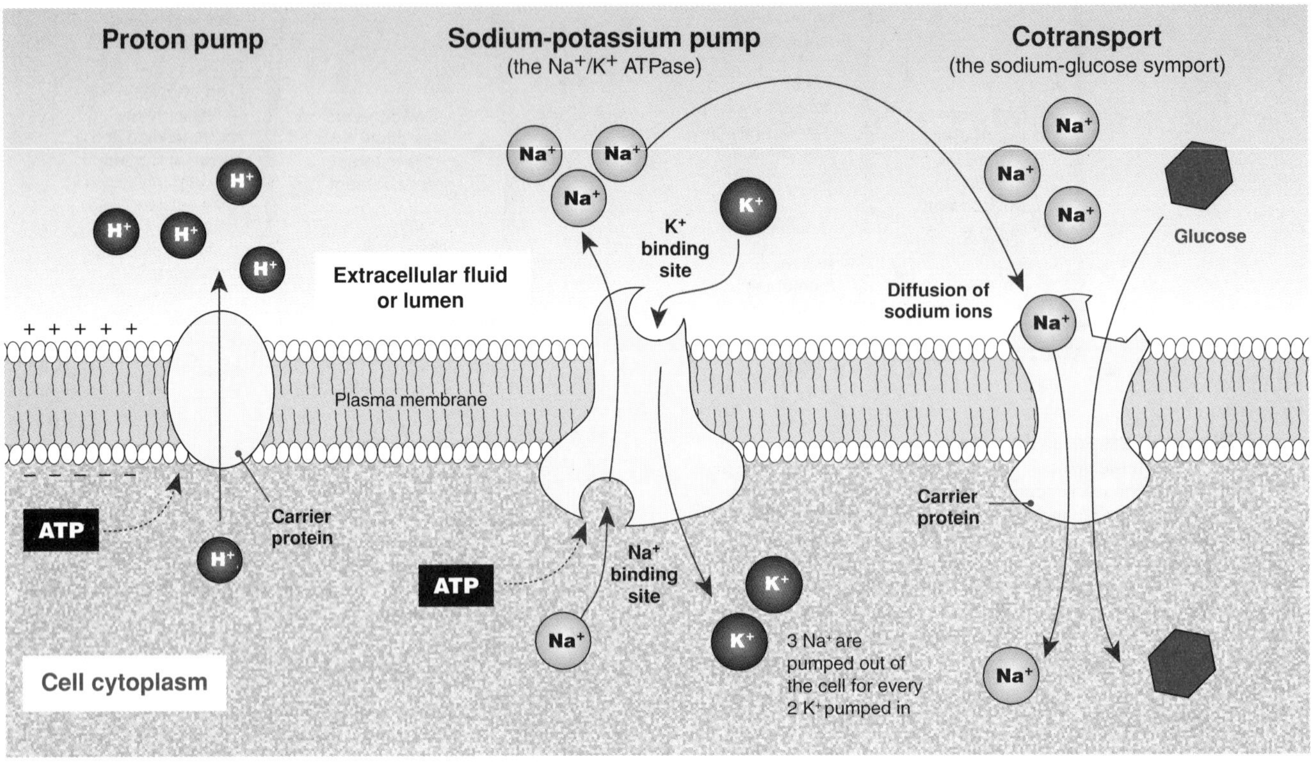
Proton pump
Sodium-potassium pump
(the Na+/K+ ATPase)
Cotransport
(the sodium-glucose symport)
H+
Extracellular fluid or lumen
+ + + + +
Plasma membrane
– – – – –
ATP
Carrier protein
Na+
K+
K+ binding site
Na+ binding site
ATP
3 Na+ are pumped out of the cell for every 2 K+ pumped in
Glucose
Diffusion of sodium ions
Carrier protein
Cell cytoplasm

Proton pumps

ATP driven proton pumps use energy to remove hydrogen ions (H^+) from inside the cell to the outside. This creates a large difference in the proton concentration either side of the membrane, with the inside of the plasma membrane being negatively charged. This potential difference can be coupled to the transport of other molecules.

Sodium-potassium pump

The sodium-potassium pump is a specific protein in the membrane that uses energy in the form of ATP to exchange sodium ions (Na^+) for potassium ions (K^+) across the membrane. The unequal balance of Na^+ and K^+ across the membrane creates large concentration gradients that can be used to drive transport of other substances (e.g. cotransport of glucose).

Cotransport (coupled transport)

A gradient in sodium ions drives the active transport of **glucose** in intestinal epithelial cells. The specific transport protein couples the return of Na^+ down its concentration gradient to the transport of glucose into the intestinal epithelial cell. A low intracellular concentration of Na^+ (and therefore the concentration gradient) is maintained by a sodium-potassium pump.

1. Explain how the transport of molecules such as sucrose can be coupled to the activity of an ion pump: ______

2. Why is ATP required for membrane pump systems to operate? ______

3. Explain what is meant by cotransport: ______

4. Describe two consequences of the extracellular accumulation of sodium ions: ______

Related activities: *Active and Passive Transport Summary,*
Weblinks: *Cellular Transport, Symport*

ISBN: 978-1-927173-73-2

Exocytosis and Endocytosis

Most cells carry out **cytosis**: a form of **active transport** involving the infolding or outfolding of the plasma membrane. The ability of cells to do this is a function of the flexibility of the plasma membrane. Cytosis results in bulk transport into or out of the cell and is achieved through the localized activity of microfilaments and microtubules in the cell cytoskeleton. **Endocytosis** involves material being engulfed. It typically occurs in protozoans and certain white blood cells of the mammalian defence system (phagocytes). **Exocytosis** is the reverse of endocytosis and involves the release of material from vesicles or vacuoles that have fused with the plasma membrane. Exocytosis is typical of cells that export material (secretory cells).

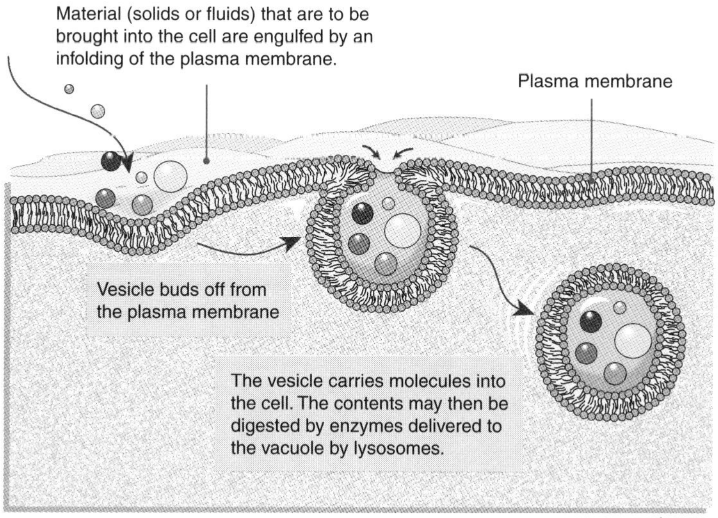
Material (solids or fluids) that are to be brought into the cell are engulfed by an infolding of the plasma membrane.
Plasma membrane
Vesicle buds off from the plasma membrane
The vesicle carries molecules into the cell. The contents may then be digested by enzymes delivered to the vacuole by lysosomes.

Endocytosis

Endocytosis (left) occurs by invagination (infolding) of the plasma membrane, which then forms vesicles or vacuoles that become detached and enter the cytoplasm. There are two main types of endocytosis:

Phagocytosis: 'cell-eating'
Phagocytosis involves the cell engulfing **solid material** to form large vesicles or vacuoles (e.g. food vacuoles). Examples: Feeding in *Amoeba*, phagocytosis of foreign material and cell debris by neutrophils and macrophages. Some endocytosis is **receptor mediated** and is triggered when receptor proteins on the extracellular surface of the plasma membrane bind to specific substances. Examples include the uptake of lipoproteins by mammalian cells.

Pinocytosis: 'cell-drinking'
Pinocytosis involves the non-specific uptake of **liquids** or fine suspensions into the cell to form small pinocytic vesicles. Pinocytosis is used primarily for absorbing extracellular fluid. Examples: Uptake in many protozoa, some cells of the liver, and some plant cells.

Both endocytosis and exocytosis require energy in the form of ATP

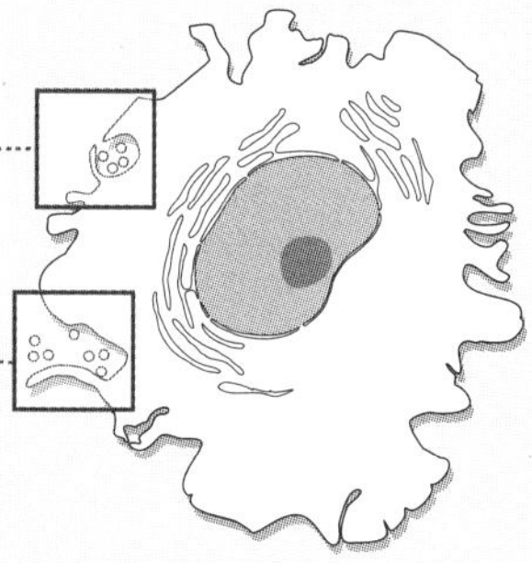
Areas of enlargement

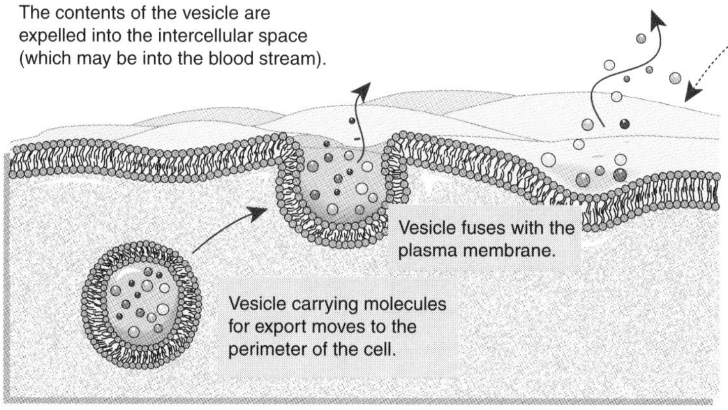
The contents of the vesicle are expelled into the intercellular space (which may be into the blood stream).
Vesicle fuses with the plasma membrane.
Vesicle carrying molecules for export moves to the perimeter of the cell.

Exocytosis

In multicellular organisms, several types of cells (e.g. lymphocytes) are specialized to manufacture and export products, such as proteins, from the cell to elsewhere in the body or outside it. Exocytosis (left) occurs by fusion of the vesicle membrane and the plasma membrane, followed by release of the vesicle's contents to the outside of the cell.

1. Distinguish between **phagocytosis** and **pinocytosis**: ______________________

2. Describe an example of phagocytosis and identify the cell type involved: ______________________

3. Describe an example of exocytosis and identify the cell type involved: ______________________

4. Why is cytosis affected by changes in oxygen level, whereas diffusion is not? ______________________

5. How does each of the following substances enter a living macrophage (for help, see *Passive Transport Processes*):

   (a) Oxygen: ______________ (c) Water: ______________

   (b) Cellular debris: ______________ (d) Glucose: ______________

ISBN: 978-1-927173-73-2

Related activities: *Active and Passive Transport Summary*
Weblinks: *Cellular Transport*

KNOW

Summary of Active and Passive Transport Processes

Cells have a need to move materials both into and out of the cell. Raw materials and other molecules necessary for metabolism must be accumulated from outside the cell. Some of these substances are scarce outside of the cell and some effort is required to accumulate them. Waste products and molecules for use in other parts of the body must be 'exported' out of the cell. Some materials (e.g. gases and water) move into and out of the cell by **passive transport** processes, without the expenditure of energy on the part of the cell. Other molecules (e.g. sucrose) are moved into and out of the cell using **active transport**. Active transport processes involve the expenditure of energy in the form of ATP, and therefore use oxygen.

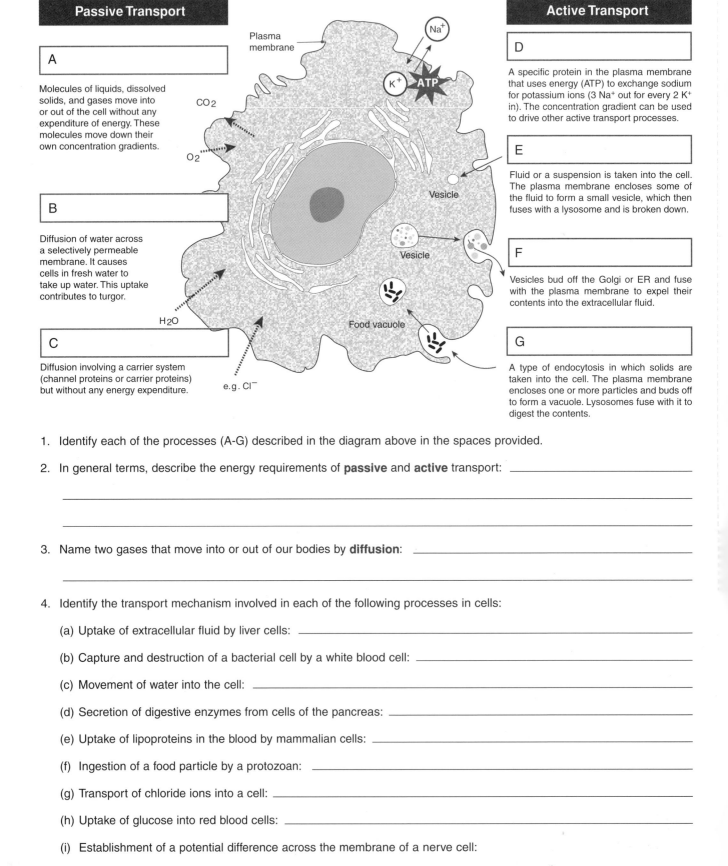

Passive Transport

A

Molecules of liquids, dissolved solids, and gases move into or out of the cell without any expenditure of energy. These molecules move down their own concentration gradients.

B

Diffusion of water across a selectively permeable membrane. It causes cells in fresh water to take up water. This uptake contributes to turgor.

C

Diffusion involving a carrier system (channel proteins or carrier proteins) but without any energy expenditure.

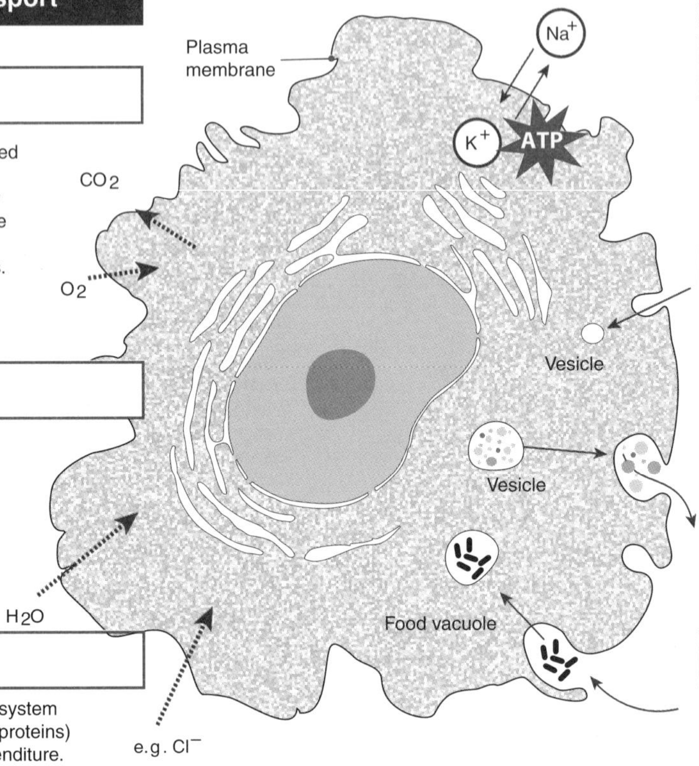
Plasma membrane
Na^+
K^+
ATP
CO_2
O_2
Vesicle
Vesicle
H_2O
Food vacuole
e.g. Cl^-

Active Transport

D

A specific protein in the plasma membrane that uses energy (ATP) to exchange sodium for potassium ions (3 Na^+ out for every 2 K^+ in). The concentration gradient can be used to drive other active transport processes.

E

Fluid or a suspension is taken into the cell. The plasma membrane encloses some of the fluid to form a small vesicle, which then fuses with a lysosome and is broken down.

F

Vesicles bud off the Golgi or ER and fuse with the plasma membrane to expel their contents into the extracellular fluid.

G

A type of endocytosis in which solids are taken into the cell. The plasma membrane encloses one or more particles and buds off to form a vacuole. Lysosomes fuse with it to digest the contents.

1. Identify each of the processes (A-G) described in the diagram above in the spaces provided.

2. In general terms, describe the energy requirements of **passive** and **active** transport: ____________________

3. Name two gases that move into or out of our bodies by **diffusion**: ____________________

4. Identify the transport mechanism involved in each of the following processes in cells:

   (a) Uptake of extracellular fluid by liver cells: ____________________

   (b) Capture and destruction of a bacterial cell by a white blood cell: ____________________

   (c) Movement of water into the cell: ____________________

   (d) Secretion of digestive enzymes from cells of the pancreas: ____________________

   (e) Uptake of lipoproteins in the blood by mammalian cells: ____________________

   (f) Ingestion of a food particle by a protozoan: ____________________

   (g) Transport of chloride ions into a cell: ____________________

   (h) Uptake of glucose into red blood cells: ____________________

   (i) Establishment of a potential difference across the membrane of a nerve cell:

Related activities: *Passive Transport Processes, Ion Pumps, Exocytosis and Endocytosis*
Weblinks: *Cellular Transport*

ISBN: 978-1-927173-73-2

Limitations to Cell Size

When an object (e.g. a cell) is small it has a large surface area in comparison to its volume. In this case diffusion will be an effective way to transport materials (e.g. gases) into the cell. As an object becomes larger, its surface area compared to its volume is smaller. Diffusion is no longer an effective way to transport materials to the inside. For this reason, there is a physical limit for the size of a cell, with the effectiveness of diffusion being the controlling factor.

Diffusion in Organisms of Different Sizes

Respiratory gases and some other substances are exchanged with the surroundings by diffusion or active transport across the plasma membrane.

The **plasma membrane**, which surrounds every cell, functions as a selective barrier that regulates the cell's chemical composition. For each square micrometre of membrane, only so much of a particular substance can cross per second.

In large multicellular organisms, the body cannot meet its need for respiratory gases by diffusion through the skin. A specialized gas exchange surface (lungs) and circulatory (blood) system are required to transport substances to the body's cells.

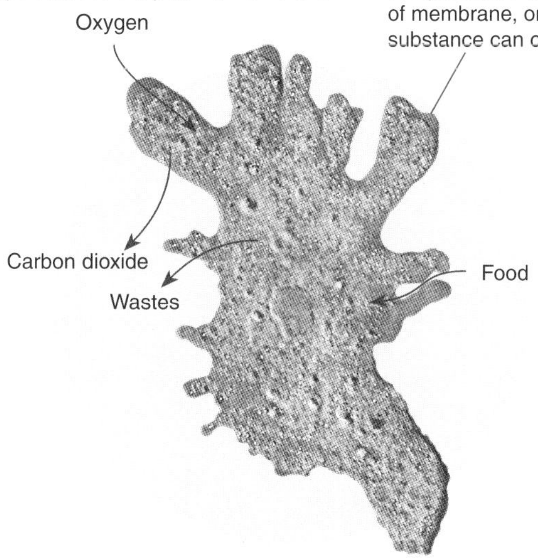
Oxygen
Carbon dioxide
Wastes
Food

Amoeba: The small size of single-celled protists, such as *Amoeba*, provides a large surface area relative to the cell's volume. This is adequate for many materials to be moved into and out of the cell by diffusion or active transport.

Multicellular organisms: Multicellular organisms (e.g. plants and animals) are often quite large, and large organisms have a small surface area compared to their volume. They require specialized systems to transport the materials they need to and from the cells and tissues in their body.

The diagram below shows four imaginary cells of different sizes (cells do not actually grow to this size, their large size is for the sake of the exercise). They range from a small 2 cm cube to a larger 5 cm cube. This exercise investigates the effect of cell size on the efficiency of diffusion.

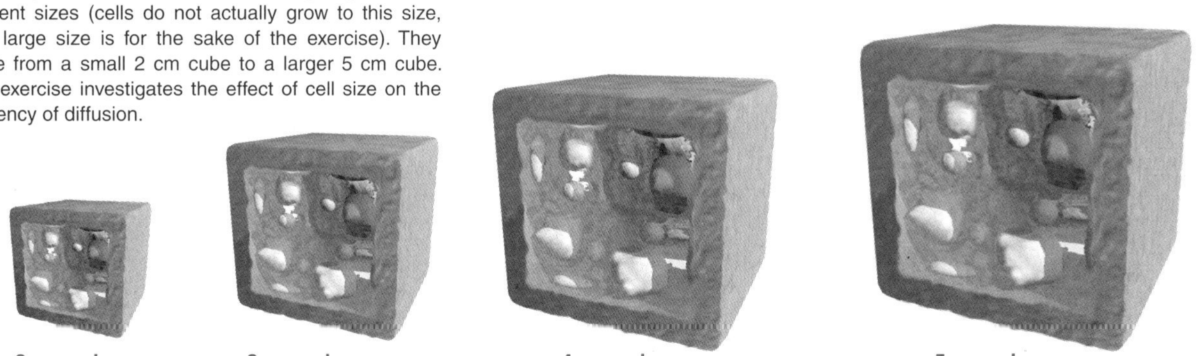

2 cm cube — 3 cm cube — 4 cm cube — 5 cm cube

1. Calculate the volume, surface area and the ratio of surface area to volume for each of the four cubes above (the first has been done for you). When completing the table below, show your calculations.

Cube size	Surface area	Volume	Surface area to volume ratio
2 cm cube	$2 \times 2 \times 6 = 24\ cm^2$ (2 cm x 2 cm x 6 sides)	$2 \times 2 \times 2 = 8\ cm^3$ (height x width x depth)	24 to 8 = 3:1
3 cm cube			
4 cm cube			
5 cm cube			

ISBN: 978-1-927173-73-2

2. Create a graph, plotting the surface area against the volume of each cube, on the grid on the right. Draw a line connecting the points and label axes and units.

3. Which increases the fastest with increasing size: the **volume** or the **surface area**?

4. Explain what happens to the ratio of surface area to volume with increasing size.

5. The diffusion of molecules into a cell can be modelled by using agar cubes infused with phenolphthalein indicator and soaked in sodium hydroxide (NaOH). Phenolphthalein turns a pink color when in the presence of a base. As the NaOH diffuses into the agar, the phenolphthalein changes to pink and thus indicates how far the NaOH has diffused into the agar. By cutting an agar block into cubes of various sizes, it is possible to show the effect of cell size on diffusion.

(a) Use the information below to fill in the table on the right:

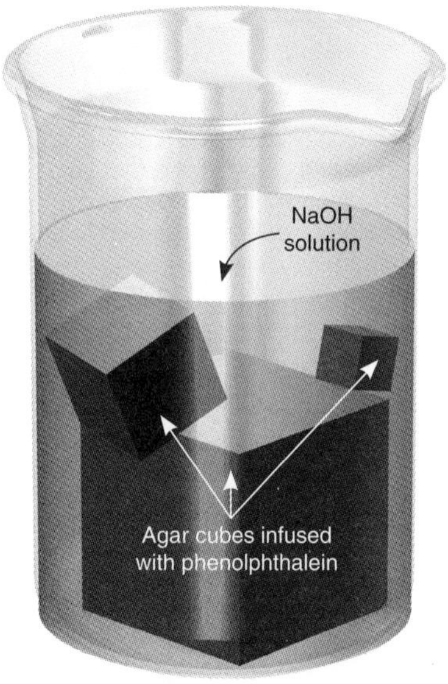
NaOH solution
Agar cubes infused with phenolphthalein

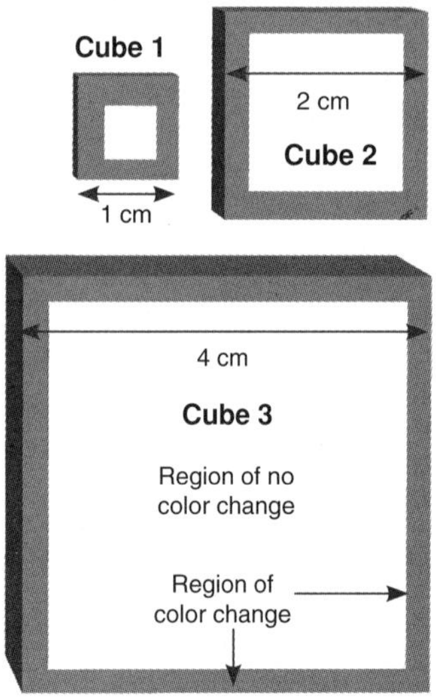
Cube 1
1 cm
2 cm
Cube 2
4 cm
Cube 3
Region of no color change
Region of color change

Cubes shown to same scale

Cube	1	2	3
1. Total volume (cm^3)			
2. Volume not pink (cm^3)			
3. Diffused volume (1. – 2.) (cm^3)			
4. Percentage diffusion			

(b) Diffusion of substances into and out of a cell occurs across the plasma membrane. For a cuboid cell, explain how increasing cell size affects the effective ability of diffusion to provide the materials required by the cell:

6. Explain why a single large cell of 2 cm x 2 cm x 2 cm is less efficient in terms of passively acquiring nutrients than eight cells of 1 cm x 1 cm x 1 cm:

ISBN: 978-1-927173-73-2

KEY TERMS: Mix and Match

INSTRUCTIONS: Test your vocabulary by matching each term to its definition, as identified by its preceding letter code.

active transport ....
amphipathic ....
aquaporin ....
carrier protein ....
cell wall ....
channel protein ....
concentration gradient ....
diffusion ....
endocytosis ....
exocytosis ....
facilitated diffusion ....
fluid mosaic model ....
glycolipids ....
glycoproteins ....
hypertonic ....
hypotonic ....
ion pump ....
isotonic ....
osmosis ....
passive transport ....
phagocytosis ....
pinocytosis ....
plasma membrane ....
plasmolysis ....
selectively permeable ....
surface area: volume ratio ....
transmembrane protein ....
turgor ....

A Passive movement of water molecules across a selectively permeable membrane down a concentration gradient.

B The model for membrane structure which proposes a double phospholipid bilayer in which proteins and cholesterol are embedded.

C A type of passive transport, facilitated by transport proteins.

D Protein that spans the plasma membrane.

E The process in plant cells where the plasma membrane pulls away from the cell wall as a result of the loss of water through osmosis.

F The energy-requiring movement of substances across a biological membrane against a concentration gradient.

G A solution with lower solute concentration relative to another solution (across a membrane).

H Active transport in which molecules are engulfed by the plasma membrane, forming a phagosome or food vacuole within the cell.

I The gradual difference in the concentration of solutes as a function of distance through the solution.

J The force exerted outward on a plant cell wall by the water contained in the cell.

K Lipids with attached carbohydrates which serve as markers for cellular recognition.

L Solutions of equal solute concentration are termed this.

M This relationship determines capacity for effective diffusion in a cell.

N The uptake of liquids or fine suspensions by endocytosis.

O The passive movement of molecules from high to low concentration.

P The movement of substances across a biological membrane without energy expenditure.

Q A solution with higher solute concentration relative to another solution (across a membrane).

R A structure, present in plants and bacteria, which is found outside the plasma membrane and gives rigidity to the cell.

S A selectively-permeable phospholipid bilayer forming the boundary of all cells.

T A transmembrane protein that moves ions across a plasma membrane against their concentration gradient.

U A specific form of endocytosis involving the engulfment of solid particles by the plasma membrane.

V Protein that provides a channel through the plasma membrane for small polar molecules and ions.

W Protein channel that increases the diffusion rate of water through the plasma membrane.

X Protein in the plasma membrane that facilitates the diffusion of a specific lipid insoluble molecule.

Y Active transport process by which membrane-bound secretory vesicles fuse with the plasma membrane and release the vesicle contents into the external environment.

Z A membrane that acts selectively to allow some substances, but not others, to pass.

AA Membrane-bound proteins with attached carbohydrates, involved in cell to cell interactions.

BB Possessing both hydrophilic and hydrophobic (lipophilic) properties.

ISBN: 978-1-927173-73-2

Chapter 4

Cellular **Energetics**

Key concepts

- ATP is the universal energy currency in cells.
- Cellular respiration and photosynthesis are important energy transformation processes.
- Both cellular respiration and photosynthesis involve the use of ATP and electron carriers.
- Cellular respiration involves the step-wise oxidation of glucose in the mitochondria.
- Photosynthesis uses light energy to fix carbon in organic compounds. It occurs in the chloroplasts.

Key terms

absorption spectrum
accessory pigment
acetyl coA
action spectrum
anaerobic metabolism
ATP
Calvin cycle
cellular respiration
chemiosmosis
chloroplast
chlorophyll
cristae
cyclic phosphorylation
electron transport chain
ethanol
fermentation
glycolysis
grana
H^+ acceptor
Krebs cycle
lactic acid
light dependent phase
matrix
mitochondrion
NAD/NADP
non-cyclic phosphorylation
photolysis
photosynthesis
ribulose bisphosphate
stroma
thylakoid discs

Learning Objectives

□ 1. Use the **KEY TERMS** to compile a glossary for this topic.

Role of ATP page 81-83

□ 2. Explain the universal role of **ATP** in metabolism, as illustrated by examples, e.g. active transport, anabolic reactions, movement, and thermoregulation.

□ 3. Describe the structure of ATP. Describe its synthesis from ADP and inorganic phosphate (Pi) and explain how it stores and releases its energy.

Cellular Respiration pages 84-89

□ 4. Describe the structure of a mitochondrion, identifying the **matrix** and **cristae**. Identify the location of the main steps in the complete oxidation of glucose: **glycolysis**, the **link reaction**, **Krebs cycle**, and **electron transport chain**.

□ 5. Describe glycolysis and recognize it as the major anaerobic pathway in cells (the starting point for both respiratory and fermentation pathways). State the net yield of ATP and $NADH_2$ from glycolysis.

□ 6. Describe the complete oxidation of glucose to CO_2, including reference to:
- The conversion of pyruvate to acetyl-coenzyme A.
- The stepwise oxidation of intermediates in the Krebs cycle.
- Generation of ATP by **chemiosmosis** in the electron transport chain.
- The role of oxygen as the terminal electron acceptor.

□ 7. Describe **fermentation** in mammalian muscle and in yeast, identifying the **H^+ acceptor** to each case. Compare and explain the differences in the yields of ATP from aerobic respiration (#6) and from fermentation.

Photosynthesis pages 90-96

□ 8. Describe the structure and role of **chloroplasts**. Explain the role of **chlorophyll a** and **b**, and **accessory pigments** (e.g. carotenoids) in light capture by green plants. Explain what is meant by the terms **absorption spectrum** and **action spectrum** with respect to light absorbing pigments.

□ 9. Describe and explain **photosynthesis** in a C_3 plant, including reference to:
- The generation of ATP and $NADPH_2$ in the **light dependent phase**, including the location and role of the photosystems.
- The **Calvin cycle** and the fixation of carbon dioxide using ATP and $NADPH_2$ in the **light independent phase**. Include reference to the reduction of G3P and the regeneration of ribulose bisphosphate.

□ 10. Compare and contrast photosynthesis in **C_3** and **C_4** plants. Explain the adaptive value of the C_4 pathway in photosynthesis.

□ 11. Describe and explain factors affecting **photosynthetic rate** and yield.

Weblinks:
www.thebiozone.com/weblink/Cellbio-3732/

BIOZONE APP:
Student Review Series
Cellular Energetics

Energy in Cells

All organisms require energy for their metabolism. The universal energy carrier for the cell is **ATP** (**adenosine triphosphate**). ATP transports chemical energy within the cell for use in metabolic processes such as biosynthesis, cell division, cell signaling, thermoregulation, cell motility, and active transport. ATP can release its energy quickly; only one chemical reaction (hydrolysis of the terminal phosphate) is required. This reaction is catalyzed by the enzyme ATPase. Once ATP has released its energy, it becomes ADP (adenosine diphosphate), a low energy molecule that can be recharged by adding a phosphate. This requires energy, which is supplied by the controlled breakdown of respiratory substrates (commonly glucose) in **cellular respiration**.

Adenosine Triphosphate (ATP)

The ATP molecule consists of three components; a purine base (**adenine**), a pentose sugar (**ribose**), and **three phosphate groups** which attach to the 5' carbon of the pentose sugar. The three dimensional structure of ATP is described below.

ATP acts as a store of energy within the cell. The bonds between the phosphate groups are **high-energy bonds**, meaning that a large amount of free energy is released when they are hydrolyzed. Typically, this hydrolysis involves the removal of one phosphate group from the ATP molecule resulting in the formation of adenosine diphosphate (ADP).

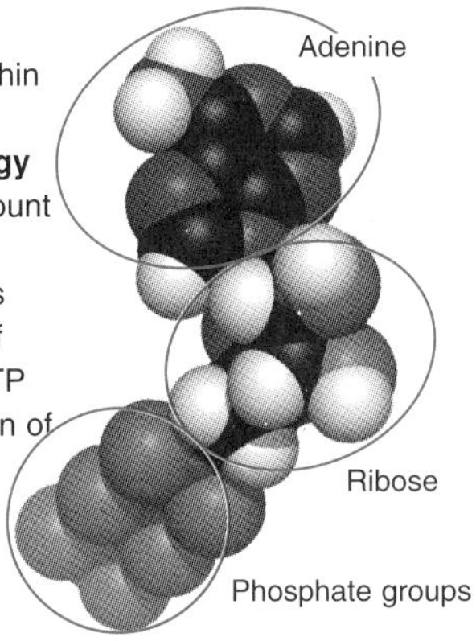
Adenine
Ribose
Phosphate groups

The Mitochondrion

Cellular respiration and ATP production occur in the mitochondria. A mitochondrion is bound by a double membrane. The inner and outer membranes are separated by an intermembrane space, compartmentalizing the regions of the mitochondrion in which the different reactions of cellular respiration take place.

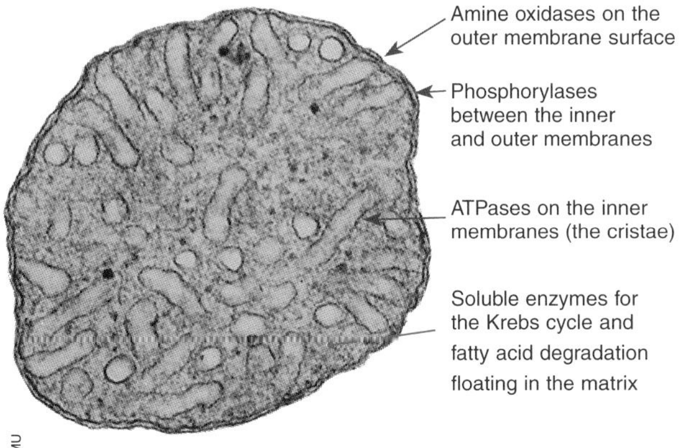
Amine oxidases on the outer membrane surface
Phosphorylases between the inner and outer membranes
ATPases on the inner membranes (the cristae)
Soluble enzymes for the Krebs cycle and fatty acid degradation floating in the matrix

WMU

ATP Powers Metabolism

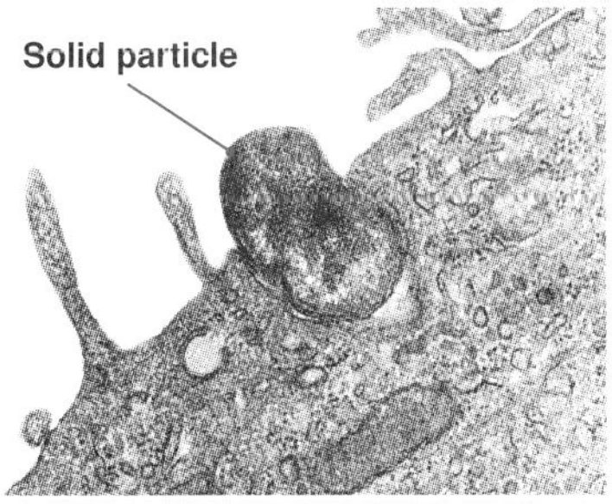
Solid particle

The energy released from the removal of a phosphate group of ATP is used to actively transport molecules and substances across the cellular membrane. **Phagocytosis** (left), which involves the engulfment of solid particles, is one such example.

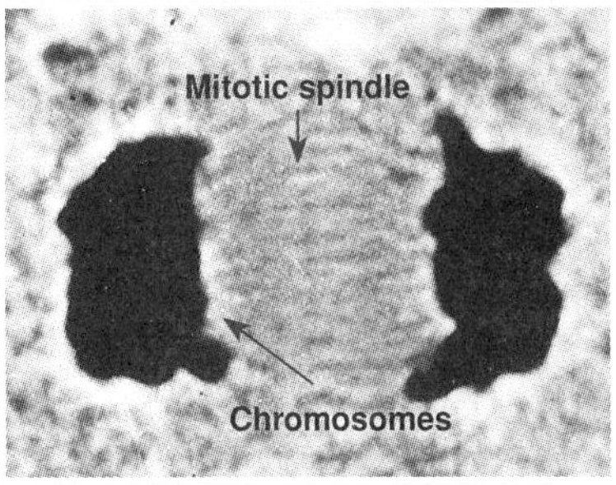
Mitotic spindle
Chromosomes

Cell division (mitosis), as observed in this onion cell, requires ATP to proceed. Formation of the mitotic spindle and chromosome separation are two aspects of cell division which require energy from ATP hydrolysis to occur.

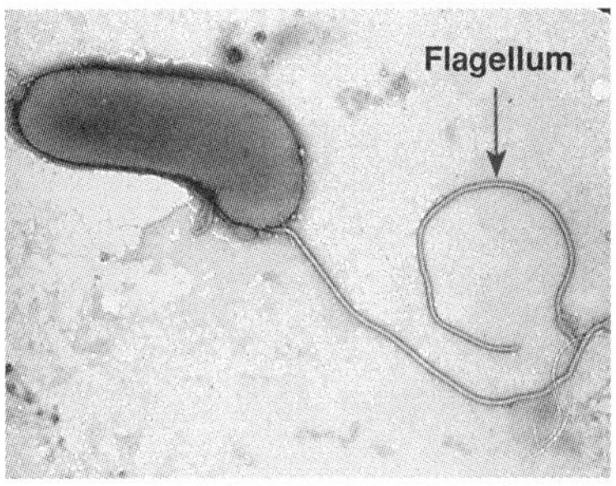
Flagellum

The hydrolysis of ATP provides the energy for motile cells to achieve movement via a tail-like structure called a flagellum. For example, the bacterium, *Helicobacter pylori* (left), is motile. Likewise, mammalian sperm must be able to move to the ovum to fertilize it.

The maintenance of body temperature requires energy. To maintain body heat, muscular activity increases (e.g. shivering, erection of body hairs). Cooling requires expenditure of energy too. For example, sweating is an energy requiring process involving secretion from glands in the skin.

1. In which organelle is ATP produced in the cell? ______________________________

2. Which enzyme catalyzes the hydrolysis of ATP? ______________________________

3. Explain how ATP is involved in:

   (a) Thermoregulation: ______________________________

   ____

   (b) Cell motility: ______________________________

   ____

   ____

ISBN: 978-1-927173-73-2

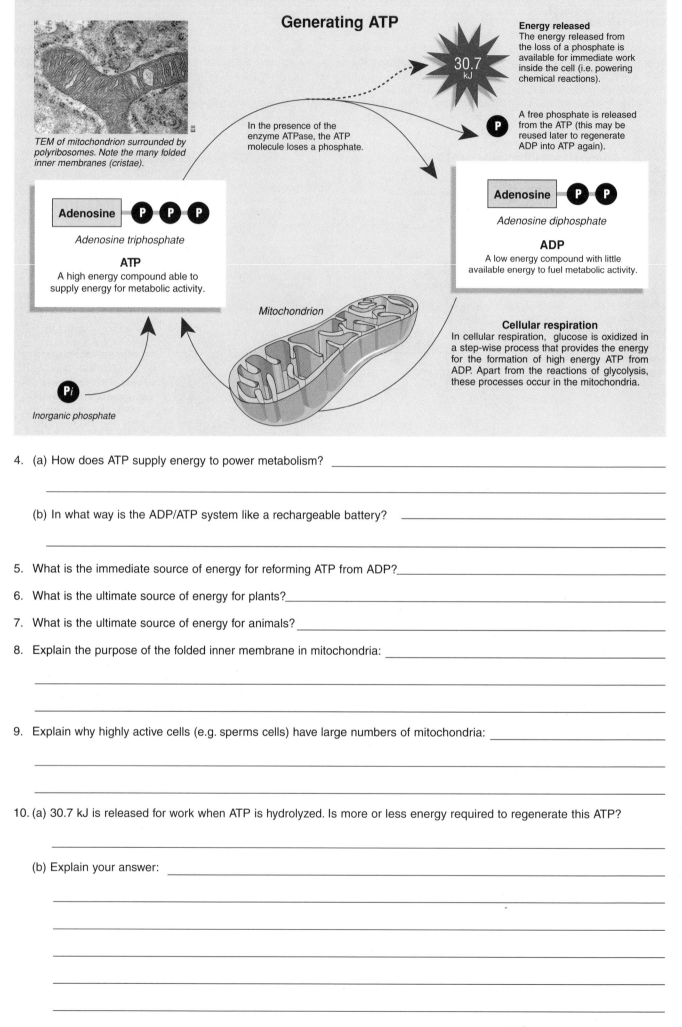

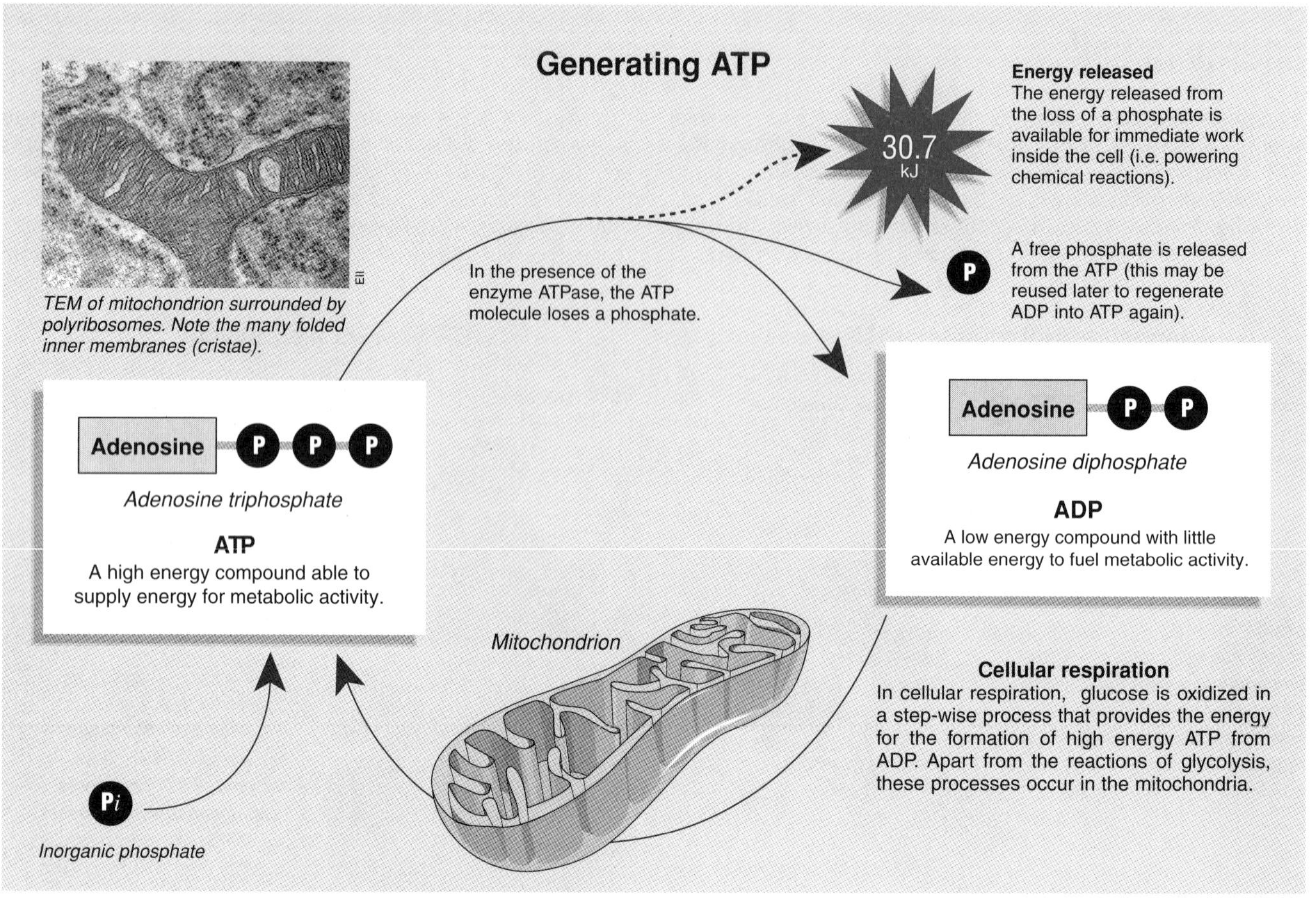
Generating ATP
Energy released
The energy released from the loss of a phosphate is available for immediate work inside the cell (i.e. powering chemical reactions).
30.7 kJ
A free phosphate is released from the ATP (this may be reused later to regenerate ADP into ATP again).
P
In the presence of the enzyme ATPase, the ATP molecule loses a phosphate.
TEM of mitochondrion surrounded by polyribosomes. Note the many folded inner membranes (cristae).
EII
Adenosine
P P P
Adenosine triphosphate
ATP
A high energy compound able to supply energy for metabolic activity.
Adenosine
P P
Adenosine diphosphate
ADP
A low energy compound with little available energy to fuel metabolic activity.
Mitochondrion
Cellular respiration
In cellular respiration, glucose is oxidized in a step-wise process that provides the energy for the formation of high energy ATP from ADP. Apart from the reactions of glycolysis, these processes occur in the mitochondria.
Pi
Inorganic phosphate

4. (a) How does ATP supply energy to power metabolism? ______________________

____

(b) In what way is the ADP/ATP system like a rechargeable battery? ______________________

____

5. What is the immediate source of energy for reforming ATP from ADP? ______________________

6. What is the ultimate source of energy for plants? ______________________

7. What is the ultimate source of energy for animals? ______________________

8. Explain the purpose of the folded inner membrane in mitochondria: ______________________

____

____

9. Explain why highly active cells (e.g. sperms cells) have large numbers of mitochondria: ______________________

____

____

10. (a) 30.7 kJ is released for work when ATP is hydrolyzed. Is more or less energy required to regenerate this ATP?

____

(b) Explain your answer: ______________________

____

____

____

____

____

ISBN: 978-1-927173-73-2

Energy Transformations in Cells

A summary of the flow of energy within a plant cell is illustrated below. Animal cells have a similar flow except the glucose is supplied by ingestion rather than by photosynthesis. The energy not immediately stored in chemical bonds is lost as heat. Note the role of ATP; it is made in cellular respiration and provides the energy for metabolic reactions, including photosynthesis.

Energy Transformations in a Photosynthetic Plant Cell

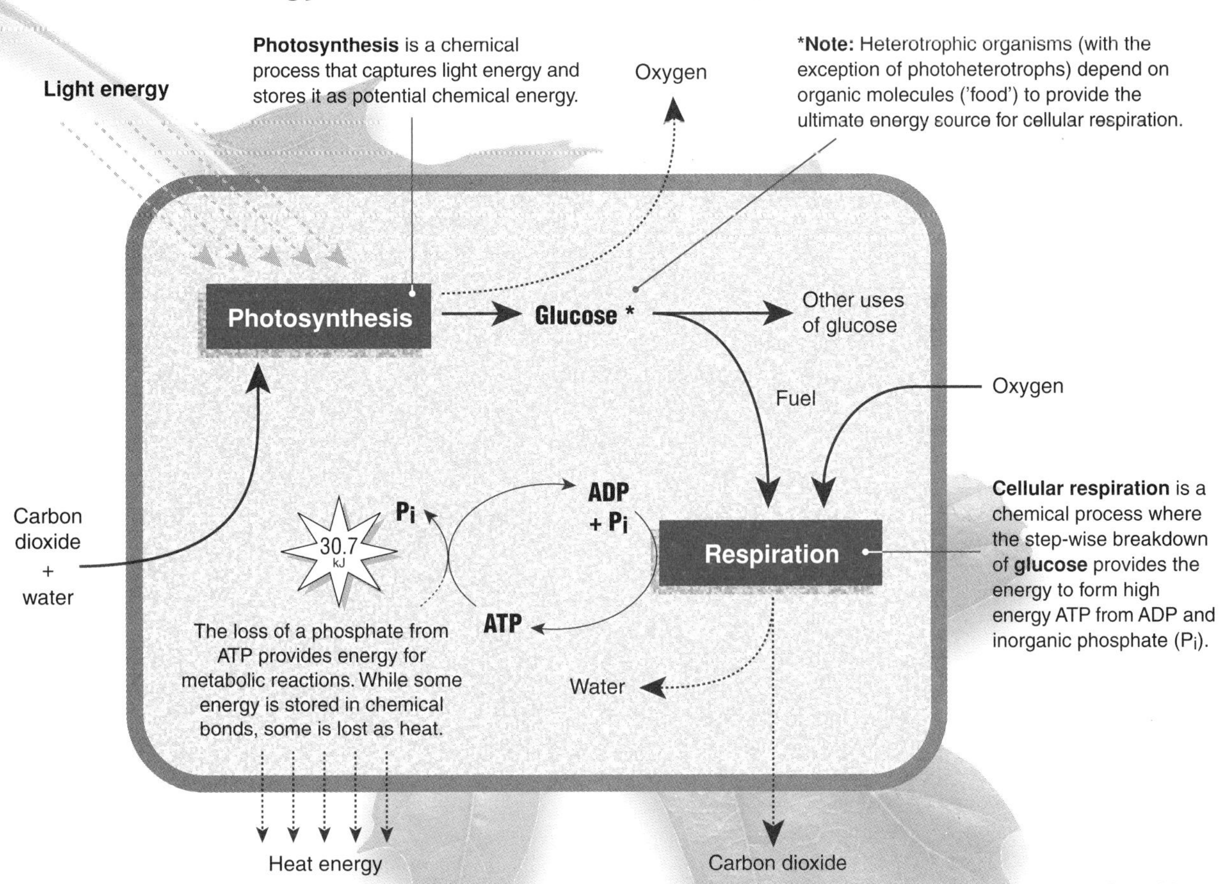
Light energy
Photosynthesis is a chemical process that captures light energy and stores it as potential chemical energy.
Oxygen
*Note: Heterotrophic organisms (with the exception of photoheterotrophs) depend on organic molecules ('food') to provide the ultimate energy source for cellular respiration.
Photosynthesis
Glucose *
Other uses of glucose
Fuel
Oxygen
Carbon dioxide + water
P_i
30.7 kJ
ADP + P_i
Respiration
Cellular respiration is a chemical process where the step-wise breakdown of **glucose** provides the energy to form high energy ATP from ADP and inorganic phosphate (P_i).
ATP
The loss of a phosphate from ATP provides energy for metabolic reactions. While some energy is stored in chemical bonds, some is lost as heat.
Water
Heat energy
Carbon dioxide

1. Discuss the differences between **heterotrophs**, **photosynthetic autotrophs**, and **chemosynthetic autotrophs** with respect to how these organisms derive their source of energy for metabolism:

2. In 1977, scientists working near the Galápagos Islands in the equatorial eastern Pacific found warm water spewing from cracks in the mid-oceanic ridges 2,600 m below the surface. Clustered around these hydrothermal vents were strange and beautiful creatures new to science. The entire community depends on sulfur-oxidizing bacteria that use hydrogen sulfide dissolved in the venting water as an energy source to manufacture carbohydrates. This process is similar to photosynthesis, but does not rely on sunlight to provide the energy for generating ATP and fixing carbon:

   (a) Explain why a community based on photosynthetic organisms is not found at this site:

   (b) Name the ultimate energy source for the bacteria:

   (c) This same chemical that provides the bacteria with energy is also toxic to the process of cellular respiration; a problem that the animals living in the habitat have resolved by evolving various adaptations. Explain what would happen if these animals did not possess adaptations to reduce the toxic effect on cellular respiration:

   (d) Name the energy source classification for these sulfur-oxidizing bacteria:

ISBN: 978-1-927173-73-2

Cell Respiration

Cell respiration is the process by which organisms break down energy rich molecules (e.g. glucose) to release the energy in a useable form (ATP). All living cells respire in order to exist, although the substrates they use may vary. **Aerobic respiration** requires oxygen. Forms of cell respiration that do not require oxygen are said to be **anaerobic**. Some plants and animals can generate ATP anaerobically for short periods of time. Other organisms use only anaerobic respiration and live in oxygen-free environments. For these organisms, there is some other final electron acceptor other than oxygen (e.g. nitrate or Fe^{2+}).

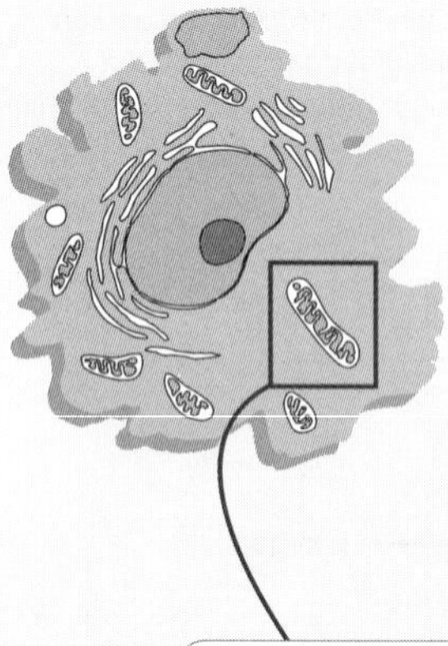

An Overview of Cell Respiration

Respiration involves three metabolic stages (plus a link reaction) summarized below. The first two stages are the catabolic pathways that decompose glucose and other organic fuels. In the third stage, the electron transport chain accepts electrons from the first two stages and passes these from one electron acceptor to another. The energy released at each stepwise transfer is used to make ATP. The final electron acceptor in this process is molecular oxygen.

1. **Glycolysis**. In the cytoplasm, glucose is broken down into two molecules of pyruvate.
2. **The link reaction**. Pyruvate is split and added to coenzyme A ready to enter the Krebs cycle.
3. **Krebs cycle**. In the mitochondrial matrix, a derivative of pyruvate is decomposed to CO_2.
4. **Electron transport chain**. This occurs in the inner membranes of the mitochondrion and accounts for almost 90% of the ATP generated by respiration.

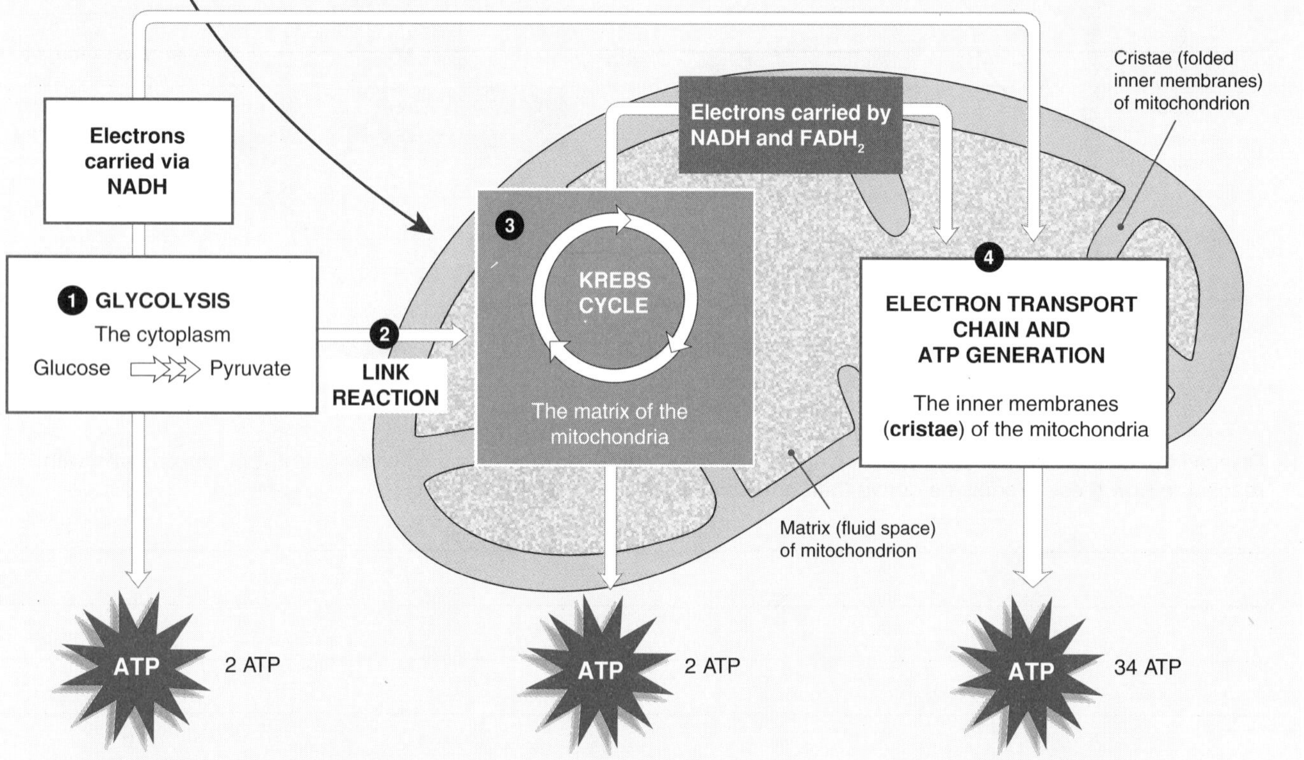

Electrons carried via NADH
Electrons carried by NADH and $FADH_2$
Cristae (folded inner membranes) of mitochondrion
1 GLYCOLYSIS
The cytoplasm
Glucose
Pyruvate
2
LINK REACTION
3
KREBS CYCLE
The matrix of the mitochondria
4
ELECTRON TRANSPORT CHAIN AND ATP GENERATION
The inner membranes (cristae) of the mitochondria
Matrix (fluid space) of mitochondrion
ATP
2 ATP
ATP
2 ATP
ATP
34 ATP

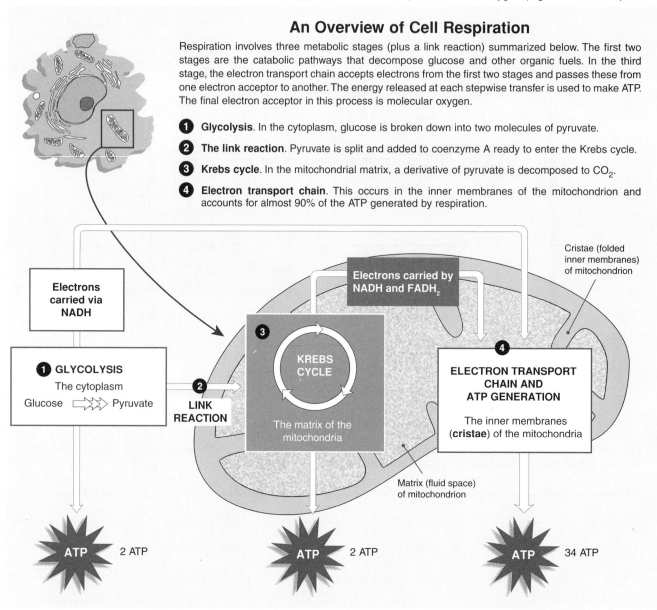

1. Describe precisely in which part of the cell the following take place and state the ATP yield from each:

   (a) Glycolysis: ______

   (b) Krebs cycle reactions: ______

   (c) Electron transport chain: ______

2. Summarize the events occurring in each of the following:

   (a) Glycolysis: ______

   (b) Krebs cycle: ______

   (c) Electron transport: ______

ISBN: 978-1-927173-73-2

The Biochemistry of Respiration

The oxidation of glucose is a catabolic, energy yielding pathway. The breakdown of glucose and other organic fuels (such as fats and proteins) to simpler molecules releases energy for ATP synthesis. Glycolysis and the Krebs cycle supply electrons to the electron transport chain, which drives **oxidative phosphorylation**. Glycolysis nets two ATP. The conversion of pyruvate (the end product of glycolysis) to **acetyl CoA** links glycolysis to the Krebs cycle. One "turn" of the cycle releases carbon dioxide, forms one ATP, and passes electrons to three NAD^+ and one FAD. Most of the ATP generated in cellular respiration is produced by oxidative phosphorylation when $NADH_2$ and $FADH_2$ donate electrons to the series of electron carriers in the electron transport chain. At the end of the chain, electrons are passed to molecular oxygen, reducing it to water. Electron transport is coupled to ATP synthesis.

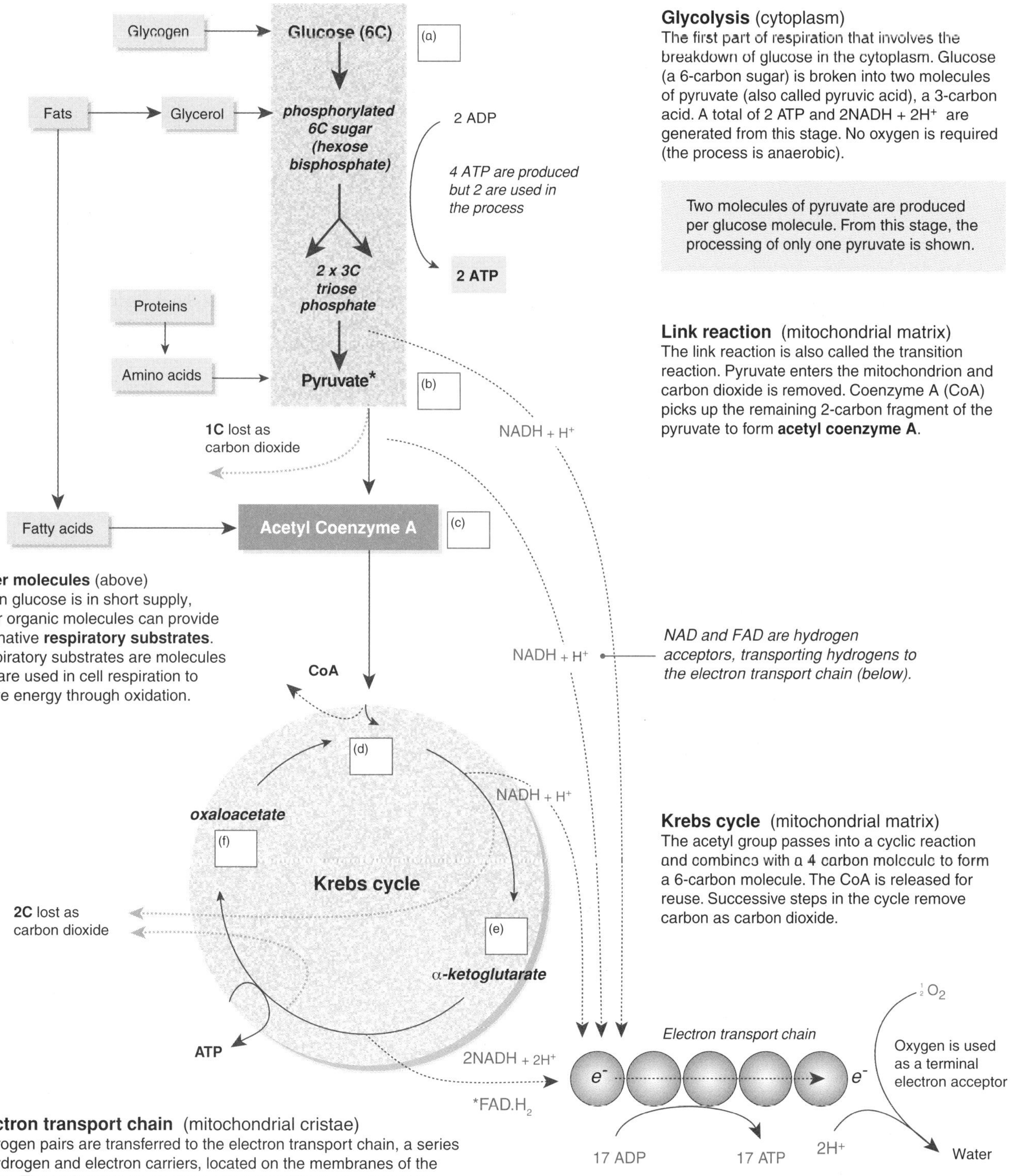
Glycogen
Glucose (6C)
(a)
Fats
Glycerol
phosphorylated 6C sugar (hexose bisphosphate)
2 ADP
4 ATP are produced but 2 are used in the process
2 ATP
2 x 3C triose phosphate
Proteins
Amino acids
Pyruvate*
(b)
1C lost as carbon dioxide
NADH + H+
Fatty acids
Acetyl Coenzyme A
(c)
NADH + H+
CoA
(d)
NADH + H+
oxaloacetate
(f)
Krebs cycle
2C lost as carbon dioxide
(e)
α-ketoglutarate
ATP
2NADH + 2H+
*FAD.H2
Electron transport chain
e-
e-
½ O2
Oxygen is used as a terminal electron acceptor
17 ADP
17 ATP
2H+
Water

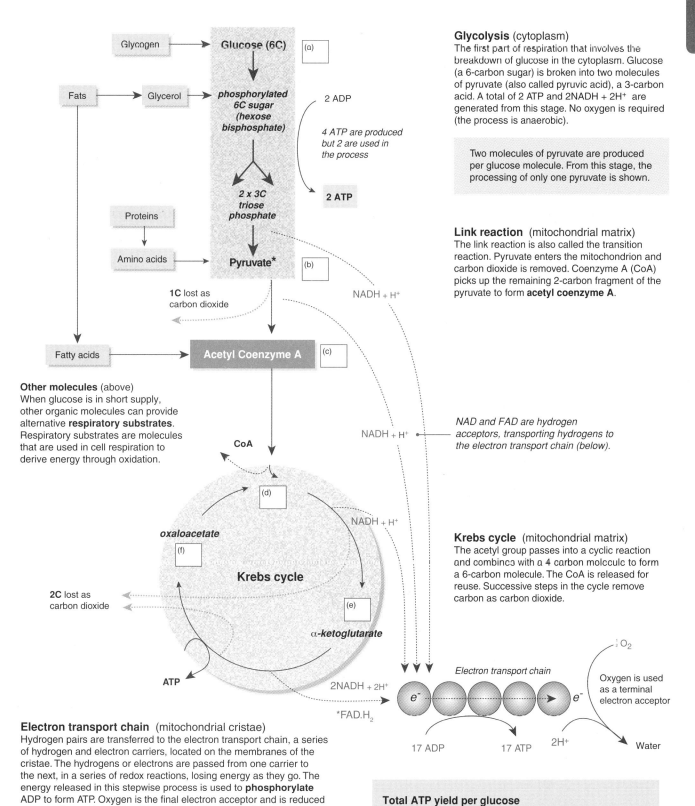

Glycolysis (cytoplasm)
The first part of respiration that involves the breakdown of glucose in the cytoplasm. Glucose (a 6-carbon sugar) is broken into two molecules of pyruvate (also called pyruvic acid), a 3-carbon acid. A total of 2 ATP and 2NADH + $2H^+$ are generated from this stage. No oxygen is required (the process is anaerobic).

Two molecules of pyruvate are produced per glucose molecule. From this stage, the processing of only one pyruvate is shown.

Link reaction (mitochondrial matrix)
The link reaction is also called the transition reaction. Pyruvate enters the mitochondrion and carbon dioxide is removed. Coenzyme A (CoA) picks up the remaining 2-carbon fragment of the pyruvate to form **acetyl coenzyme A**.

Other molecules (above)
When glucose is in short supply, other organic molecules can provide alternative **respiratory substrates**. Respiratory substrates are molecules that are used in cell respiration to derive energy through oxidation.

NAD and FAD are hydrogen acceptors, transporting hydrogens to the electron transport chain (below).

Krebs cycle (mitochondrial matrix)
The acetyl group passes into a cyclic reaction and combines with a 4 carbon molecule to form a 6-carbon molecule. The CoA is released for reuse. Successive steps in the cycle remove carbon as carbon dioxide.

Electron transport chain (mitochondrial cristae)
Hydrogen pairs are transferred to the electron transport chain, a series of hydrogen and electron carriers, located on the membranes of the cristae. The hydrogens or electrons are passed from one carrier to the next, in a series of redox reactions, losing energy as they go. The energy released in this stepwise process is used to **phosphorylate** ADP to form ATP. Oxygen is the final electron acceptor and is reduced to water (hence the term **oxidative phosphorylation**).
Note FAD enters the electron transport chain at a lower energy level than NAD, and only 2ATP are generated per $FAD.H_2$.

Total ATP yield per glucose
Glycolysis: 2 ATP, *Krebs cycle*: 2 ATP, *Electron transport*: 34 ATP

ISBN: 978-1-927173-73-2

Related activities: *Cellular Respiration*
Weblinks: *Glycolysis, The Citric Acid Cycle*

Glycolysis and Fermentation	Aerobic Respiration
Occurs in the cytoplasm of the cell.	Occurs in the mitochondria of eukaryotic cells.
Oxygen is not required.	Oxygen is required.
Glycolysis: glucose is converted to pyruvic acid with a net production of 2ATP molecules (a very low energy yield).	Pyruvic acid is converted to carbon dioxide, water, and a further 36 ATP molecules from the Krebs cycle and electron transport chain (a high energy yield per glucose molecule).
Very inefficient production of energy.	An energy efficient process.
In the absence of oxygen, pyruvic acid cannot enter the mitochondrion. It is converted to ethanol and carbon dioxide in plants, and lactic acid in animals.	When oxygen is present, pyruvic acid can be oxidized further via the Krebs cycle and electron transport chain.

1. Explain the purpose of the link reaction: ____________________

2. On the diagram of cell respiration (previous page), state the number of carbon atoms in each of the molecules (a)-(f):

3. Determine how many ATP molecules **per molecule of glucose** are generated during the following stages of respiration:

   (a) Glycolysis: ________ (b) Krebs cycle: ________ (c) Electron transport chain: ________ (d) Total: ________

4. Explain what happens to the carbon atoms lost during respiration: ____________________

5. Describe the role of each of the following in cell respiration:

   (a) Hydrogen atoms: ____________________

   (b) NAD and FAD: ____________________

   (c) Oxygen: ____________________

   (d) Acetyl coenzyme A: ____________________

6. Explain what happens when the supply of glucose for cell respiration is limited: ____________________

7. Distinguish between reduction and oxidation: ____________________

8. Explain what happens during oxidative phosphorylation: ____________________

ISBN: 978-1-927173-73-2

Chemiosmosis

Chemiosmosis is the process in which electron transport is coupled to ATP synthesis. It takes place in the membranes of the mitochondria of all eukaryotic cells, the chloroplasts of plants, and across the plasma membrane of bacteria. Chemiosmosis involves the establishment of a proton (hydrogen) gradient across biological membranes (shown below for cell respiration). The concentration gradient is a form of potential energy, which in chemiosmosis is used to generate ATP. Chemiosmosis has two key components: an **electron transport chain** (ETC) sets up a proton gradient as electrons pass along it to a final electron acceptor, and an enzyme called **ATP synthase** which uses the proton gradient to catalyze ATP synthesis In cell respiration, electron transport carriers on the inner membrane of the mitochondrion oxidize NADH + H^+ and $FADH_2$. Energy from this process forces protons to move, against their concentration gradient, from the mitochondrial matrix into the space between the two membranes. The protons then flow back into the matrix via ATP synthase molecules in the membrane. As the protons flow down their concentration gradient, energy is released and ATP is synthesized. In the chloroplasts of green plants, the process is similar as ATP is produced when protons pass from the thylakoid lumen to the chloroplast stroma via ATP synthase.

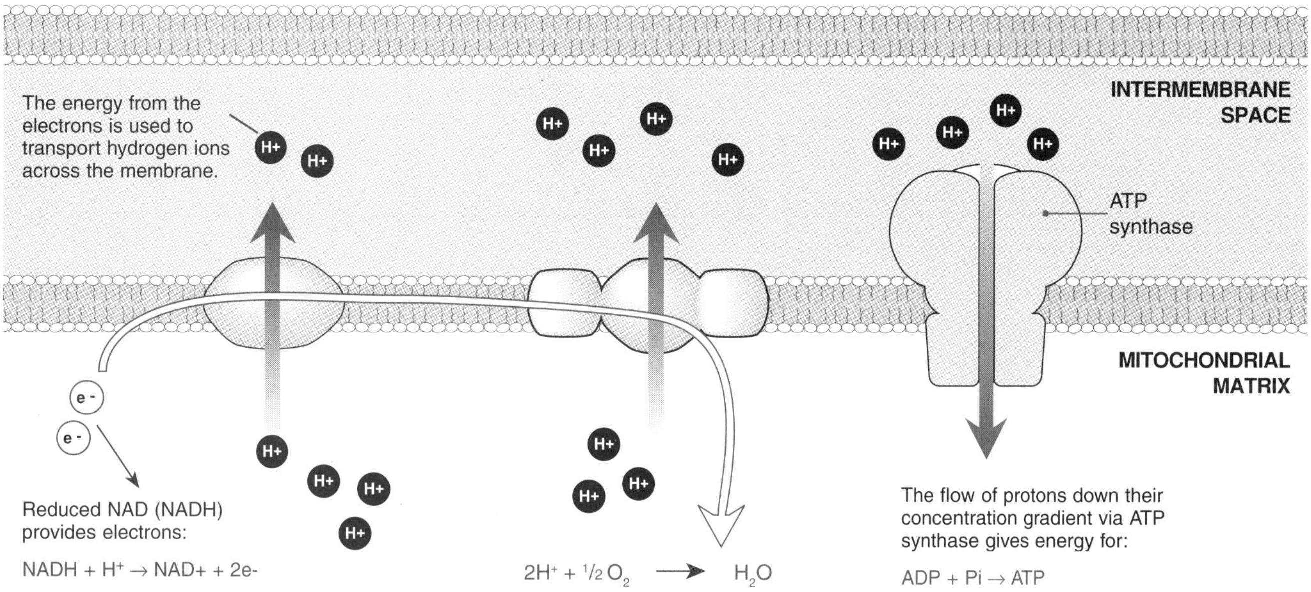
The energy from the electrons is used to transport hydrogen ions across the membrane.
H+
INTERMEMBRANE SPACE
ATP synthase
MITOCHONDRIAL MATRIX
e -
Reduced NAD (NADH) provides electrons:
NADH + H⁺ → NAD+ + 2e-
2H⁺ + 1/2 O₂ → H₂O
The flow of protons down their concentration gradient via ATP synthase gives energy for:
ADP + Pi → ATP

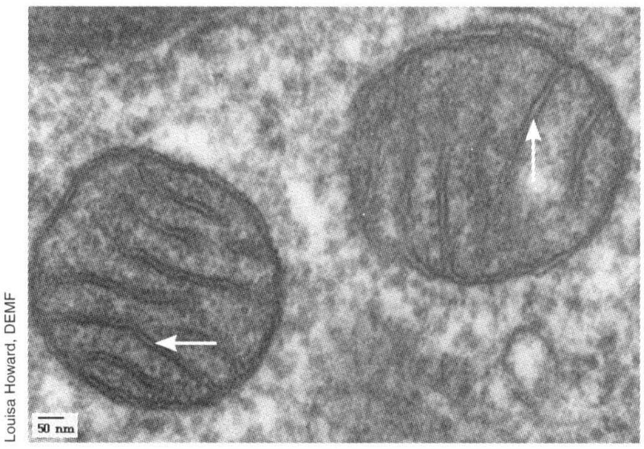
50 nm
Louisa Howard, DEMF
The intermembrane spaces can be seen (arrows) in this transverse section of miotchondria.

The Evidence for Chemiosmosis

The British biochemist Peter Mitchell proposed the chemiosmotic hypothesis in 1961. He proposed that, because living cells have membrane potential, electrochemical gradients could be used to do work, i.e. provide the energy for ATP synthesis. Scientists at the time were skeptical, but the evidence for chemiosmosis was extensive and came from studies of isolated mitochondria and chloroplasts. Evidence included:

- The outer membranes of mitochondria were removed leaving the inner membranes intact. Adding protons to the treated mitochondria increased ATP synthesis.
- When isolated chloroplasts were illuminated, the medium in which they were suspended became alkaline.
- Isolated chloroplasts were kept in the dark and transferred first to a low pH medium (to acidify the thylakoid interior) and then to an alkaline medium (low protons). They then spontaneously synthesized ATP (no light was needed).

1. Summarize the process of chemiosmosis: ______________________________

____

____

2. Why did the addition of protons to the treated mitochondria increase ATP synthesis? ______________________________

____

3. Why did the suspension of isolated chloroplasts become alkaline when illuminated? ______________________________

____

4. (a) What was the purpose of transferring the chloroplasts first to an acid then to an alkaline medium? ______________________________

____

(b) Why did ATP synthesis occur spontaneously in these treated chloroplasts? ______________________________

____

ISBN: 978-1-927173-73-2

Related activities: *The Biochemistry of Respiration*
Weblinks: *Electron Transport Chain Movie, Oxidative Phosphorylation*

Measuring Respiration

In small animals or germinating seeds, the rate of cellular respiration can be measured using a simple respirometer: a sealed unit where the carbon dioxide produced by the respiring tissues is absorbed by soda lime and the volume of oxygen consumed is detected by fluid displacement in a manometer. Germinating seeds are also often used to calculate the **respiratory quotient** (RQ): the ratio of the amount of carbon dioxide produced during cellular respiration to the amount of oxygen consumed. RQ provides a useful indication of the respiratory substrate being used.

Respiratory Substrates and RQ

The respiratory quotient (RQ) can be expressed simply as:

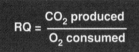

$$RQ = \frac{CO_2 \text{ produced}}{O_2 \text{ consumed}}$$

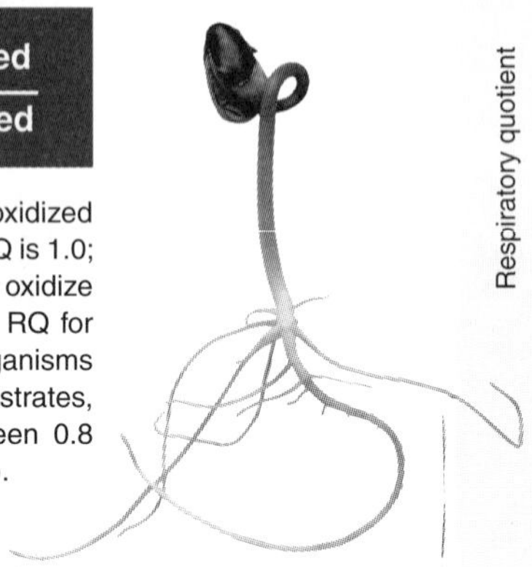

When pure carbohydrate is oxidized in cellular respiration, the RQ is 1.0; more oxygen is required to oxidize fatty acids (RQ = 0.7). The RQ for protein is about 0.9. Organisms usually respire a mix of substrates, giving RQ values of between 0.8 and 0.9 (see table 1, below).

RQ	Substrate
> 1.0	Carbohydrate with some anaerobic respiration
1.0	Carbohydrates e.g. glucose
0.9	Protein
0.7	Fat
0.5	Fat with associated carbohydrate synthesis
0.3	Carbohydrate with associated organic acid synthesis

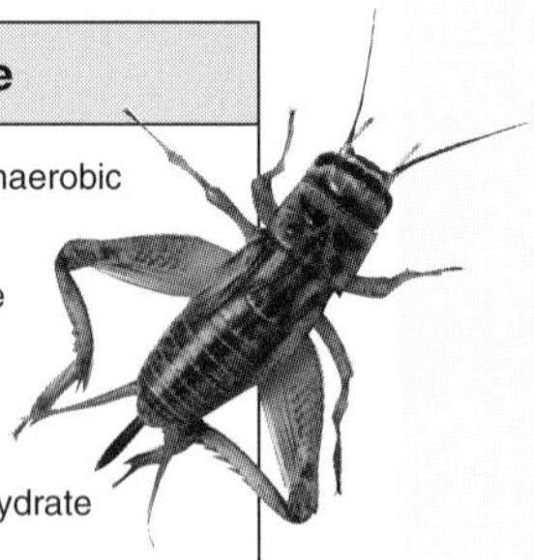

Using RQ to determine respiratory substrate

Fig. 1: RQ in relation to germination stage in wheat

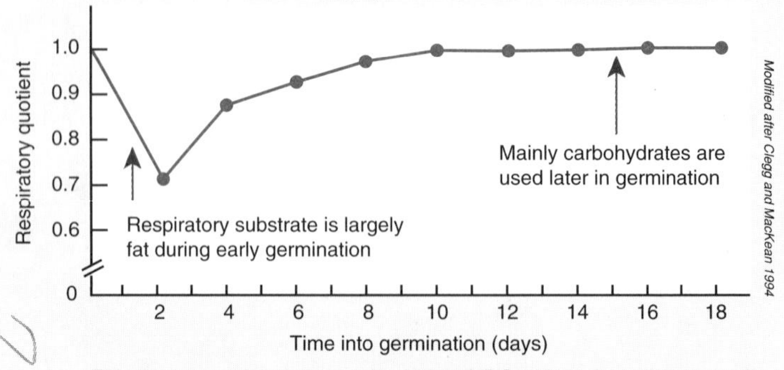
Respiratory quotient
1.0
0.9
0.8
0.7
0.6
0
Respiratory substrate is largely fat during early germination
Mainly carbohydrates are used later in germination
2
4
6
8
10
12
14
16
18
Time into germination (days)
Modified after Clegg and MacKean 1994

Fig. 1, above, shows how experimental RQ values have been used to determine the respiratory substrate utilized by germinating wheat seeds (*Triticum sativum*) over the period of their germination.

Table 2: Rates of O_2 consumption and CO_2 production in crickets

Time after last fed (h)	Temperature (°C)	Rate of O_2 consumption (mL g^{-1} h^{-1})	Rate of CO_2 production (mL g^{-1} h^{-1})
1	20	2.82	2.82
48	20	2.82	1.97
1	30	5.12	5.12
48	30	5.12	3.57

Table 2 shows the rates of oxygen consumption and carbon dioxide production of crickets kept under different experimental conditions.

1. Table 2 above shows the results of an experiment to measure the rates of oxygen consumption and carbon dioxide production of crickets 1 hour and 48 hours after feeding at different temperatures:

   (a) Calculate the RQ of a cricket kept at 20°C, 48 hours after feeding (show working): ________________

   (b) Compare this RQ to the RQ value obtained for the cricket 1 hour after being fed (20°C). Explain the difference:

2. The RQs of two species of seeds were calculated at two day intervals after germination. Results are tabulated to the right:

   (a) Plot the change in RQ of the two species during early germination:

   (b) Explain the values in terms of the possible substrates being respired:

Days after germination	RQ	
	Seedling A	Seedling B
2	0.65	0.70
4	0.35	0.91
6	0.48	0.98
8	0.68	1.00
10	0.70	1.00

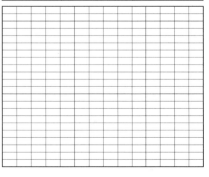

ISBN: 978-1-927173-73-2

Anaerobic Pathways

All organisms can metabolize glucose anaerobically (without oxygen) using **glycolysis** in the cytoplasm, but the energy yield from this process is low and few organisms can obtain sufficient energy for their needs this way. In the absence of oxygen, glycolysis soon stops unless there is an alternative acceptor for the electrons produced from the glycolytic pathway. In yeasts and the root cells of higher plants this acceptor is ethanal, and the pathway is called **alcoholic fermentation**. In the skeletal muscle of mammals, the acceptor is pyruvate itself and the end product is **lactic acid**. In both cases, the duration of the fermentation is limited by the toxic effects of the organic compound produced. Although fermentation is often used synonymously with anaerobic respiration, they are not the same. Respiration always involves hydrogen ions passing down a chain of carriers to a terminal acceptor, and this does not occur in fermentation. In anaerobic respiration, the terminal H^+ acceptor is a molecule other than oxygen, e.g. Fe^{2+} or nitrate.

Alcoholic Fermentation

In alcoholic fermentation, the H^+ acceptor is ethanal which is reduced to ethanol with the release of CO_2. Yeasts respire aerobically when oxygen is available but can use alcoholic fermentation when it is not. At levels above 12-15%, the ethanol produced by alcoholic fermentation is toxic to the yeast cells and this limits their ability to use this pathway indefinitely. The root cells of plants also use fermentation as a pathway when oxygen is unavailable but the ethanol must be converted back to respiratory intermediates and respired aerobically.

Lactic Acid Fermentation

In the absence of oxygen, the skeletal muscle cells of mammals are able to continue using glycolysis for ATP production by reducing pyruvate to lactic acid (the H^+ acceptor is pyruvate itself). This process is called lactic acid fermentation. Lactic acid is toxic and this pathway cannot continue indefinitely. The lactic acid must be removed from the muscle and transported to the liver, where it is converted back to respiratory intermediates and respired aerobically.

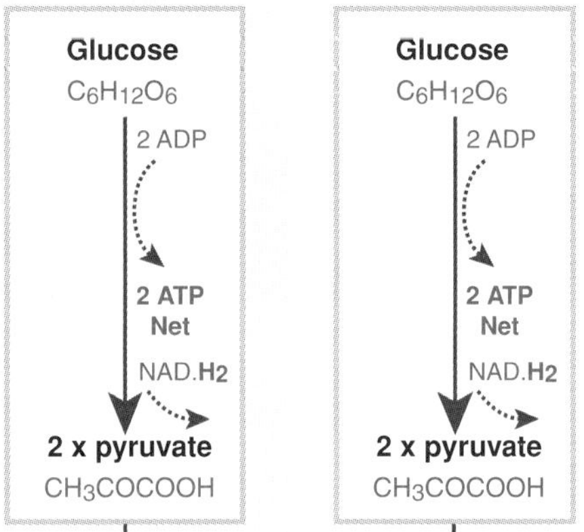
Glucose
C6H12O6
2 ADP
2 ATP
Net
NAD.H2
2 x pyruvate
CH3COCOOH
Glucose
C6H12O6
2 ADP
2 ATP
Net
NAD.H2
2 x pyruvate
CH3COCOOH

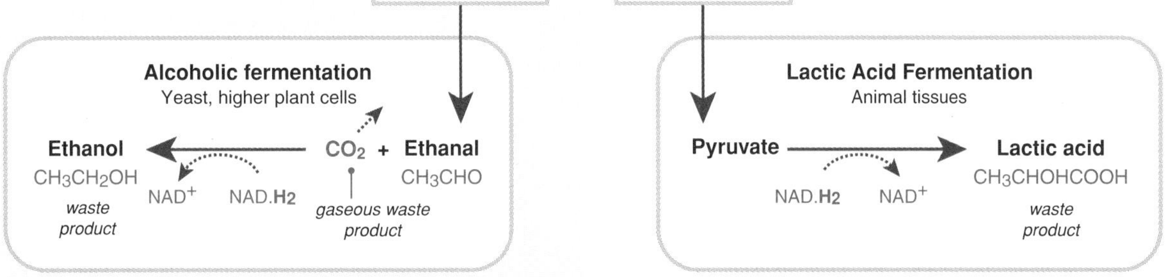
Alcoholic fermentation
Yeast, higher plant cells
Ethanol
CH3CH2OH
waste product
NAD+
NAD.H2
CO2 + Ethanal
CH3CHO
gaseous waste product
Lactic Acid Fermentation
Animal tissues
Pyruvate
NAD.H2
NAD+
Lactic acid
CH3CHOHCOOH
waste product

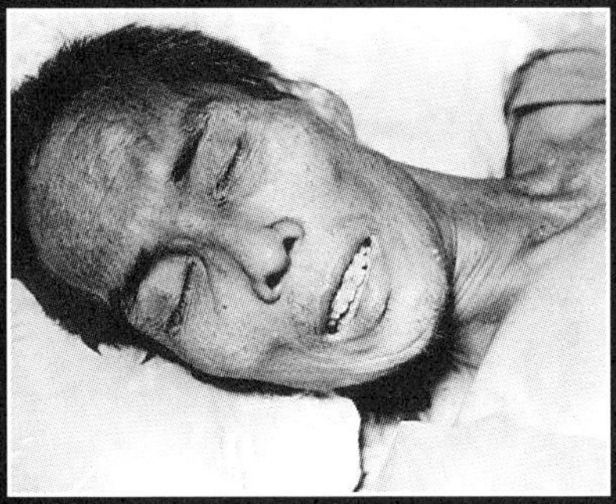

CDC

Some organisms respire only in the absence of oxygen and are known as obligate anaerobes. Many of these organisms are bacterial pathogens and cause diseases such as tetanus (above), gangrene, and botulism.

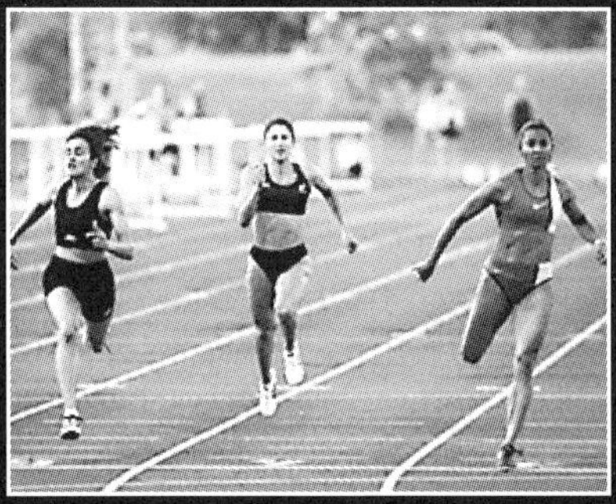

Vertebrate skeletal muscle is facultatively anaerobic because it has the ability to generate ATP for a short time in the absence of oxygen. The energy from this pathway comes from glycolysis and the yield is low.

The products of alcoholic fermentation have been utilized by humans for centuries. The alcohol and carbon dioxide produced from this process form the basis of the brewing and baking industries.

1. Describe the key difference between aerobic respiration and fermentation: ______________________

____

2. (a) Refer to page 86 and determine the efficiency of fermentation compared to aerobic respiration: __________ %

(b) Why is the efficiency of these anaerobic pathways so low? ______________________

____

3. Why can't fermentation go on indefinitely? ______________________

____

____

ISBN: 978-1-927173-73-2

Photosynthesis

Photosynthesis transforms sunlight energy into chemical energy stored in molecules, releases free oxygen gas, and absorbs carbon dioxide (a waste product of cellular metabolism). Photosynthetic organisms use pigments, called **chlorophylls**, to absorb light of specific wavelengths and thereby capture the light energy. Visible light is a small fraction of the total **electromagnetic radiation** reaching Earth from the sun. Of the visible spectrum, only certain wavelengths (red and blue) are absorbed by chlorophyll. Other wavelengths, particularly green, are reflected or transmitted, and so leaves appear green. The diagram below summarizes the process of photosynthesis.

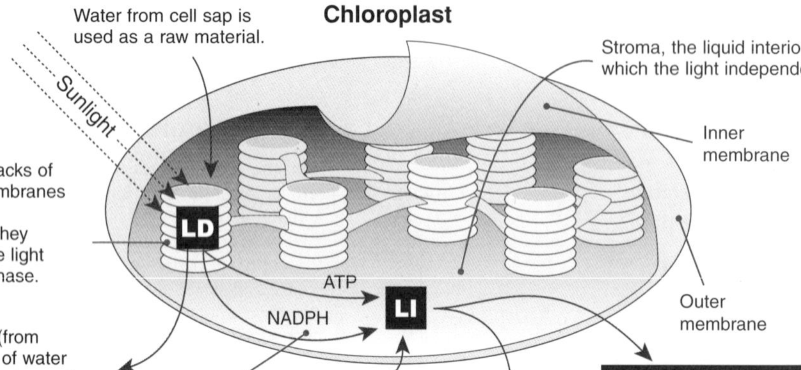
Chloroplast
Water from cell sap is used as a raw material.
Sunlight
Stroma, the liquid interior of the chloroplast, in which the light independent phase takes place.
Inner membrane
Grana are stacks of thylakoid membranes that contain chlorophyll. They are site of the light dependent phase.
LD
ATP
NADPH
LI
Outer membrane
Oxygen gas (from the break-up of water molecules) is given off as a waste product.
Hydrogen (from the break-up of water molecules) is used as a raw material.
Carbon dioxide from the air provides carbon and oxygen as raw materials.
Water is given off as a waste product.

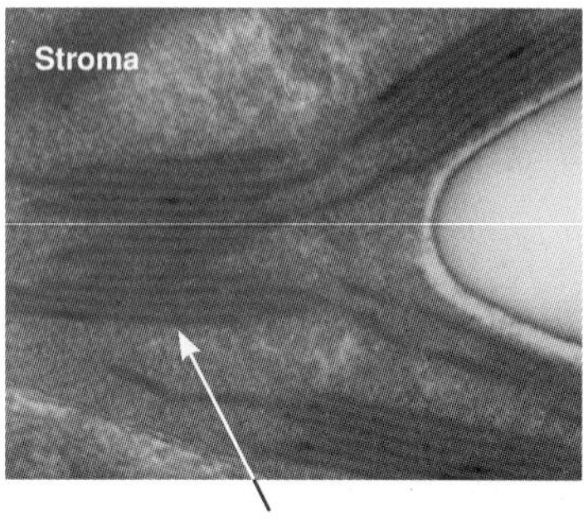
Stroma

Image: Dartmouth College

Grana are stacks of thylakoid membranes containing chlorophyll

triose phosphate
(a 3-carbon sugar)

Converted via a number of steps to:

Lipids and amino acids

Monosaccharides	**Cellulose**	**Starch**	**Disaccharides**
Glucose is the fuel for cell respiration and supplies energy for metabolism. Glucose can be converted to fructose.	Glucose is used as a building block for creating cellulose, a component of plant cell walls.	Stored as a reserve supply of energy in starch granules, to be converted back into glucose when required.	Monosaccharides join to form disaccharides, e.g. fructose and glucose form sucrose, found in sugar cane.

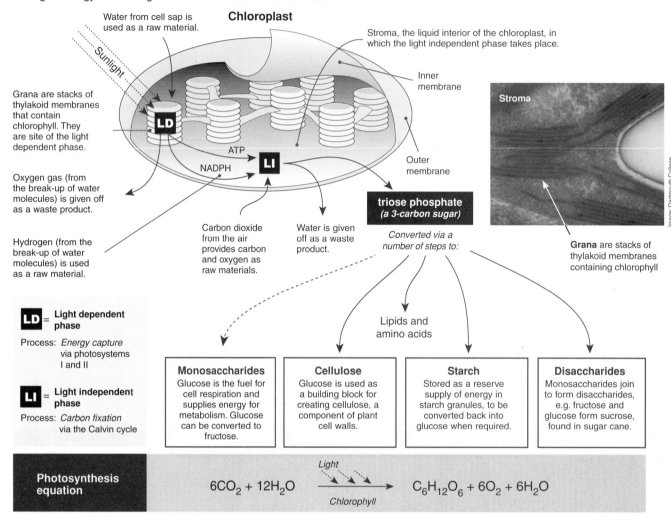

LD = **Light dependent phase**
Process: *Energy capture* via photosystems I and II

LI = **Light independent phase**
Process: *Carbon fixation* via the Calvin cycle

Photosynthesis equation

$$6CO_2 + 12H_2O \xrightarrow[\textit{Chlorophyll}]{\textit{Light}} C_6H_{12}O_6 + 6O_2 + 6H_2O$$

1. Distinguish between the two different regions of a chloroplast and describe the biochemical processes that occur in each:

(a) ______________________________

(b) ______________________________

2. State the origin and fate of the following molecules involved in photosynthesis:

(a) Carbon dioxide: ______________________________

(b) Oxygen: ______________________________

(c) Hydrogen: ______________________________

3. How might scientists have determined the fate of these molecules? ______________________________

4. Explain why the leaves of most plants look green: ______________________________

ISBN: 978-1-927173-73-2

Pigments and Light Absorption

As light meets matter, it may be reflected, transmitted, or absorbed. Substances that absorb visible light are called **pigments**, and different pigments absorb light of different wavelengths. The ability of a pigment to absorb particular wavelengths of light can be measured with a spectrophotometer. The light absorption vs the wavelength is called the **absorption spectrum** of that pigment. The absorption spectrum of different photosynthetic pigments provides clues to their role in photosynthesis, since light can only perform work if it is absorbed. An **action spectrum** profiles the effectiveness of different wavelength light in fuelling photosynthesis. It is obtained by plotting wavelength against some measure of photosynthetic rate (e.g. CO_2 production). Some features of photosynthetic pigments and their light absorbing properties are outlined below.

The Electromagnetic Spectrum

Light is a form of energy known as electromagnetic radiation. The segment of the electromagnetic spectrum most important to life is the narrow band between about 380 nm and 750 nm. This radiation is known as visible light because it is detected as colors by the human eye (although some other animals, such as insects, can see in the UV range). It is the visible light that drives photosynthesis.

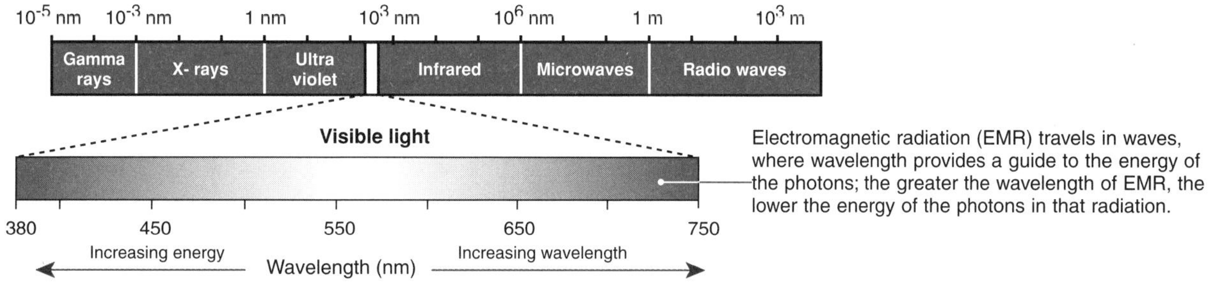
10^-5 nm
10^-3 nm
1 nm
10^3 nm
10^6 nm
1 m
10^3 m
Gamma rays
X- rays
Ultra violet
Infrared
Microwaves
Radio waves
Visible light
380
450
550
650
750
Increasing energy
Wavelength (nm)
Increasing wavelength
Electromagnetic radiation (EMR) travels in waves, where wavelength provides a guide to the energy of the photons; the greater the wavelength of EMR, the lower the energy of the photons in that radiation.

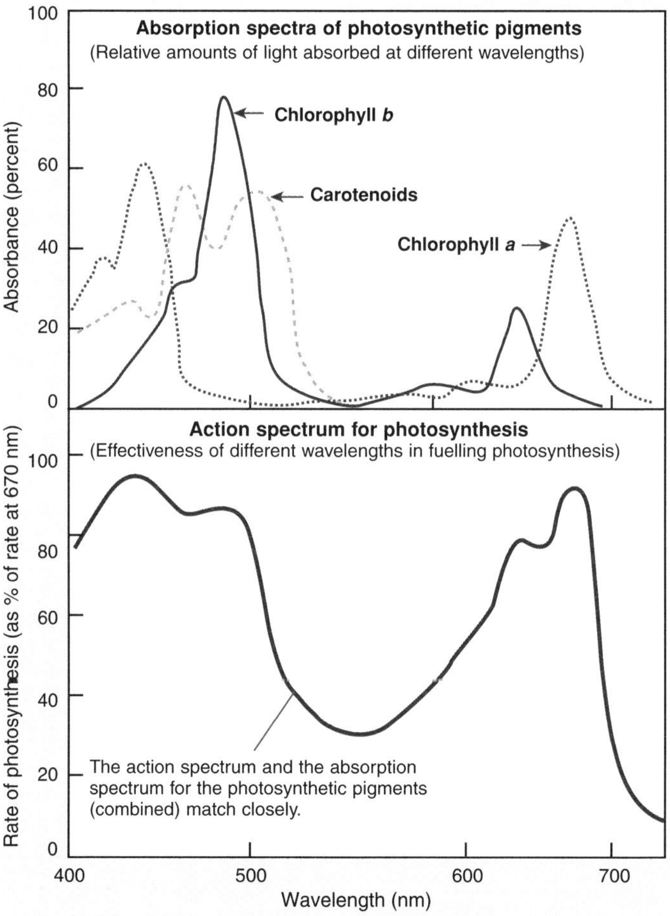
Absorption spectra of photosynthetic pigments
(Relative amounts of light absorbed at different wavelengths)
Absorbance (percent)
100
80
60
40
20
0
Chlorophyll b
Carotenoids
Chlorophyll a
Action spectrum for photosynthesis
(Effectiveness of different wavelengths in fuelling photosynthesis)
Rate of photosynthesis (as % of rate at 670 nm)
100
80
60
40
20
0
The action spectrum and the absorption spectrum for the photosynthetic pigments (combined) match closely.
400
500
600
700
Wavelength (nm)

The photosynthetic pigments of plants

The photosynthetic pigments of plants fall into two categories: chlorophylls (which absorb red and blue-violet light) and carotenoids (which absorb strongly in the blue-violet and appear orange, yellow, or red). The pigments are located on the chloroplast membranes (the thylakoids) and are associated with membrane transport systems.

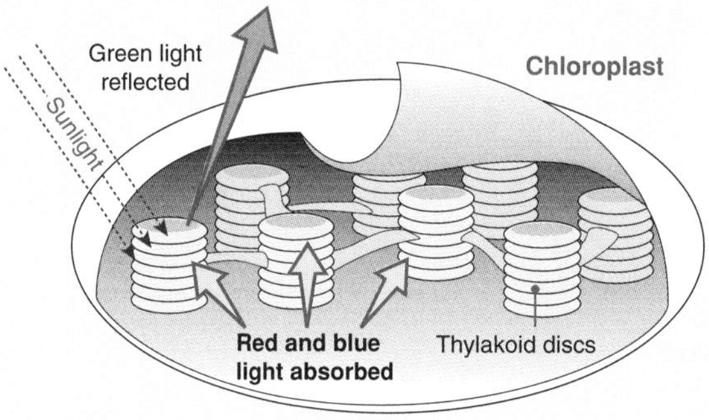
Green light reflected
Sunlight
Chloroplast
Red and blue light absorbed
Thylakoid discs

The pigments of chloroplasts in higher plants (above) absorb blue and red light, and the leaves therefore appear green (which is reflected). Each photosynthetic pigment has its own characteristic absorption spectrum (left, top graph). Although only chlorophyll a can participate directly in the light reactions of photosynthesis, the accessory pigments (chlorophyll *b* and carotenoids) can absorb wavelengths of light that chlorophyll *a* cannot. The accessory pigments pass the energy (photons) to chlorophyll a, thus broadening the spectrum that can effectively drive photosynthesis.

Left: Graphs comparing absorption spectra of photosynthetic pigments compared with the action spectrum for photosynthesis.

1. What is meant by the absorption spectrum of a pigment? ______________________

____

2. Why doesn't the **action spectrum** for photosynthesis exactly match the absorption spectrum of chlorophyll *a*?

____

ISBN: 978-1-927173-73-2

Light Dependent Reactions

Like cell respiration, photosynthesis is a redox process, but in photosynthesis, water is split and electrons, together with hydrogen ions, are transferred from water to CO_2, reducing it to sugar. The electrons increase in potential energy as they move from water to sugar. The energy to do this is provided by light. Photosynthesis consists of two phases. In the **light dependent reactions**, light energy is converted to chemical energy (ATP and reducing power). In the **light independent reactions** (**Calvin cycle**), the chemical energy is used to synthesize carbohydrate. The light dependent phase most commonly operates by **non-cyclic phosphorylation**, which produces both ATP and NADPH (steps 1-5 below). In **cyclic phosphorylation**, the electrons lost from photosystem II are replaced by those from photosystem I. ATP is generated, but not NADPH.

Non-cyclic phosphorylation

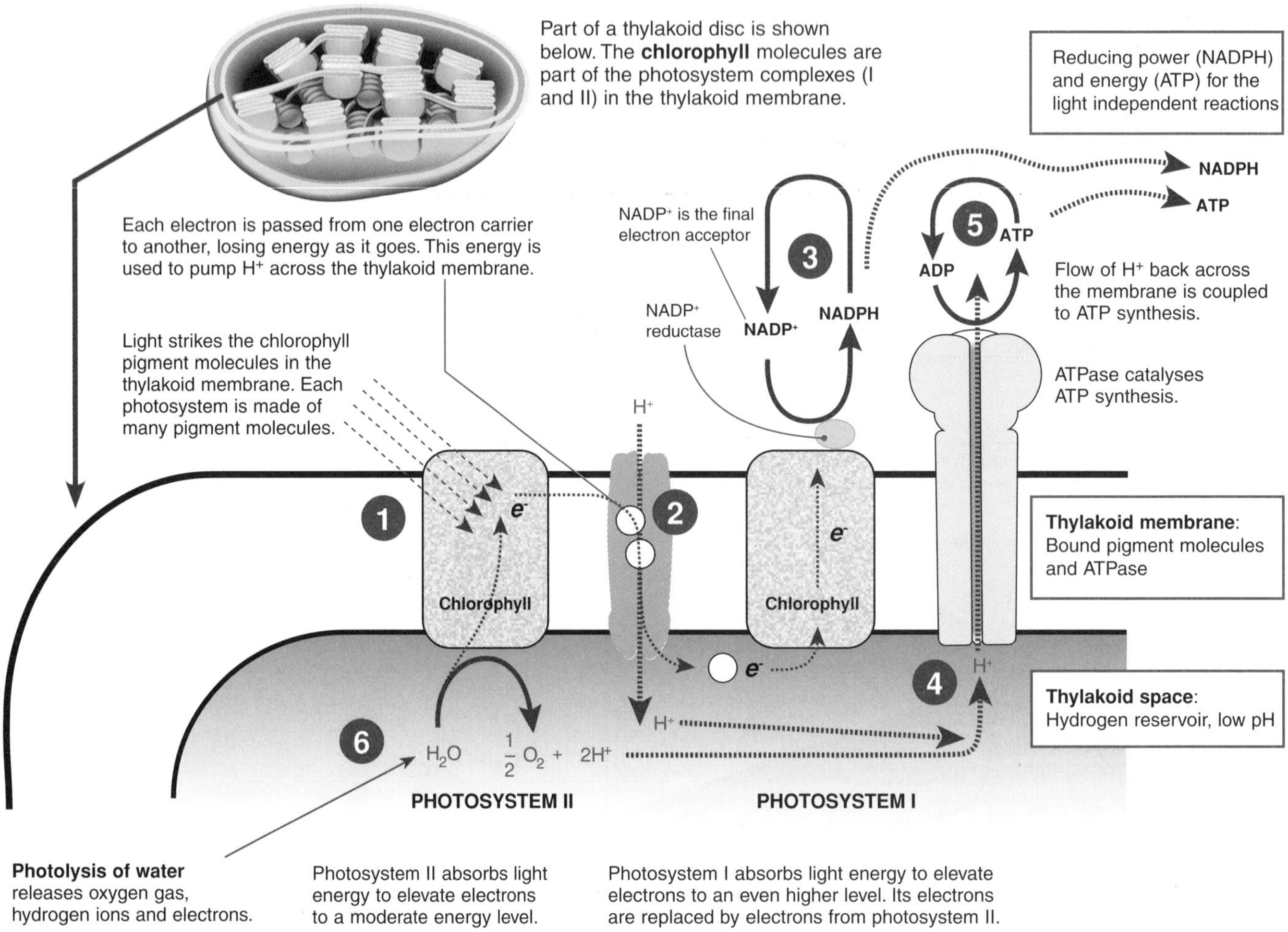
Part of a thylakoid disc is shown below. The **chlorophyll** molecules are part of the photosystem complexes (I and II) in the thylakoid membrane.
Reducing power (NADPH) and energy (ATP) for the light independent reactions
NADPH
ATP
Each electron is passed from one electron carrier to another, losing energy as it goes. This energy is used to pump H+ across the thylakoid membrane.
NADP+ is the final electron acceptor
NADP+ reductase
NADP+
NADPH
3
5
ADP
ATP
Flow of H+ back across the membrane is coupled to ATP synthesis.
ATPase catalyses ATP synthesis.
Light strikes the chlorophyll pigment molecules in the thylakoid membrane. Each photosystem is made of many pigment molecules.
H+
1
e-
2
e-
Chlorophyll
Chlorophyll
Thylakoid membrane: Bound pigment molecules and ATPase
e-
H+
4
Thylakoid space: Hydrogen reservoir, low pH
6
H2O
1/2 O2 + 2H+
H+
PHOTOSYSTEM II
PHOTOSYSTEM I
Photolysis of water releases oxygen gas, hydrogen ions and electrons.
Photosystem II absorbs light energy to elevate electrons to a moderate energy level.
Photosystem I absorbs light energy to elevate electrons to an even higher level. Its electrons are replaced by electrons from photosystem II.

Cyclic phosphorylation

Cyclic phosphorylation involves only photosystem I and NADPH is not generated. Electrons from photosystem I are shunted back to the electron carriers in the membrane. This pathway produces ATP only. The Calvin cycle uses more ATP than NADPH, so cyclic phosphorylation makes up the difference. It is activated when NADPH levels build up, and remains active until enough ATP is made to meet demand.

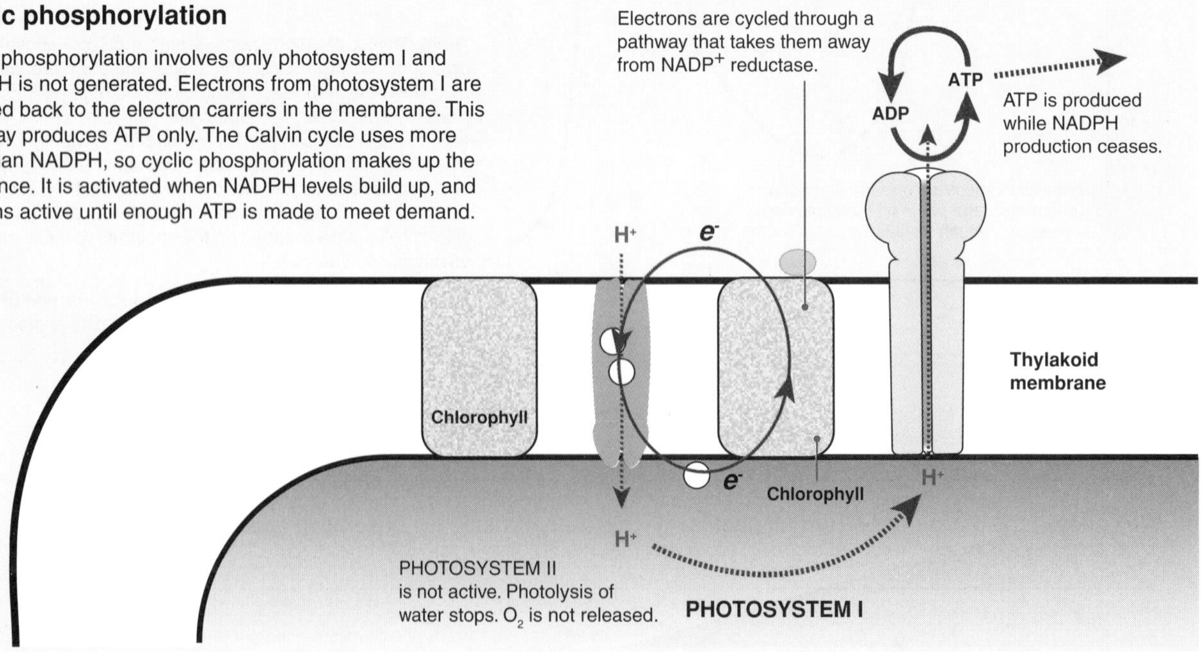
Electrons are cycled through a pathway that takes them away from NADP+ reductase.
ADP
ATP
ATP is produced while NADPH production ceases.
H+
e-
Thylakoid membrane
Chlorophyll
e-
Chlorophyll
H+
H+
PHOTOSYSTEM II is not active. Photolysis of water stops. O2 is not released.
PHOTOSYSTEM I

ISBN: 978-1-927173-73-2

1. Describe the role of the carrier molecule **NADP** in photosynthesis:

2. Explain the role of chlorophyll molecules in photosynthesis:

3. Summarize the events of the light dependent reactions and identify where they occur:

4. Describe how ATP is produced as a result of light striking chlorophyll molecules during the light dependent phase:

5. (a) Explain what you understand by the term **non-cyclic phosphorylation**:

   (b) Suggest why this process is also known as non-cyclic **photo**phosphorylation:

6. (a) Describe how **cyclic photophosphorylation** differs from non-cyclic photophosphorylation:

   (b) Both cyclic and noncyclic pathways operate to varying degrees during photosynthesis. Since the non-cyclic pathway produces both ATP and NAPH, explain the purpose of the cyclic pathway of electron flow:

7. Explain how the independence of photosystem I gives a mechanism for evolution of the photosynthetic pathway:

ISBN: 978-1-927173-73-2

Light Independent Reactions

The **light independent reactions** of photosynthesis (the **Calvin cycle**) take place in the stroma of the chloroplast, and do not require light to proceed. Here, hydrogen (H^+) is added to CO_2 and a 5C intermediate to make carbohydrate. The H^+ and ATP are supplied by the light dependent reactions. The Calvin cycle uses more ATP than NADPH, but the cell uses cyclic phosphorylation (which does not produce NADPH) when it runs low on ATP to make up the difference.

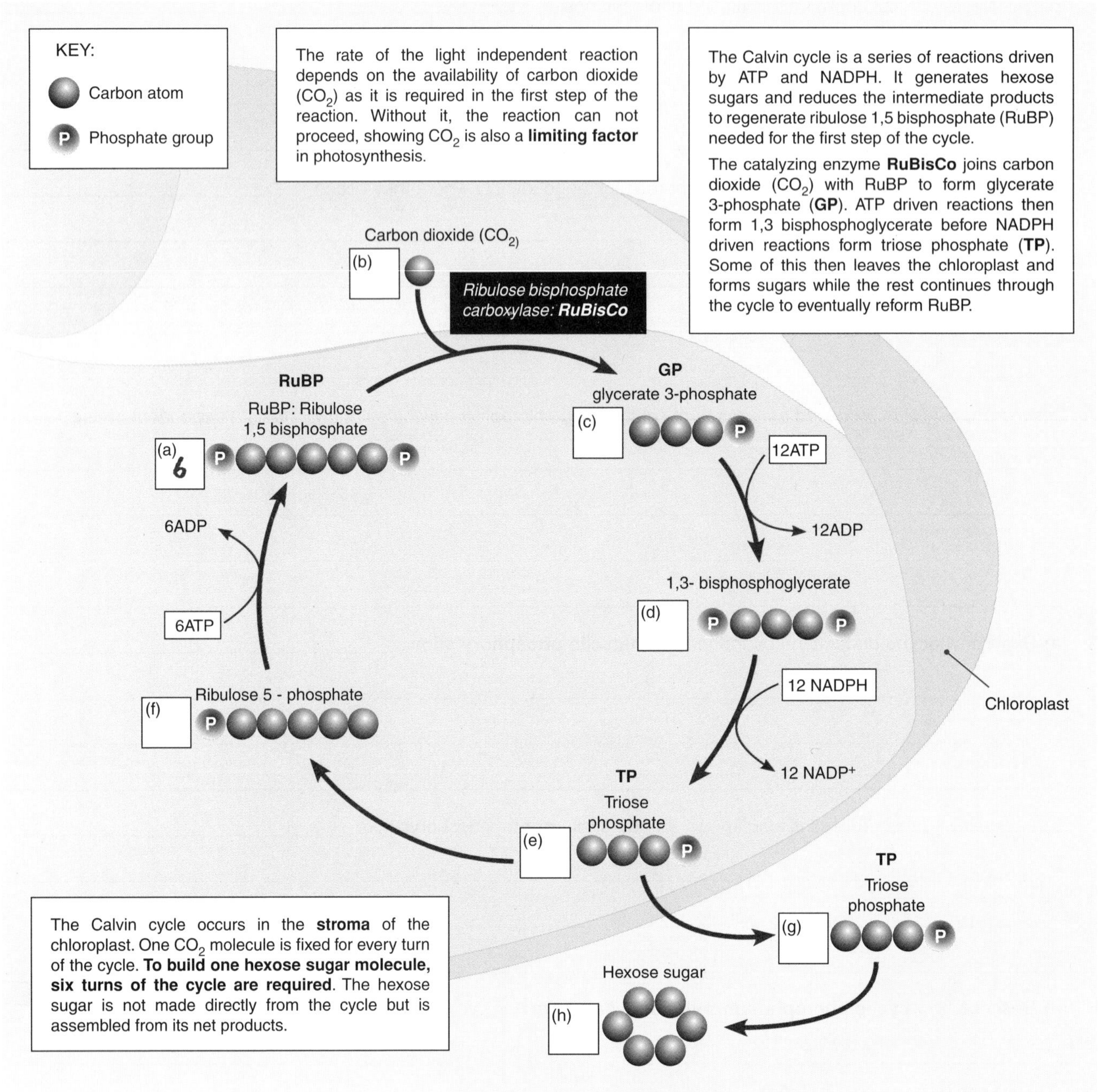
KEY:
Carbon atom
P Phosphate group
Carbon dioxide (CO_2)
(b)
Ribulose bisphosphate carboxylase: RuBisCo
RuBP
RuBP: Ribulose 1,5 bisphosphate
(a) 6
GP
glycerate 3-phosphate
(c)
12ATP
12ADP
6ADP
6ATP
1,3- bisphosphoglycerate
(d)
12 NADPH
12 NADP+
Chloroplast
Ribulose 5 - phosphate
(f)
TP
Triose phosphate
(e)
TP
Triose phosphate
(g)
Hexose sugar
(h)

The rate of the light independent reaction depends on the availability of carbon dioxide (CO_2) as it is required in the first step of the reaction. Without it, the reaction can not proceed, showing CO_2 is also a **limiting factor** in photosynthesis.

The Calvin cycle is a series of reactions driven by ATP and NADPH. It generates hexose sugars and reduces the intermediate products to regenerate ribulose 1,5 bisphosphate (RuBP) needed for the first step of the cycle.

The catalyzing enzyme **RuBisCo** joins carbon dioxide (CO_2) with RuBP to form glycerate 3-phosphate (**GP**). ATP driven reactions then form 1,3 bisphosphoglycerate before NADPH driven reactions form triose phosphate (**TP**). Some of this then leaves the chloroplast and forms sugars while the rest continues through the cycle to eventually reform RuBP.

The Calvin cycle occurs in the **stroma** of the chloroplast. One CO_2 molecule is fixed for every turn of the cycle. **To build one hexose sugar molecule, six turns of the cycle are required**. The hexose sugar is not made directly from the cycle but is assembled from its net products.

1. In the boxes on the diagram above, write the number of molecules formed at each step during the formation of **one hexose sugar molecule**. The first one has been done for you:

2. Explain the importance of RuBisCo in the Calvin cycle: ______________________________

____

3. Identify the actual end product on the Calvin cycle: ______________________________

4. Write the equation for the production of one hexose sugar molecule from carbon dioxide: ______________________________

____

5. Explain why the Calvin cycle is likely to cease in the dark for most plants, even though it is independent of light:

____

KNOW

Related activities: *Light Dependent Reactions*
Weblinks: *Photosynthesis Biochemistry*

ISBN: 978-1-927173-73-2

Photosynthesis in C_4 Plants

When photosynthesis takes place, the first detectable compound which is made by a plant is usually a 3-carbon compound called GP (glycerate 3-phosphate). Plants which do this are called C_3 plants. In some plants, however, a 4-carbon molecule called oxaloacetate, is the first to be made. Such plants, which include cereals and tropical grasses, are called C_4 plants. These plants have a high rate of photosynthesis, thriving in environments with high light levels and warm temperatures. Their yield of photosynthetic products is higher than that of C_3 plants, giving them a competitive advantage in tropical climates. The high productivity of the C_4 system is also an important property of crop plants such as sugar cane and maize.

Structure of a Leaf from a C_4 Plant

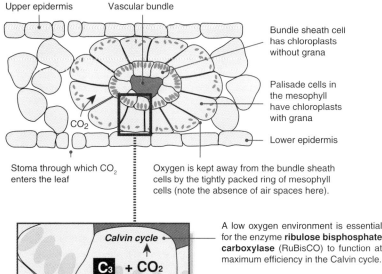

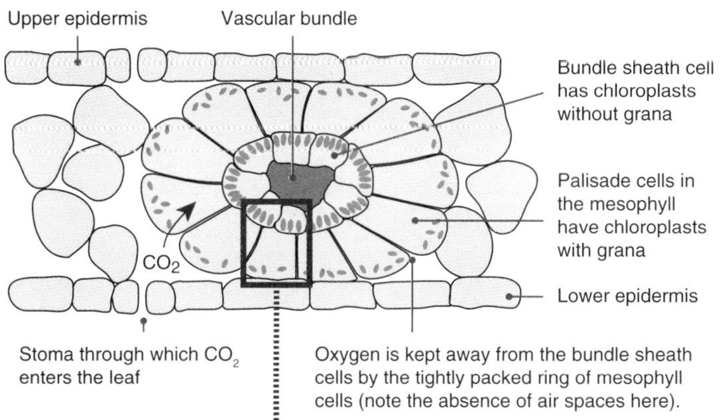
Upper epidermis
Vascular bundle
Bundle sheath cell has chloroplasts without grana
Palisade cells in the mesophyll have chloroplasts with grana
CO2
Lower epidermis
Stoma through which CO2 enters the leaf
Oxygen is kept away from the bundle sheath cells by the tightly packed ring of mesophyll cells (note the absence of air spaces here).

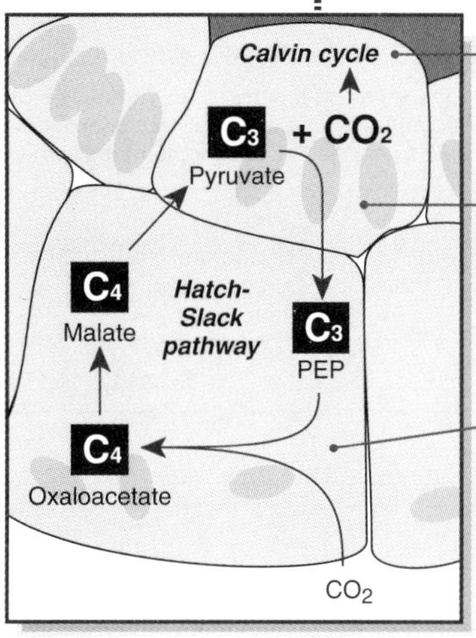
Calvin cycle
C3
+ CO2
Pyruvate
C4
Malate
Hatch-Slack pathway
C3
PEP
C4
Oxaloacetate
CO2

A low oxygen environment is essential for the enzyme **ribulose bisphosphate carboxylase** (RuBisCO) to function at maximum efficiency in the Calvin cycle.

Bundle sheath cells
Malate moves from the palisade cells to the inner bundle sheath cells where it is broken down to pyruvate, releasing free carbon dioxide. This is used as a raw material to feed into the Calvin cycle.

Palisade mesophyll cells
Photosynthesis in these cells fixes carbon dioxide in the cytoplasm and captures light energy in the chloroplasts. The enzyme **PEP carboxylase** has an extremely high affinity for CO_2 even when the latter is in low concentration. This allows the plant to fix large quantities of CO_2 rapidly.

Examples of C_4 plants

- Sugar cane *(Saccharum officinale)*
- Maize *(Zea mays)*
- Sorghum *(Sorghum bicolor)*
- Sun plant *(Portulaca grandifolia)*

Distribution of grasses using C_4 mechanism in North America

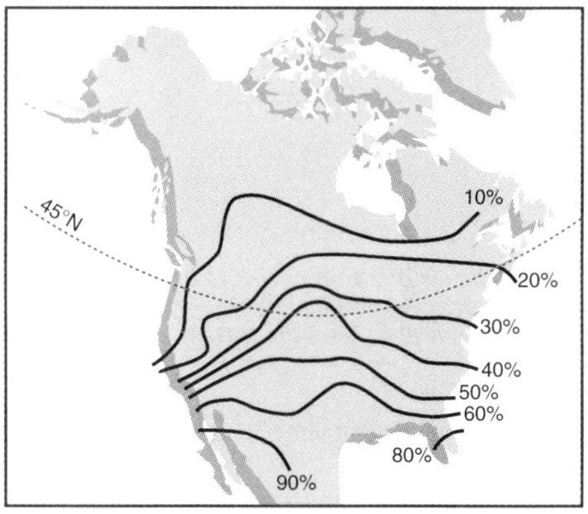
45°N
10%
20%
30%
40%
50%
60%
80%
90%

The photosynthetic strategy that a plant possesses is an important factor in determining where it lives. Because many of the enzymes of C_4 plants have optimum temperatures well above 25°C, they thrive in hot tropical and sub-tropical climates. Under these conditions, they can out-compete most C_3 plants because they achieve faster rates of photosynthesis. The proportion of grasses using the C_4 mechanism in North America is greatest near the tropics and diminishes northwards.

1. Explain why C4 plants have a competitive advantage over C3 plants in the tropics: ____________________

2. Explain why the bundle sheath cells are arranged in a way that keeps them isolated from air spaces in the leaf:

3. Study the map of North America above showing the distribution of C_4 plants. Explain the distribution pattern in terms of their competitive advantage and the environmental conditions required for this advantage:

4. In C_3 plants, the rate of photosynthesis is enhanced by higher atmospheric CO_2 concentrations. Explain why this is not the case for C_4 plants:

ISBN: 978-1-927173-73-2

Factors Affecting Photosynthetic Rate

The rate at which plants make carbohydrate (the photosynthetic rate) is dependent on environmental factors, the most important of which are the availability of **light** and **carbon dioxide** (CO_2). and **temperature**. The effect of these factors can be tested experimentally by altering one of the factors while holding the others constant (a controlled experiment). In reality, a plant in its natural environment is subjected to variations in many different environmental factors, all of which will influence, directly or indirectly, the rate at which photosynthesis can occur.

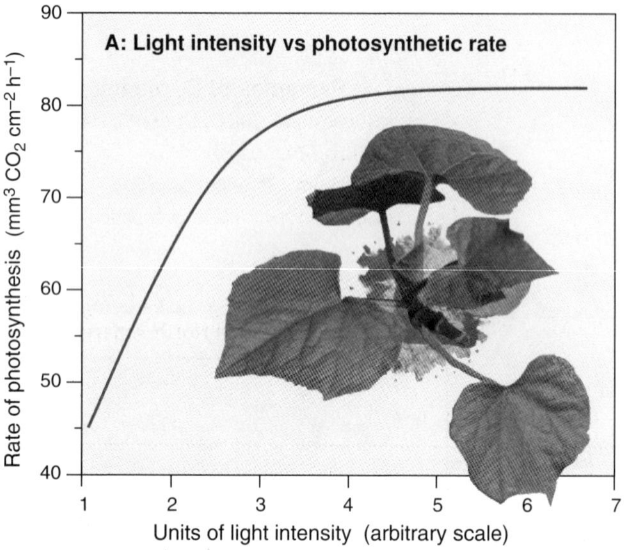
A: Light intensity vs photosynthetic rate
Rate of photosynthesis (mm³ CO₂ cm⁻² h⁻¹)
90
80
70
60
50
40
1 2 3 4 5 6 7
Units of light intensity (arbitrary scale)

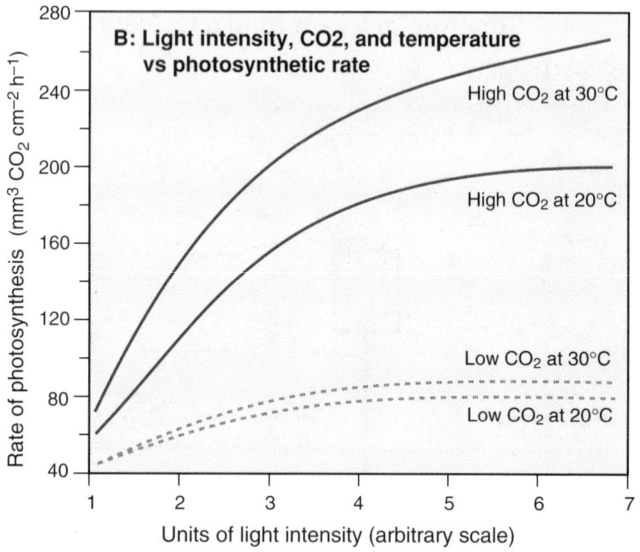
B: Light intensity, CO2, and temperature vs photosynthetic rate
Rate of photosynthesis (mm³ CO₂ cm⁻² h⁻¹)
280
240
200
160
120
80
40
High CO2 at 30°C
High CO2 at 20°C
Low CO2 at 30°C
Low CO2 at 20°C
1 2 3 4 5 6 7
Units of light intensity (arbitrary scale)

These figures illustrate the effect of different limiting factors on the rate of photosynthesis in cucumber plants. Figure A shows the effect of different light intensities when the temperature and carbon dioxide (CO_2) level are kept constant. Figure B shows the effect of different light intensities at two temperatures and two CO_2 concentrations. In each of these experiments, either CO_2 level or temperature was changed at each light intensity in turn.

1. Based on the figures above, summarize and explain the effect of each of the following factors on photosynthetic rate:

   (a) CO_2 concentration: ____________________

   (b) Light intensity: ____________________

   (c) Temperature: ____________________

2. Explain why photosynthetic rate declines when the CO_2 level is reduced: ____________________

3. (a) In figure B, explain how the effects of CO_2 concentration were distinguished from the effects of temperature:

   (b) Identify which factor (CO_2 or temperature) had the greatest effect on photosynthetic rate: ____________________

   (c) Explain how you can tell this from the graph: ____________________

4. Explain how glasshouses can be used to create an environment in which photosynthetic rates are maximized:

5. Design an experiment to demonstrate the effect of temperature on photosynthetic rate. You should include a hypothesis, list of equipment, and methods. Staple your experiment to this page.

ISBN: 978-1-927173-73-2

KEY TERMS: Crossword

Complete the crossword below, which will test your understanding of key terms in this chapter and their meanings.

Clues Across

7. Organelles responsible for producing the cell's ATP.
8. The light independent phase of photosynthesis can also be called this. (2 words: 6, 5)
11. An intermediary molecule, which transfers carbon atoms within the acetyl group to the Krebs cycle to be oxidized for energy production. (3 words 6,8,1)
12. The biochemical process by which plants manufacture food.
13. A profile of the effectiveness of different wavelengths of light in fueling photosynthesis.
16. Plant pigments that absorb wavelengths of light that chlorophyll a does not absorb. (2 words 9,7)
17. The name for the inner membranes of the mitochondria.
19. The inner region of the mitochondrion enclosed by the inner mitochondrial membrane.
22. The term to describe the light absorption vs the wavelength of a pigment. (2 words: 10, 8)
23. A high energy compound involved in energy transfers in cells. (Acronym)
24. In this phase of photosynthesis chemical energy is used for the synthesis of carbohydrate. (2 words: 5, 11)
25. The phosphorylation of ADP to ATP in photosynthesis using photosystem I to replace electrons lost from photosystem II.
26. The organelle in plant cells where photosynthesis takes place.

Clues Down

1. An anaerobic process in which pyruvate is converted to lactic acid or to ethanol and carbon dioxide.
2. The phase in photosynthesis when light energy is converted to chemical energy. (2 words: 5, 9)
3. The anaerobic breakdown of glucose into two molecules of pyruvate.
4. The catabolic process in which the chemical energy in complex organic molecules is coupled to ATP production. (2 words: 8, 11)
5. Stacks of membrane bound compartments in chloroplasts.
6. The stage of in cellular respiration in which a derivative of pyruvate is broken down to carbon dioxide. (2 words: 5, 5)
9. In skeletal muscle, pyruvate is reduced to this, in the absence of oxygen. (2 words: 6, 4)
10. The process where the synthesis of ATP is coupled to electron transport and the movement of protons.
14. Phosphorylation process in photosynthesis in which light energy is used to generate ATP and NADPH
15. The green pigment involved in the light dependent reactions of photosynthesis.
16. Metabolism that yields energy without the need for molecular oxygen.
18. The liquid interior of the chloroplast where the light independent phase takes place.
20. A molecule that accepts hydrogen ions. (2 words 1,8)
21. The stacks of thylakoids within the chloroplasts of plants.

ISBN: 978-1-927173-73-2

Chapter 5

The Nucleus and Cell Division

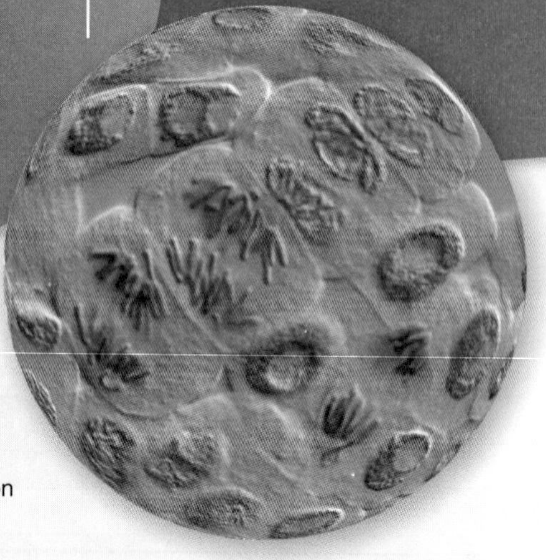

Key concepts

- DNA is a self-replicating molecule constructed according to strict base-pairing rules.
- DNA replication is a semi-conservative process controlled by enzymes.
- In the cell cycle, interphase alternates with cell division. New cells arise through cell division.
- Stem cells have properties that allow them to develop into any cell type.
- Meiosis is a reduction division and is essential for sexual reproduction.

Key terms

apoptosis
anaphase
cell cycle
cellular differentiation
cell division
cytokinesis
DNA
DNA polymerase
DNA replication
double-helix
helicase
interphase
lagging strand
leading strand
meiosis
metaphase
mitosis
nucleic acids
prophase
reduction division
semi-conservative
specialized cell
stem cell
telophase

Learning Objectives

☐ 1. Use the **KEY TERMS** to compile a glossary for this topic.

DNA

pages 99-104

☐ 2. Recall the structure of nucleotides and **nucleic acids** and the Watson-Crick **double-helix model** of DNA structure, including the anti-parallel nature of DNA, the base-pairing rule, and hydrogen bonding.

☐ 3. Describe the **semi-conservative replication** of DNA. Demonstrate understanding of the base-pairing rule for creating a complementary strand from a single strand of DNA.

☐ 4. Explain the significance of DNA replication in the **5' to 3' direction**. Relate this to the formation of the **leading strand** and the **lagging strand**.

☐ 5. Recognize **DNA replication** as a necessary precursor to cell division.

Cell Division and Differentiation

pages 105-114

☐ 6. Describe the **cell cycle** in eukaryotes, including reference to: **mitosis** and **interphase**.

☐ 7. Describe stages in mitosis: **prophase**, **metaphase**, **anaphase**, and **telophase**. Recognize these stages in light and electron micrographs.

☐ 8. Describe and explain **cytokinesis.** Explain how cytokinesis differs in plant cells and animal cells.

☐ 9. Define the term **apoptosis**. Explain the role of apoptosis in normal cell differentiation and morphogenesis. Describe the consequences of excessive or insufficient apoptosis during development.

☐ 10. In a plant root tip distinguish between the structure and activity of different regions of the root tip: root cap, meristem, zone of elongation, zone of differentiation.

☐ 11. Identify and describe the structural adaptations, role, and location of some **specialized cells** in humans, e.g. blood cells, nerve cells, or intestinal epithelial cells.

☐ 12. Know that **meiosis**, like mitosis, involves DNA replication during interphase in the parent cell, but that this is followed by two cycles of nuclear division. Know that meiosis is a **reduction division** and explain what this means.

☐ 13. Distinguish between **meiosis I** and **meiosis II**, Identifying the main features of these stages.

☐ 13. Distinguish between **meiosis** and **mitosis** in terms of their cellular outcomes.

Weblinks:
www.thebiozone.com/weblink/Cellbio-3732/

BIOZONE APP:
Student Review Series
Processes in the Nucleus

DNA Molecules

Even the smallest DNA molecules are extremely long. The DNA from the small *Polyoma* virus, for example, is 1.7 μm long; about three times longer than the longest proteins. The DNA in a bacterial chromosome is 1000 times longer than the cell it is packed in. The amount of DNA in the nucleus of a eukaryotic cell varies widely. In vertebrate sex cells, the quantity of DNA ranges from 40,000 **kb** to 80,000,000 **kb**, with humans about in the middle of the range. The traditional focus of DNA research has been on protein-coding DNA sequences, yet protein-coding DNA accounts for less than 2% of the DNA in human chromosomes. The rest of the DNA was once called 'junk', meaning it did not code for anything. We now know that much of it codes for regulatory RNA molecules and it is not junk at all. The genomes of more complex organisms contain more of these RNA-only 'hidden' genes than the genomes of simple organisms. The sequences are short and difficult to identify, but they are highly conserved (they do not change much through evolution). This tells us that they must have an important role.

Total length of DNA in viruses, bacteria, and eukayotes

Taxon	Organism	Base pairs (in 1000s, or kb)	Length
Viruses	Polyoma or SV40	5.1	1.7 μm
	Lambda phage	48.6	17 μm
	T2 phage	166	56 μm
	Vaccinia	190	65 μm
Bacteria	Mycoplasma	760	260 μm
	E.coli (from human gut)	4600	1.56 mm
Eukaryotes	Yeast	13,500	4.6 mm
	Drosophila (fruit fly)	165,000	5.6 cm
	Human	2,900,000	99 cm

Kilobase (kb)

A kilobase (kb) is 1000 base pairs of a double-stranded nucleic acid molecule (or 1000 bases of a single-stranded molecule). One kb of double stranded DNA has a length of approximately 0.34 μm (1 μm = 1/1000 mm).

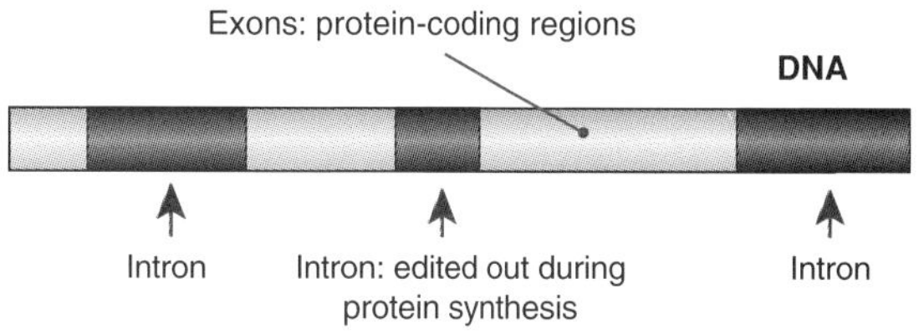

Exons: protein-coding regions
DNA
Intron
Intron: edited out during protein synthesis
Intron

Most protein-coding genes in eukaryotic DNA are not continuous. The protein-coding regions (**exons**) are interrupted by non-protein-coding regions called **introns**. Introns range in frequency from 1 to over 30 in a single 'gene' and also in size (100 to more than 10,000 bases). Introns are edited out of the protein-coding sequence during protein synthesis. After processing, the introns may go on to serve a regulatory function.

Giant Lampbrush Chromosomes

Lampbrush chromosomes are large chromosomes found in amphibian eggs, with lateral loops of DNA that produce a brushlike appearance under the microscope. The two scanning electron micrographs (below and right) show minute strands of DNA giving a fuzzy appearance in the high power view.

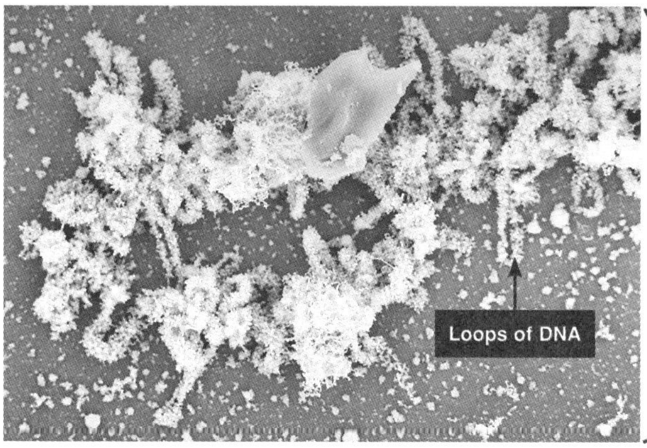

Loops of DNA

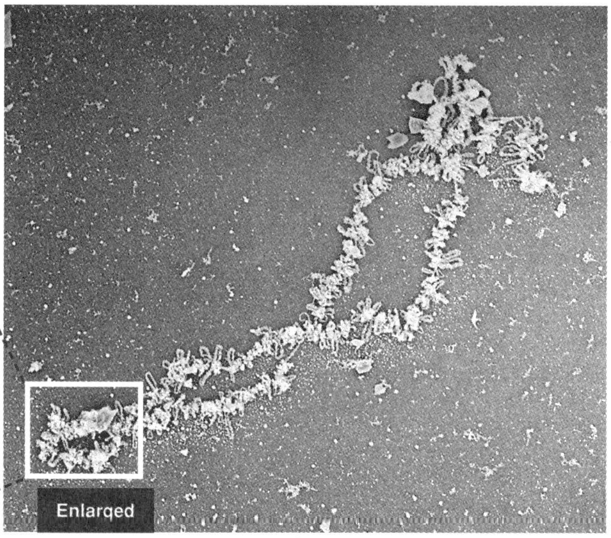

Enlarged

1. Consult the table above and make the following comparisons. Determine how much more DNA is present in:

   (a) The bacterium *E. coli* compared to the Lambda Phage virus: ____________________

   (b) Human cells compared to the bacteria *E. coli:* ____________________

2. What proportion of DNA in a eukaryotic cell is used to code for proteins? ____________________

3. (a) Describe the organization of protein-coding regions in eukaryotic DNA: ____________________

   ____

   ____

   (b) What might be the purpose of the introns? ____________________

   ____

   ____

ISBN: 978-1-927173-73-2

The Role of DNA in Cells

All the DNA within a cell constitutes its **genome**. The genetic information in a genome is held within sections of DNA called **genes**. Genes code for proteins and are the hereditary units that determine an organism's characteristics. Every cell in the body of an organism contains all the genes an organism required to function. When a cell becomes specialized for a specific role, such as transmitting nerve impulses, the genes requires by that cell are switched on and others are switched off. In eukaryotes, most of the DNA is located in the nucleus. A small amount is also found in the mitochondria and (in green plants) the chloroplasts. The genetic instructions from the nucleus pass to the cytoplasm where they are used to make proteins by protein synthesis. Many of these proteins are the enzymes that regulate the many biochemical processes that constitute metabolism.

DNA and the Nucleus

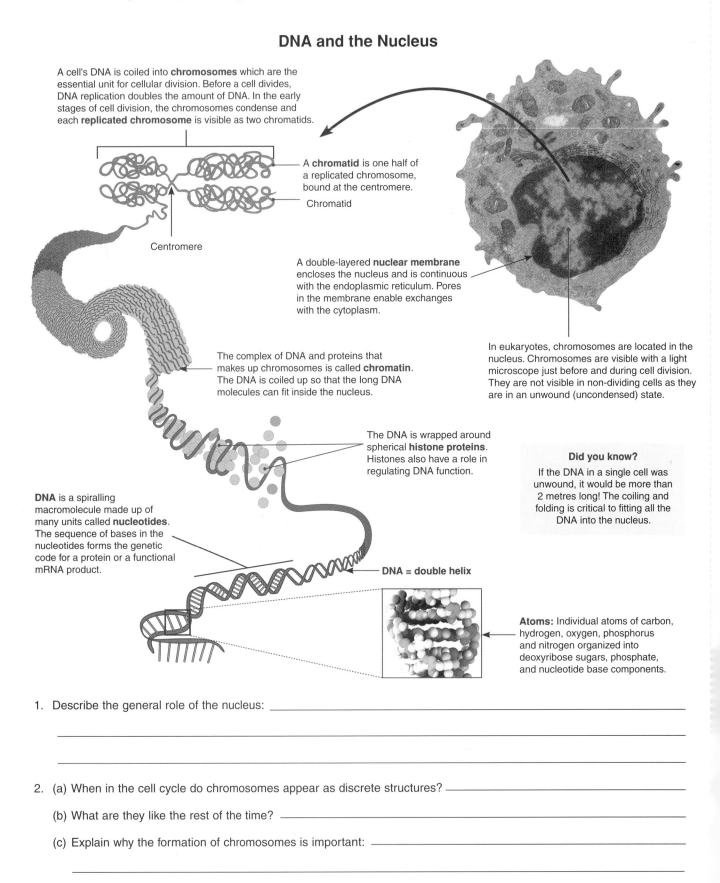

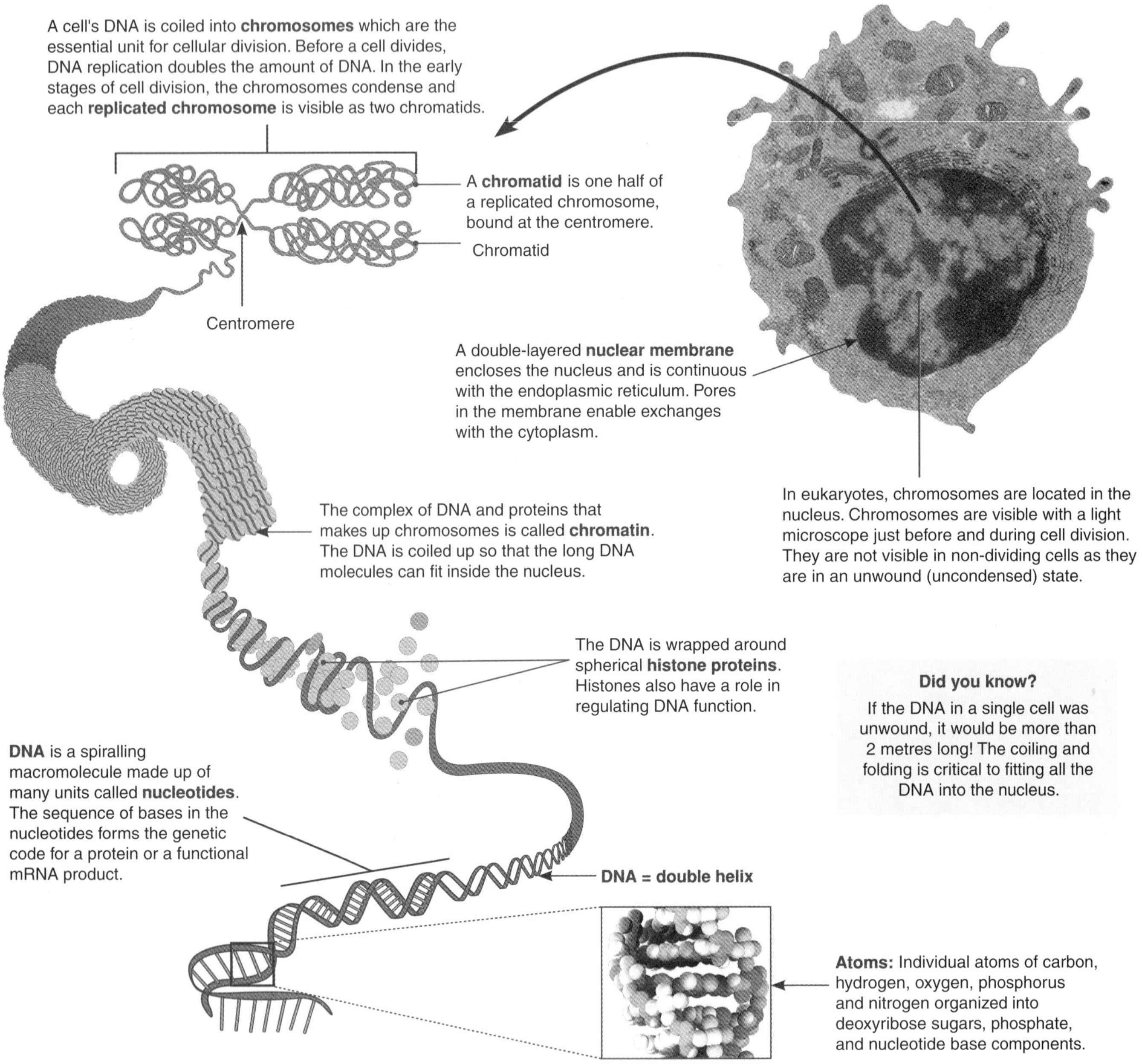
A cell's DNA is coiled into chromosomes which are the essential unit for cellular division. Before a cell divides, DNA replication doubles the amount of DNA. In the early stages of cell division, the chromosomes condense and each replicated chromosome is visible as two chromatids.
A chromatid is one half of a replicated chromosome, bound at the centromere.
Chromatid
Centromere
A double-layered nuclear membrane encloses the nucleus and is continuous with the endoplasmic reticulum. Pores in the membrane enable exchanges with the cytoplasm.
In eukaryotes, chromosomes are located in the nucleus. Chromosomes are visible with a light microscope just before and during cell division. They are not visible in non-dividing cells as they are in an unwound (uncondensed) state.
The complex of DNA and proteins that makes up chromosomes is called chromatin. The DNA is coiled up so that the long DNA molecules can fit inside the nucleus.
The DNA is wrapped around spherical histone proteins. Histones also have a role in regulating DNA function.
DNA is a spiralling macromolecule made up of many units called nucleotides. The sequence of bases in the nucleotides forms the genetic code for a protein or a functional mRNA product.
DNA = double helix
Atoms: Individual atoms of carbon, hydrogen, oxygen, phosphorus and nitrogen organized into deoxyribose sugars, phosphate, and nucleotide base components.

Did you know?

If the DNA in a single cell was unwound, it would be more than 2 metres long! The coiling and folding is critical to fitting all the DNA into the nucleus.

1. Describe the general role of the nucleus:

2. (a) When in the cell cycle do chromosomes appear as discrete structures?

   (b) What are they like the rest of the time?

   (c) Explain why the formation of chromosomes is important:

ISBN: 978-1-927173-73-2

Related activities: DNA Molecules

DNA Replication

Cells carry out the process of **DNA replication** (DNA duplication) prior to cell division (mitosis and meiosis). This process ensures that each resulting cell is able to receive a complete set of genes from the original cell. After the DNA has replicated, each chromosome is made up of two chromatids, which are joined at the centromere. Each chromatid contains half original (parent) DNA and half new (daughter) DNA. The two chromatids will become separated during cell division to form two separate chromosomes. During DNA replication, new nucleotides become added at a region called the **replication fork**. The position of the replication fork moves along the chromosome as the replication progresses. This whole process occurs simultaneously for each chromosome of a cell and the entire process is tightly controlled by enzymes.

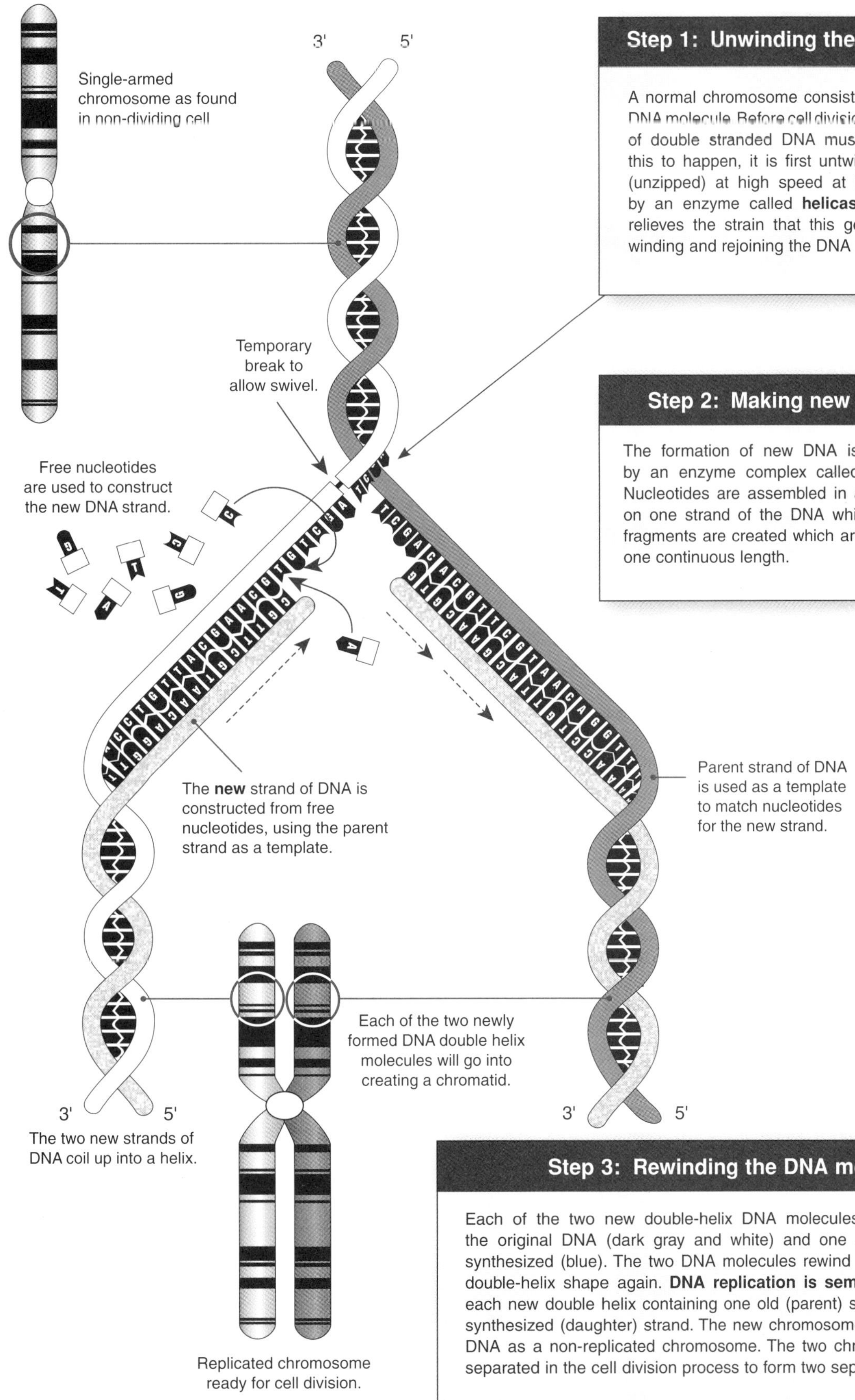

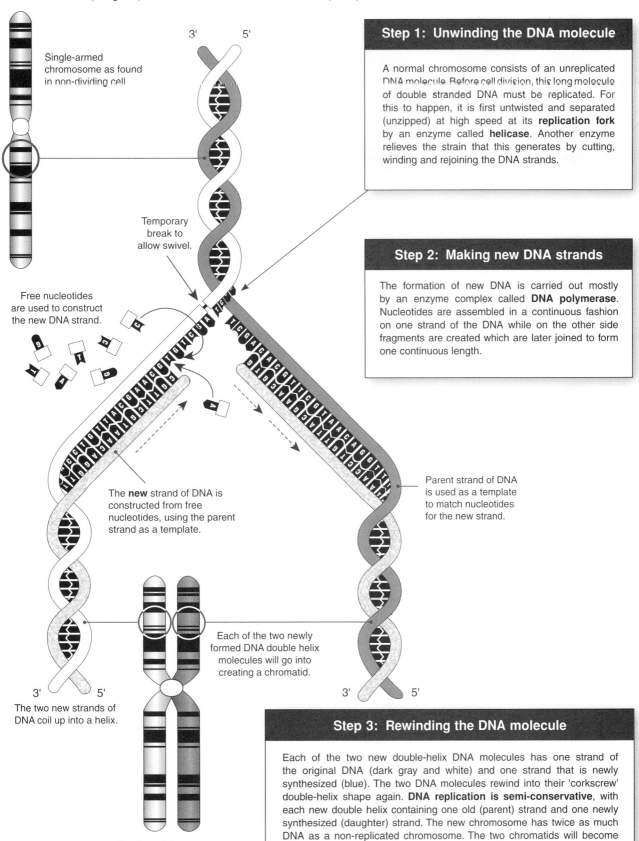

3'
5'
Single-armed chromosome as found in non-dividing cell
Temporary break to allow swivel.
Free nucleotides are used to construct the new DNA strand.
The **new** strand of DNA is constructed from free nucleotides, using the parent strand as a template.
Parent strand of DNA is used as a template to match nucleotides for the new strand.
Each of the two newly formed DNA double helix molecules will go into creating a chromatid.
3'
5'
3'
5'
The two new strands of DNA coil up into a helix.
Replicated chromosome ready for cell division.

Step 1: Unwinding the DNA molecule

A normal chromosome consists of an unreplicated DNA molecule. Before cell division, this long molecule of double stranded DNA must be replicated. For this to happen, it is first untwisted and separated (unzipped) at high speed at its **replication fork** by an enzyme called **helicase**. Another enzyme relieves the strain that this generates by cutting, winding and rejoining the DNA strands.

Step 2: Making new DNA strands

The formation of new DNA is carried out mostly by an enzyme complex called **DNA polymerase**. Nucleotides are assembled in a continuous fashion on one strand of the DNA while on the other side fragments are created which are later joined to form one continuous length.

Step 3: Rewinding the DNA molecule

Each of the two new double-helix DNA molecules has one strand of the original DNA (dark gray and white) and one strand that is newly synthesized (blue). The two DNA molecules rewind into their 'corkscrew' double-helix shape again. **DNA replication is semi-conservative**, with each new double helix containing one old (parent) strand and one newly synthesized (daughter) strand. The new chromosome has twice as much DNA as a non-replicated chromosome. The two chromatids will become separated in the cell division process to form two separate chromosomes.

ISBN: 978-1-927173-73-2

1. What is the purpose of DNA replication? ______________________________

____

2. Summarize the three main steps involved in DNA replication:

(a) ______________________________

____

(b) ______________________________

____

(c) ______________________________

____

3. For a cell with 22 chromosomes, state how many chromatids would exist following DNA replication: ______________

4. What does it mean when we say DNA replication is semi-conservative? ______________________________

____

5. DNA replication occurs during the S (synthesis) phase of the **cell cycle**. This is part of a larger phase called interphase. It is the phase in which the cell is not dividing (in mitosis).

The light micrograph (right) shows a section of cells in an onion root tip. These cells have a cell cycle of approximately 24 hours. The cells can be seen to be in various stages of the cell cycle. By counting the number of cells in the various stages it is possible to calculate how long the cell spends in each stage of the cycle.

Count and record the number of cells in the image which are undergoing mitosis and those that are in interphase. Estimate the amount of time a cell spends in each phase.

Stage	No. of cells	% of total cells	Estimated time in stage
Interphase			
Mitosis			
Total		100	

Onion Root Tip Cells

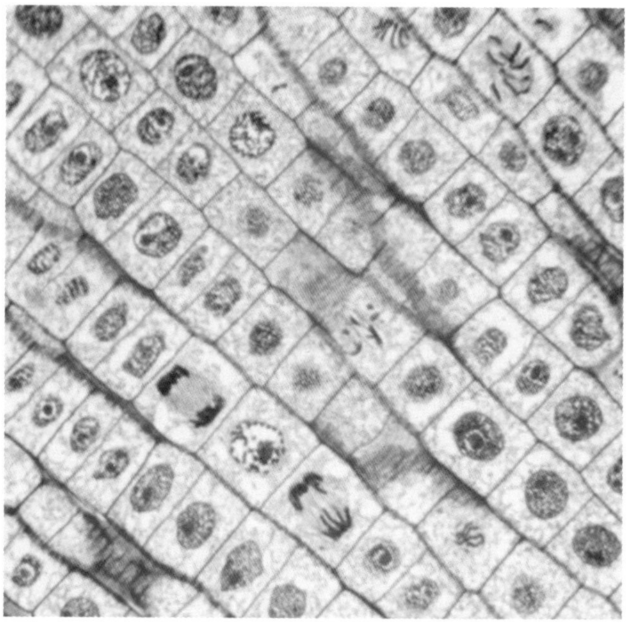

6. Match the statements in the table below to form complete sentences, then put the sentences in order to make a coherent paragraph about DNA replication and its role:

The enzymes also proofread the DNA during replication...	...is required before mitosis or meiosis can occur.
DNA replication is the process by which the DNA molecule...	...by enzymes.
Replication is tightly controlled...	...to correct any mistakes.
After replication, the chromosome...	...and half new DNA.
DNA replication...	...during mitosis.
The chromatids separate...	...is copied to produce two identical DNA strands.
A chromatid contains half original ...	...is made up of two chromatids.

Write the complete paragraph here: ______________________________

____

____

____

____

____

ISBN: 978-1-927173-73-2

Enzyme Control of DNA Replication

DNA replication involves many enzyme controlled steps. They are shown below as separate, but many of the enzymes are clustered together as enzyme complexes. As the DNA is replicated, enzymes 'proof-read' it and correct mistakes. The polymerase enzyme can only work in one direction, so that one new strand is constructed as a continuous length (the leading strand) while the other new strand (the lagging strand) is made in short segments to be later joined together.

DNA replication occurs during interphase of the cell cycle at an astounding rate. As many as 4000 nucleotides per second are replicated. This explains how bacterial cells, with as many as 4 million nucleotides, can complete a cell cycle in about 20 minutes. Note that the nucleotides are present as deoxynucleoside triphosphates. When hydrolysed, these provide the energy for incorporating the nucleotide into the strand.

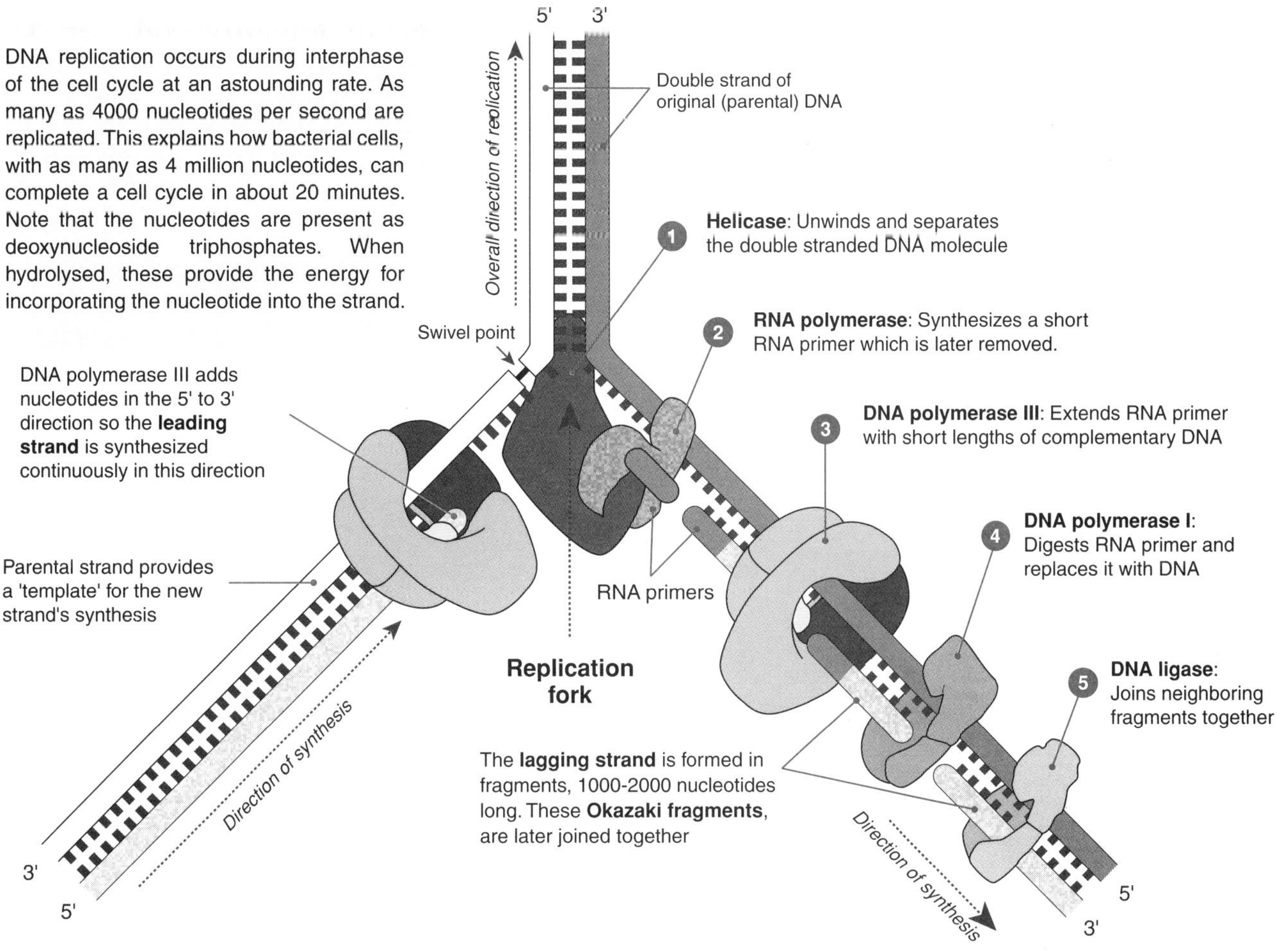

5'
3'
Overall direction of replication
Double strand of original (parental) DNA
1 Helicase: Unwinds and separates the double stranded DNA molecule
Swivel point
2 RNA polymerase: Synthesizes a short RNA primer which is later removed.
DNA polymerase III adds nucleotides in the 5' to 3' direction so the leading strand is synthesized continuously in this direction
3 DNA polymerase III: Extends RNA primer with short lengths of complementary DNA
4 DNA polymerase I: Digests RNA primer and replaces it with DNA
Parental strand provides a 'template' for the new strand's synthesis
RNA primers
Replication fork
5 DNA ligase: Joins neighboring fragments together
The lagging strand is formed in fragments, 1000-2000 nucleotides long. These Okazaki fragments, are later joined together
Direction of synthesis
Direction of synthesis
3'
5'
5'
3'

1. Describe the general role of enzymes in DNA replication: ______________________________

____

____

____

____

____

2. State the specific role of each of the following enzymes in DNA replication:

   (a) Helicase: ______________________________

   (b) DNA polymerase I: ______________________________

   (c) DNA polymerase III: ______________________________

   (d) Ligase: ______________________________

3. Determine the time it would take for a bacteria to replicate its DNA (see note in diagram above):

4. How is the energy for incorporating the nucleotides into the strand provided? ______________________________

____

____

ISBN: 978-1-927173-73-2

Related activities: *DNA Replication*
Weblinks: *DNA Replication (Advanced)*

Review of DNA Replication

The diagram below summarizes the main steps in DNA replication. You should use this activity to test your understanding of the main features of DNA replication, using the knowledge gained in the previous activity to fill in the missing information. You should attempt this from what you have learned, but refer to the previous activity if you require help.

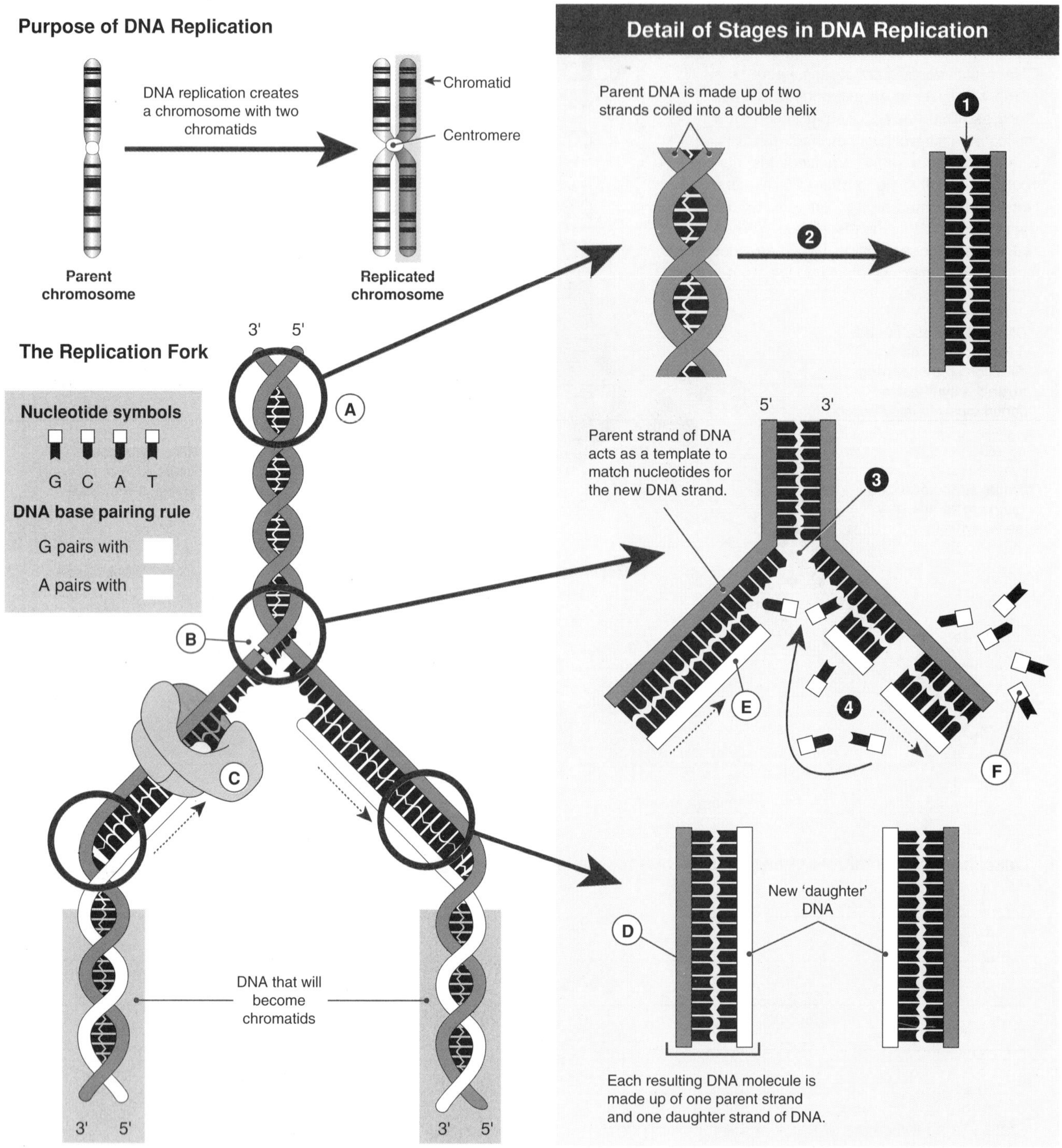
Purpose of DNA Replication
DNA replication creates a chromosome with two chromatids
Chromatid
Centromere
Parent chromosome
Replicated chromosome
The Replication Fork
3'
5'
Nucleotide symbols
G C A T
DNA base pairing rule
G pairs with
A pairs with
A
B
C
DNA that will become chromatids
3' 5'
3' 5'
Detail of Stages in DNA Replication
Parent DNA is made up of two strands coiled into a double helix
1
2
5' 3'
Parent strand of DNA acts as a template to match nucleotides for the new DNA strand.
3
4
E
F
D
New 'daughter' DNA
Each resulting DNA molecule is made up of one parent strand and one daughter strand of DNA.

1. In the white boxes on the diagram above, state the base pairing rule for making a strand of DNA.

2. Identify each of the structures marked with a letter. (A-F):

A: ______________________ C: ______________________ E: ______________________

B: ______________________ D: ______________________ F: ______________________

3. Match each of the processes (1-4) in the diagram above to the correct summary of the process provided below:

☐ Unwinding of parent DNA double helix

☐ Unzipping of parent DNA

☐ Free nucleotides occupy spaces alongside exposed bases

☐ DNA strands are joined by base pairing

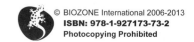

ISBN: 978-1-927173-73-2

Cell Division

The life cycle of a diploid sexually reproducing organism, such as a human, with **gametic meiosis** is illustrated below. In this life cycle, **gametogenesis** involves meiotic division to produce male and female gametes for the purpose of sexual reproduction. The life cycle in flowering plants is different in that the gametes are produced through mitosis in haploid gametophytes. The male gametes are produced inside the pollen grain and the female gametes are produced inside the embryo sac of the ovule. The gametophytes develop and grow from haploid spores, which are produced from meiosis.

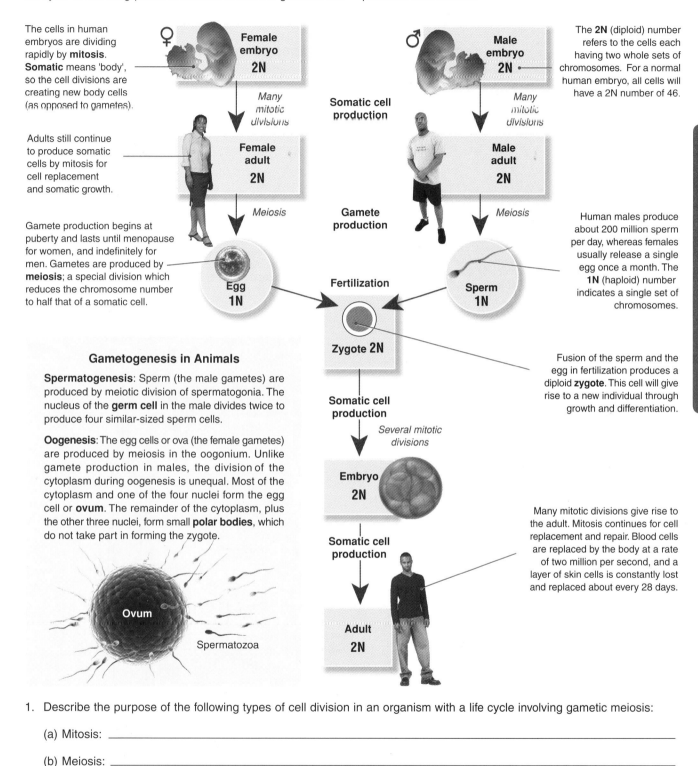

The cells in human embryos are dividing rapidly by **mitosis**. **Somatic** means 'body', so the cell divisions are creating new body cells (as opposed to gametes).

The **2N** (diploid) number refers to the cells each having two whole sets of chromosomes. For a normal human embryo, all cells will have a 2N number of 46.

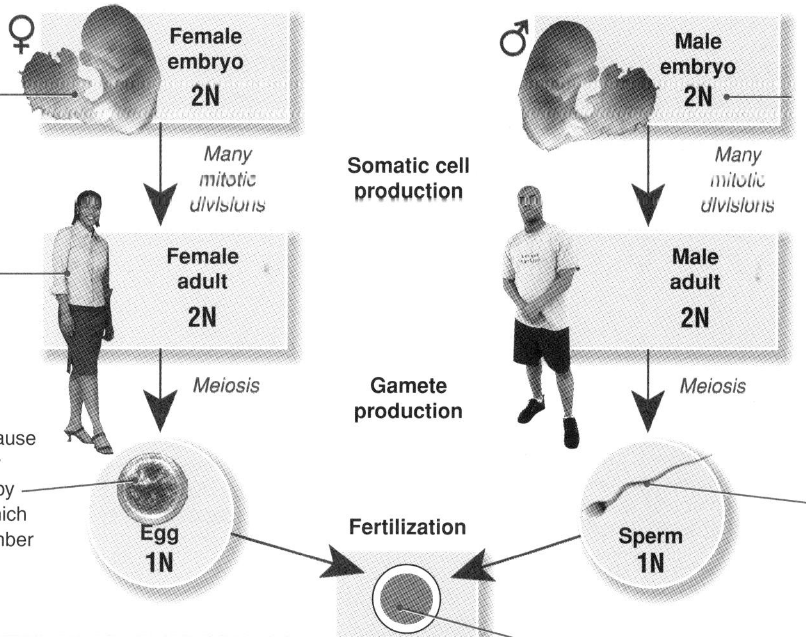
♀
Female embryo
2N
Many mitotic divisions
Female adult
2N
Meiosis
Egg
1N
Somatic cell production
Gamete production
Fertilization
♂
Male embryo
2N
Many mitotic divisions
Male adult
2N
Meiosis
Sperm
1N

Adults still continue to produce somatic cells by mitosis for cell replacement and somatic growth.

Gamete production begins at puberty and lasts until menopause for women, and indefinitely for men. Gametes are produced by **meiosis**; a special division which reduces the chromosome number to half that of a somatic cell.

Human males produce about 200 million sperm per day, whereas females usually release a single egg once a month. The **1N** (haploid) number indicates a single set of chromosomes.

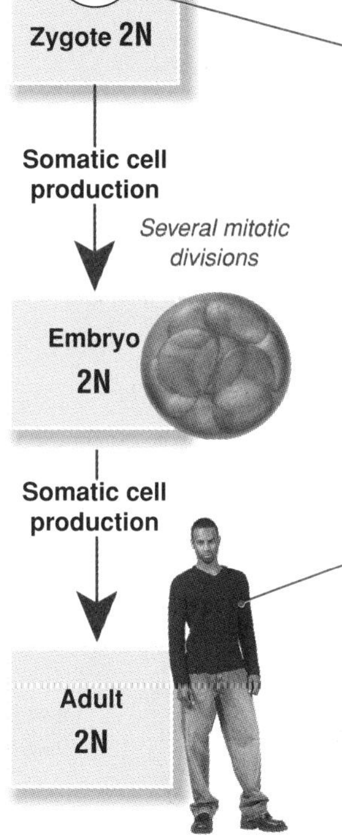
Zygote 2N
Somatic cell production
Several mitotic divisions
Embryo
2N
Somatic cell production
Adult
2N

Fusion of the sperm and the egg in fertilization produces a diploid **zygote**. This cell will give rise to a new individual through growth and differentiation.

Many mitotic divisions give rise to the adult. Mitosis continues for cell replacement and repair. Blood cells are replaced by the body at a rate of two million per second, and a layer of skin cells is constantly lost and replaced about every 28 days.

Gametogenesis in Animals

Spermatogenesis: Sperm (the male gametes) are produced by meiotic division of spermatogonia. The nucleus of the **germ cell** in the male divides twice to produce four similar-sized sperm cells.

Oogenesis: The egg cells or ova (the female gametes) are produced by meiosis in the oogonium. Unlike gamete production in males, the division of the cytoplasm during oogenesis is unequal. Most of the cytoplasm and one of the four nuclei form the egg cell or **ovum**. The remainder of the cytoplasm, plus the other three nuclei, form small **polar bodies**, which do not take part in forming the zygote.

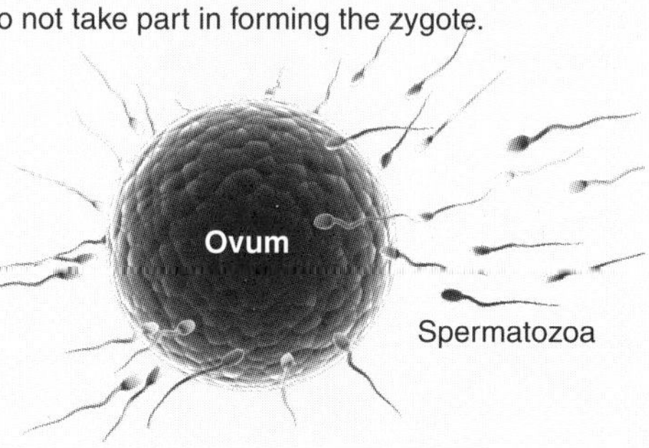
Ovum
Spermatozoa

1. Describe the purpose of the following types of cell division in an organism with a life cycle involving gametic meiosis:

   (a) Mitosis: ______________________________

   (b) Meiosis: ______________________________

2. Describe the basic difference between the cell divisions involved in spermatogenesis and oogenesis:

   ____

   ____

3. How does gametogenesis differ between humans and flowering plants? ______________________________

   ____

ISBN: 978-1-927173-73-2

Related activities: *Mitosis and the Cell Cycle, Stages in Meiosis*

Mitosis and the Cell Cycle

Mitosis is one stage of the cell cycle. The activities carried out during the cell cycle include growth of the cell, replication of the DNA, condensation of the chromosomes, mitosis, and cytokinesis. **Mitosis** is part of the cell cycle in which the parent cell divides in two to produce two genetically identical daughter cells. Mitosis is one of the shortest stages of the cell cycle. When a cell is not undergoing mitosis, it is said to be in interphase, which accounts for 90% of the cell cycle. Interphase is not a stage in mitosis. Mitosis is continuous, but it is divided into stages for easier reference (1-7 below). In plant cells, cytokinesis (division of the cytoplasm) involves construction of a cell plate in the middle of the cell where a new cell wall will form. In animal cells, cytokinesis involves the formation of a constriction that divides the cell in two and there is no cell plate.

The animal cell cycle and stages of mitosis

Interphase

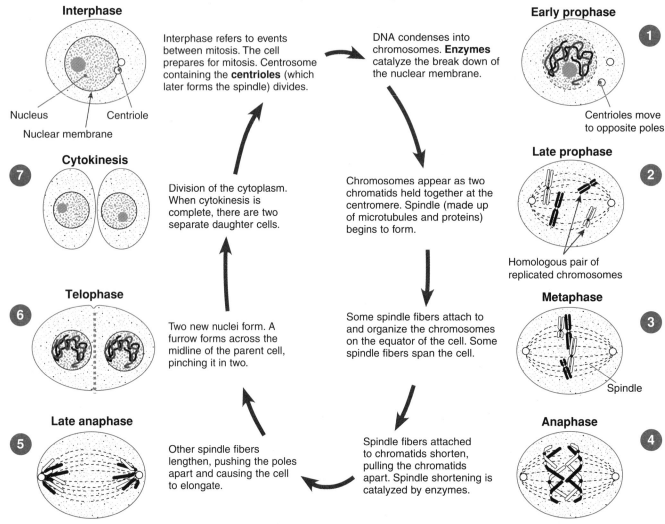

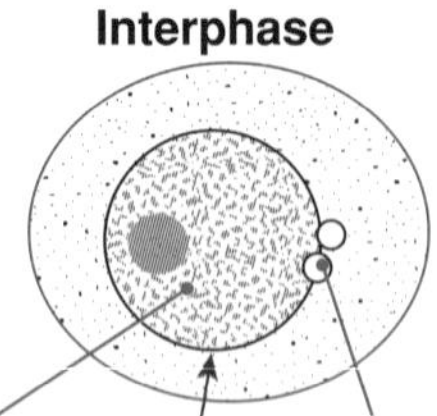
Nucleus
Centriole
Nuclear membrane

Interphase refers to events between mitosis. The cell prepares for mitosis. Centrosome containing the **centrioles** (which later forms the spindle) divides.

1 Early prophase

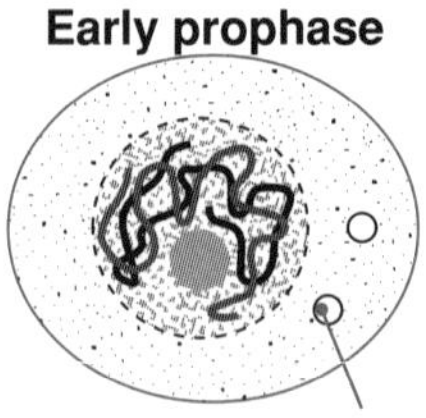
Centrioles move to opposite poles

DNA condenses into chromosomes. **Enzymes** catalyze the break down of the nuclear membrane.

2 Late prophase

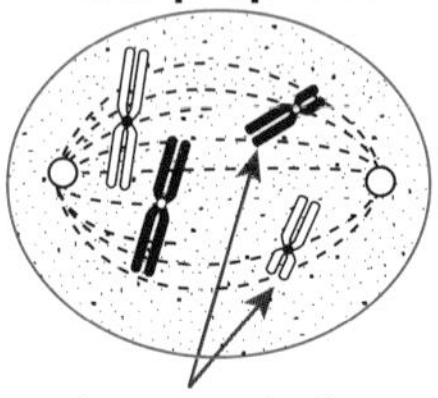
Homologous pair of replicated chromosomes

Chromosomes appear as two chromatids held together at the centromere. Spindle (made up of microtubules and proteins) begins to form.

3 Metaphase

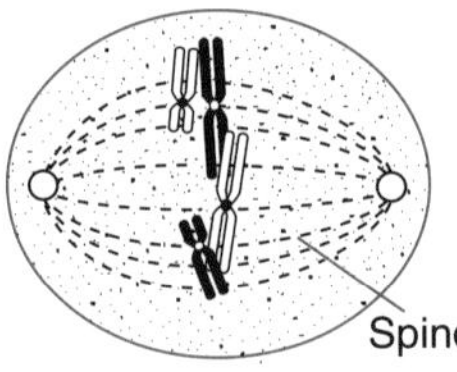
Spindle

Some spindle fibers attach to and organize the chromosomes on the equator of the cell. Some spindle fibers span the cell.

4 Anaphase

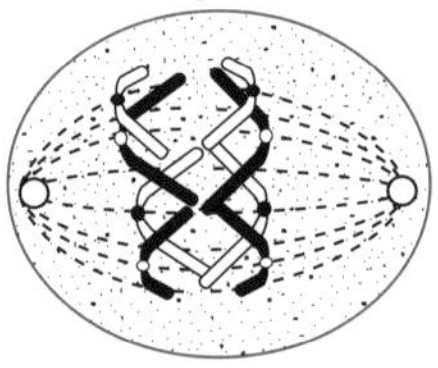

Spindle fibers attached to chromatids shorten, pulling the chromatids apart. Spindle shortening is catalyzed by enzymes.

5 Late anaphase

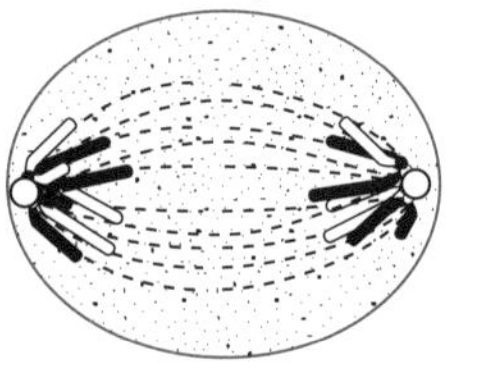

Other spindle fibers lengthen, pushing the poles apart and causing the cell to elongate.

6 Telophase

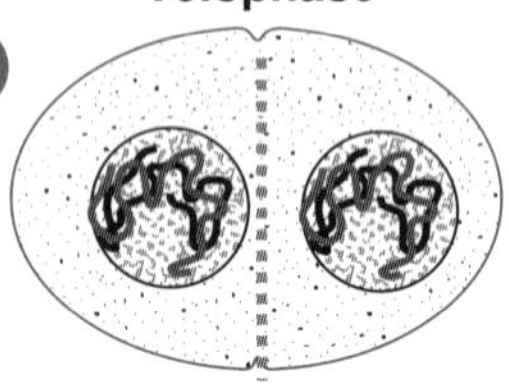

Two new nuclei form. A furrow forms across the midline of the parent cell, pinching it in two.

7 Cytokinesis

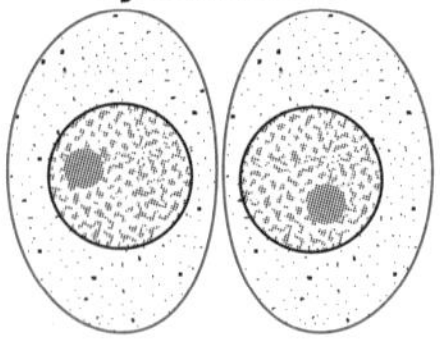

Division of the cytoplasm. When cytokinesis is complete, there are two separate daughter cells.

Interphase

Cells spend most of their time in interphase. Interphase is divided into three stages (right):

- The first gap phase.
- The S-phase.
- The second gap phase.

During interphase the cell grows, carries out its normal activities, and replicates its DNA in preparation for cell division.
Interphase is not a stage in mitosis.

Mitosis

During mitosis, the cell nucleus (containing the replicated DNA) divides in two equal parts. Mitosis consists of several phases (see next page). The last phase of mitosis is cytokinesis. During cytokinesis the cell cytoplasm divides, and the production of the two new daughter cells is complete.

The Cell Cycle Overview

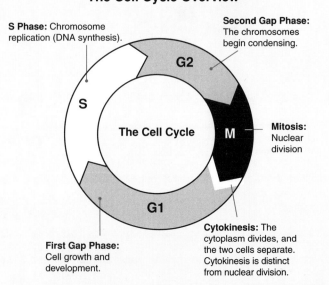

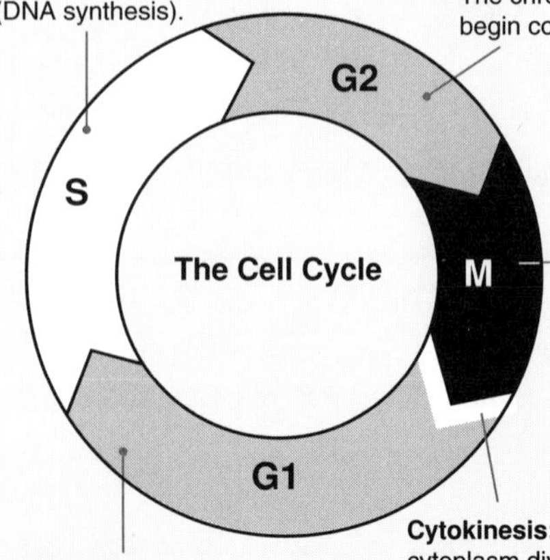
S Phase: Chromosome replication (DNA synthesis).
Second Gap Phase: The chromosomes begin condensing.
G2
S
The Cell Cycle
M
Mitosis: Nuclear division
G1
First Gap Phase: Cell growth and development.
Cytokinesis: The cytoplasm divides, and the two cells separate. Cytokinesis is distinct from nuclear division.

ISBN: 978-1-927173-73-2

The functions of mitosis

1 Growth

In multicellular organisms, mitosis is responsible for growth to an adult size.

In plants, growth occurs only at meristems (growing tips) where mitosis produces new cells and increase in length.

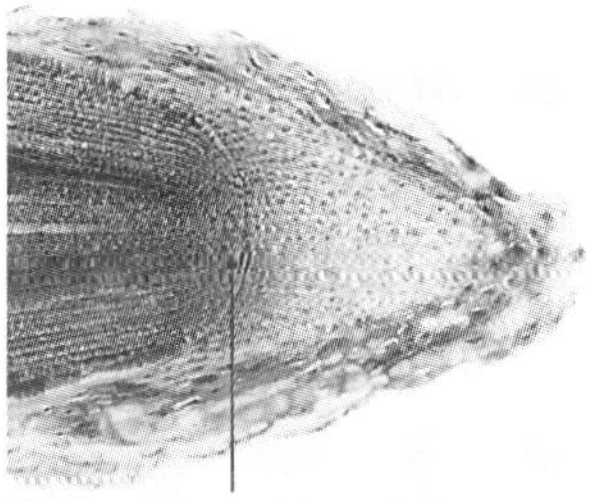

Cells of the root meristem divide by mitosis

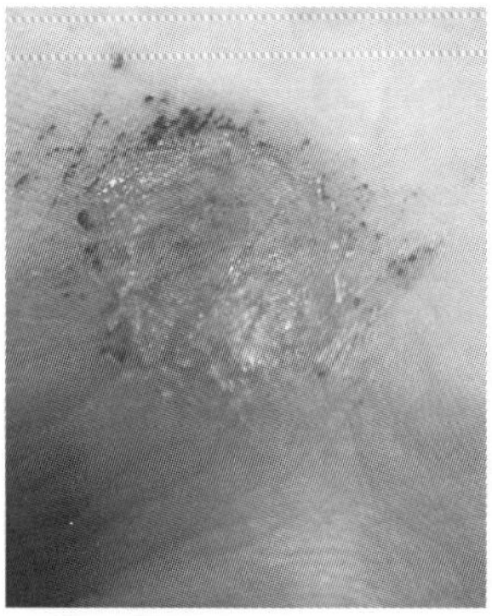

JP Barrass, Public Domain

2 Repair

Mitosis creates new cells to repair damaged tissue, such as this skin abrasion. Cells of the epithelial linings of the gut and skin are always dividing.

Some animals, e.g. lizards and starfish, can also generate new appendages by mitosis.

3 Reproduction

Some simple multicellular animals reproduce **asexually** by mitosis. The cells of this *Hydra* (right) undergo mitosis, forming a 'bud' on the side of the parent organism. Eventually the bud, which is genetically identical to its parent, detaches to continue the life cycle.

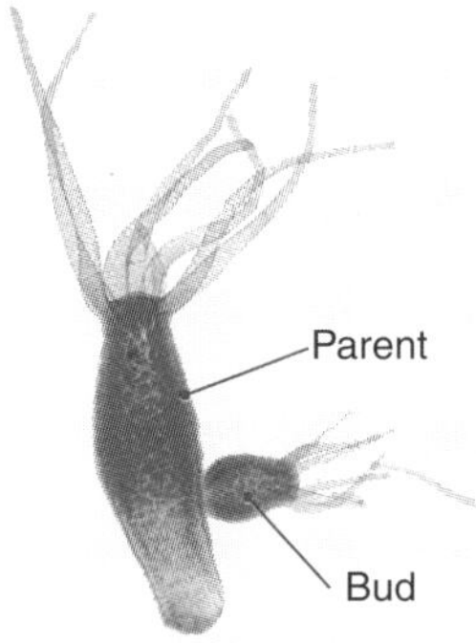
Parent
Bud

The Budding Yeast Cell Cycle

Yeasts can reproduce asexually through **budding**. In *Saccharomyces cerevisiae* (baker's yeast), budding involves mitotic division in the parent cell, with the formation of a daughter cell (or bud). As budding begins, a ring of chitin stabilizes the area where the bud will appear and enzymatic activity and turgor pressure act to weaken and extrude the cell wall. New cell wall material is incorporated during this phase. The nucleus of the parent cell also divides in two, to form a daughter nucleus, which migrates into the bud. The daughter cell is genetically identical to its parent cell and continues to grow, eventually separating from the parent cell.

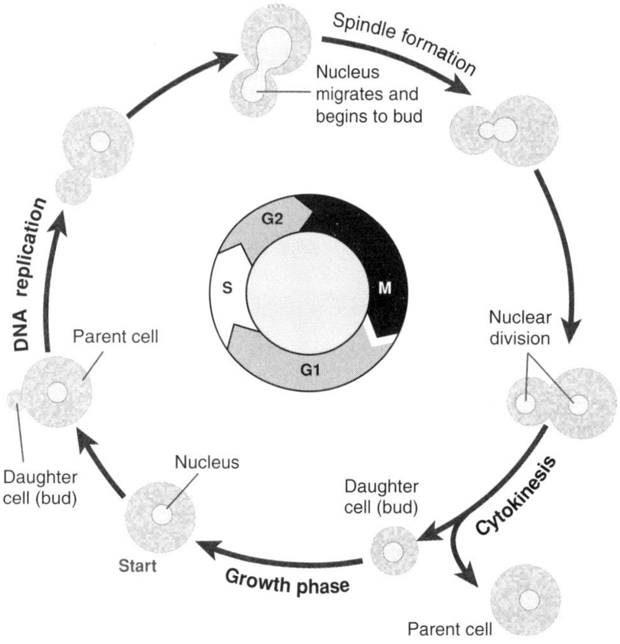
Spindle formation
Nucleus migrates and begins to bud
Nuclear division
Cytokinesis
Daughter cell (bud)
Parent cell
Growth phase
Start
Nucleus
Daughter cell (bud)
Parent cell
DNA replication
G2
S
M
G1

1. The photographs below were taken at various stages through mitosis in a plant cell. They are not in any particular order. Study the diagram on the previous page and determine the stage represented in each photograph (e.g. anaphase).

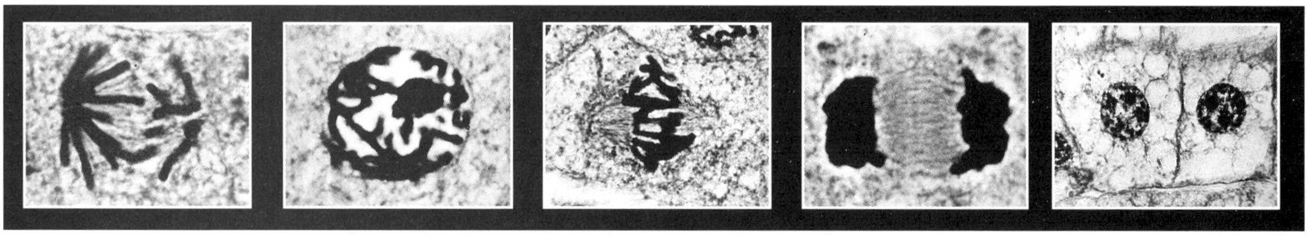

Photos: RCN

(a) ________________ (b) ________________ (c) ________________ (d) ________________ (e) ________________

2. State two important changes that chromosomes must undergo before cell division can take place: ________________

____

3. Briefly summarize the stages of the cell cycle by describing what is happening in the following stages (use the diagram on the previous page to help you):

(a) Interphase: ________________

(b) Late prophase: ________________

(c) Metaphase: ________________

(d) Late anaphase: ________________

(e) Telophase: ________________

(f) Cytokinesis: ________________

ISBN: 978-1-927173-73-2

Regulation of the Cell Cycle

Mitosis is virtually the same for all eukaryotes but aspects of the cell cycle can vary enormously between species and even between cells of the same organism. For example, the length of the cell cycle varies between cells such as intestinal and liver cells. Intestinal cells divide around twice a day, while cells in the liver divide once a year. However, if these tissues are damaged, cell division increases rapidly until the damage is repaired. Variation in the length of the cell cycle can be explained by regulatory mechanisms that slow down or speed up the cell cycle in response to changing conditions.

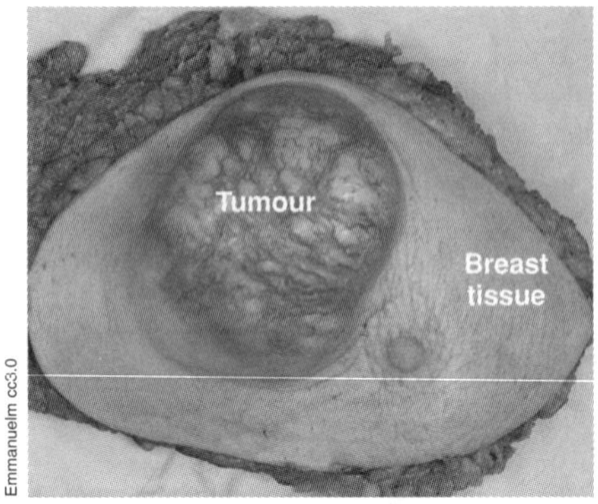
Tumour
Breast tissue
Emmanuelm cc3.0

Regulation of the cell cycle is important in detecting and repairing of genetic damage, and preventing uncontrolled cell division. Tumors and cancers, such as this breast cancer (above) are the result of uncontrolled cell division.

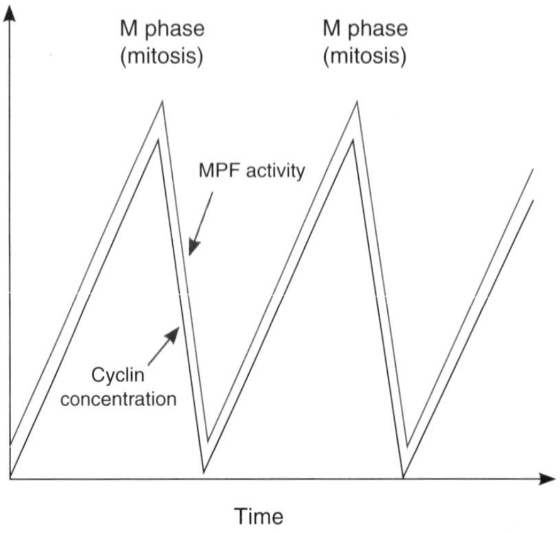
M phase (mitosis)
M phase (mitosis)
MPF activity
Cyclin concentration
Time

A substance called an M-phase promoting factor (MPF) controls cell regulation. MPF is made up of two regulatory molecules, **cyclins** and **cyclin-dependent kinases** (CDKs).

Cyclins are proteins that control the progression of cells through the cell cycle by activating CDKs (which are enzymes).

CDKs phosphorylate other proteins to signal a cell is ready to proceed to the next stage in the cell cycle. Without cyclin, CDK has little kinase activity; only the cyclin-CDK complex is active. CDK is constantly present in the cell, cyclin is not.

Checkpoints During the Cell cycle

There are three **checkpoints** during the cell cycle. A checkpoint is a critical regulatory point in the cell cycle. At each checkpoint, a set of conditions determines whether or not the cell will continue into the next phase. For example, cell size is important in regulating whether or not the cell can pass through the G_1 checkpoint.

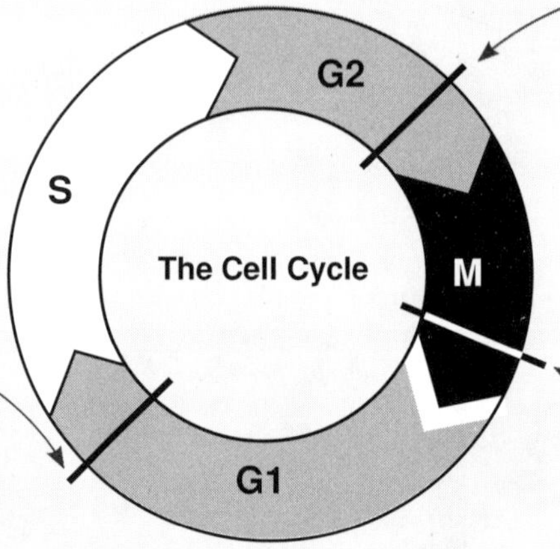
G2
S
The Cell Cycle
M
G1

G_2 Checkpoint:
Pass this checkpoint if:
- Cell size is large enough.
- Replication of chromosomes has been successfully completed.

G_1 checkpoint
Pass this checkpoint if:
- Cell size is large enough.
- Sufficient nutrients are available.
- Signals from other cells have been received.

Metaphase checkpoint
Pass this checkpoint if:
- All chromosomes are attached to the mitotic spindle.

1. What would happen if the cell cycle was not regulated? ______________________________

____

____

2. (a) Suggest why the cell cycle is shorter in epithelial cells (such as intestinal cells) than in liver cells:

____

____

____

(b) Describe another situation in which the cell cycle shortens to allow for a temporary rapid rate of cell division:

____

____

____

KNOW

ISBN: 978-1-927173-73-2

Apoptosis: Programmed Cell Death

Apoptosis or programmed cell death (PCD) is a normal and necessary mechanism in multicellular organisms to trigger the death of a cell. Apoptosis has a number of crucial roles in the body, including the maintenance of adult cell numbers, and defence against damaged or dangerous cells, such as virus-infected cells and cells with DNA damage. Apoptosis also has a role in "sculpting" embryonic tissue during its development, e.g. in the formation of fingers and toes in a developing human embryo. Programmed cell death involves an orderly series of biochemical events that result in set changes in cell morphology and end in cell death. The process is carried out in such a way as to safely dispose of cell remains and fragments. This is in contrast to another type of cell death, called **necrosis**, in which traumatic damage to the cell results in spillage of cell contents. Apoptosis is tightly regulated by a balance between the factors that promote cell survival and those that trigger cell death. An imbalance between these regulating factors leads to defective apoptotic processes and is implicated in an extensive variety of diseases. For example, low rates of apoptosis result in uncontrolled proliferation of cells and cancers.

Stages in Apoptosis

Apoptosis is a normal cell suicide process in response to particular cell signals. It characterized by an overall compaction (shrinking) of the cell and its nucleus, and the orderly dissection of chromatin by endonucleases. Death is finalized by a rapid engulfment of the dying cell by phagocytosis. The cell contents remain membrane-bound and there is no inflammation.

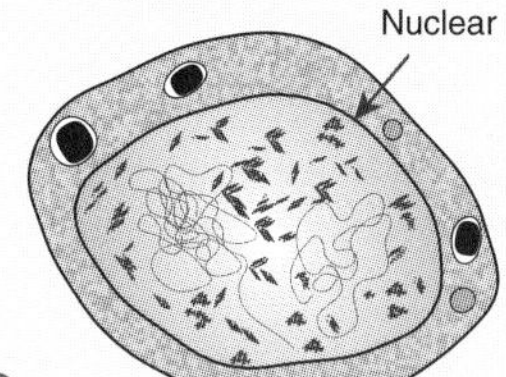
Nuclear membrane

1 The cell shrinks and loses contact with neighboring cells. The chromatin condenses and begins to degrade.

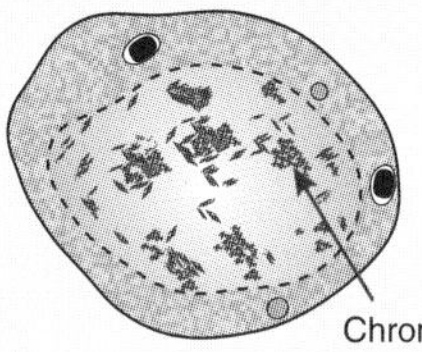
Chromatin

2 The nuclear membrane degrades. The cell loses volume. The chromatin clumps into **chromatin bodies**.

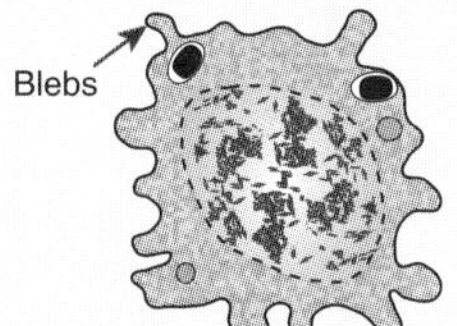
Blebs

3 **Zeiosis**: The plasma membrane forms bubble like **blebs** on its surface.

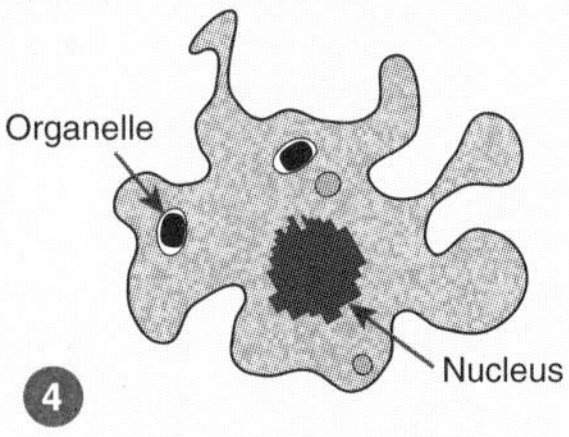
Organelle
Nucleus

4 The nucleus collapses, but many membrane-bound organelles are not affected.

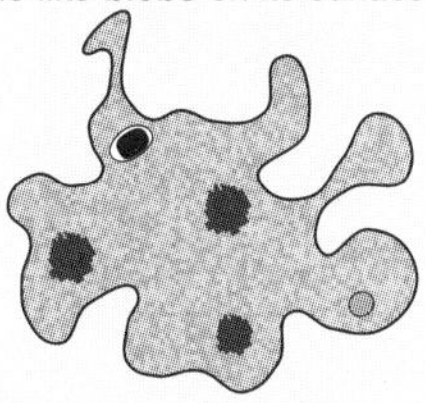

5 The nucleus breaks up into spheres and the DNA breaks up into small fragments.

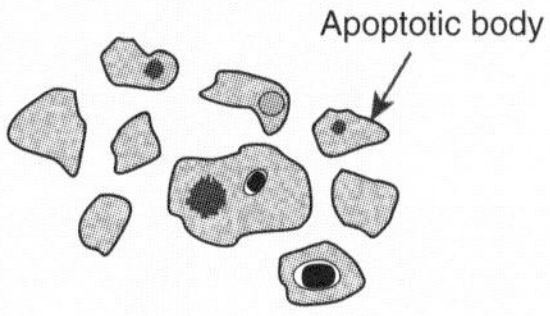
Apoptotic body

6 The cell breaks into numerous **apoptotic bodies**, which are quickly resorbed by phagocytosis.

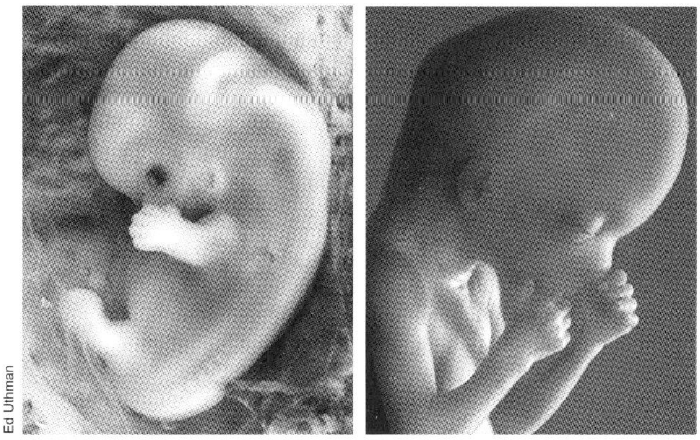
Ed Uthman

In humans, the mesoderm initially formed between the fingers and toes is removed by apoptosis. Forty one days after fertilization (top left), the digits of the hands and feet are webbed, making them look like small paddles. Apoptosis selectively destroys this superfluous webbing, sculpting them into digits when can be seen later in development (top right).

Regulating Apoptosis

Apoptosis is a complicated and tightly controlled process, distinct from cell necrosis (uncontrolled cell death), when the cell contents are spilled. Apoptosis is regulated through both:

Positive signals, which prevent apoptosis and allow a cell to function normally. They include:

- interleukin-2
- bcl-2 protein and growth factors

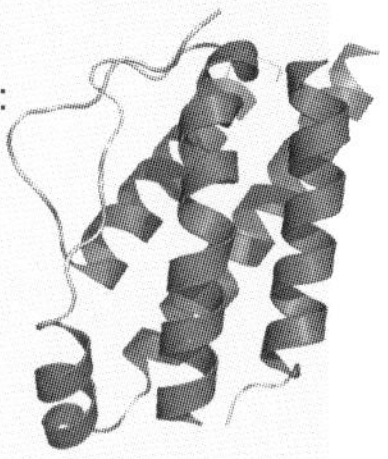

Interleukin-2 is a positive signal for cell survival. Like other signaling molecules, it binds to cell surface receptors to regulate metabolism.

Negative signals (death activators), which trigger the changes leading to cell death. They include:

- inducer signals generated from within the cell itself in response to stress, e.g. DNA damage or cell starvation.
- signaling proteins and peptides such as lymphotoxin.

1. The photograph on the right shows a condition called syndactyly. Explain what might have happened during development to result in this condition:

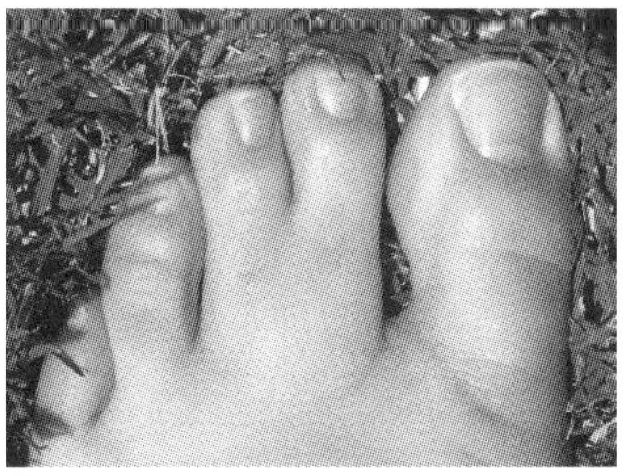

2. Describe one difference between apoptosis and necrosis:

3. Describe two situations, other than digit formation in development, in which apoptosis plays a crucial role:

(a)

(b)

ISBN: 978-1-927173-73-2

Root Cell Development

In plants, cell division for growth (mitosis) is restricted to growing tips called **meristematic** tissue. These are located at the tips of every stem and root. This is unlike mitosis in a growing animal where cell divisions can occur all over the body. The diagram below illustrates the position and appearance of developing and growing cells in a plant root. Similar zones of development occur in the growing stem tips, which may give rise to specialized structures such as leaves and flowers.

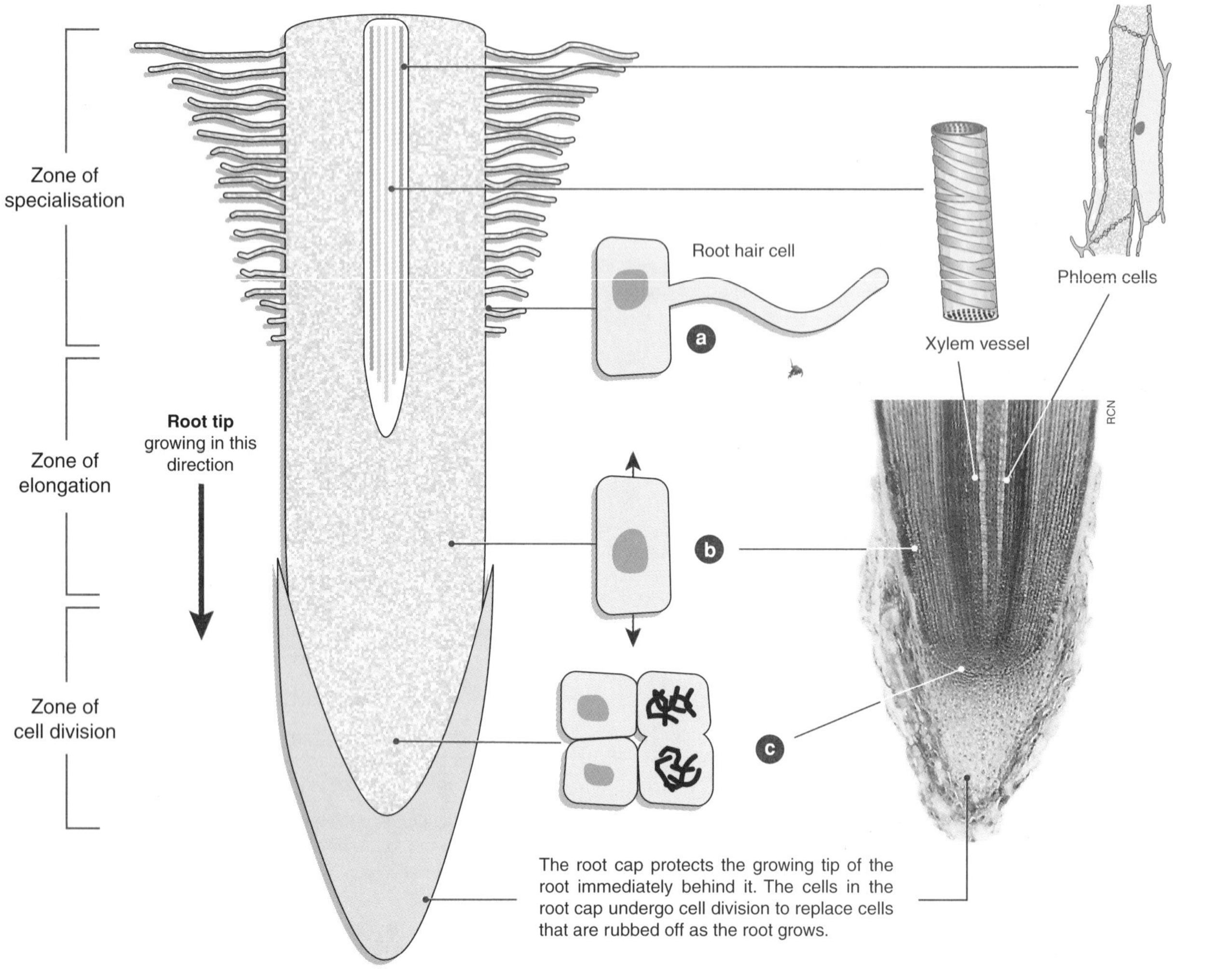
Zone of specialisation
Zone of elongation
Zone of cell division
Root tip
growing in this direction
Root hair cell
Phloem cells
Xylem vessel
a
b
c
RCN
The root cap protects the growing tip of the root immediately behind it. The cells in the root cap undergo cell division to replace cells that are rubbed off as the root grows.

1. Briefly describe what is happening to the plant cells at each of the points labelled **a** to **c** in the diagram above:

   (a) ______________________________

   (b) ______________________________

   (c) ______________________________

2. The light micrograph (below) shows a section of the cells of an onion root tip, stained to show up the chromosomes.

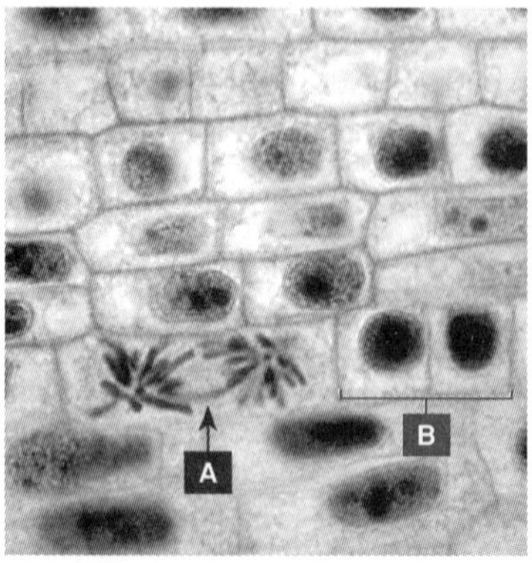
A
B

   (a) State the mitotic stage of the cell labeled **A** and explain your answer:

   ____

   (b) State the mitotic stage just completed in the cells labeled **B** and explain:

   ____

   (c) If, in this example, 250 cells were examined and 25 were found to be in the process of mitosis, state the proportion of the cell cycle occupied by mitosis:

   ____

   ____

3. Identify the cells that divide and specialize when a tree increases its girth (diameter): ______________________________

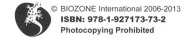

ISBN: 978-1-927173-73-2

Differentiation of Human Cells

A zygote commences development by dividing into a small ball of a few dozen identical cells called **embryonic stem cells**. These cells start to take different developmental paths to become specialized cells such as nerve stem cells which means they can no longer produce any other type of cell. **Differentiation** is cell specialization that occurs at the end of a developmental pathway.

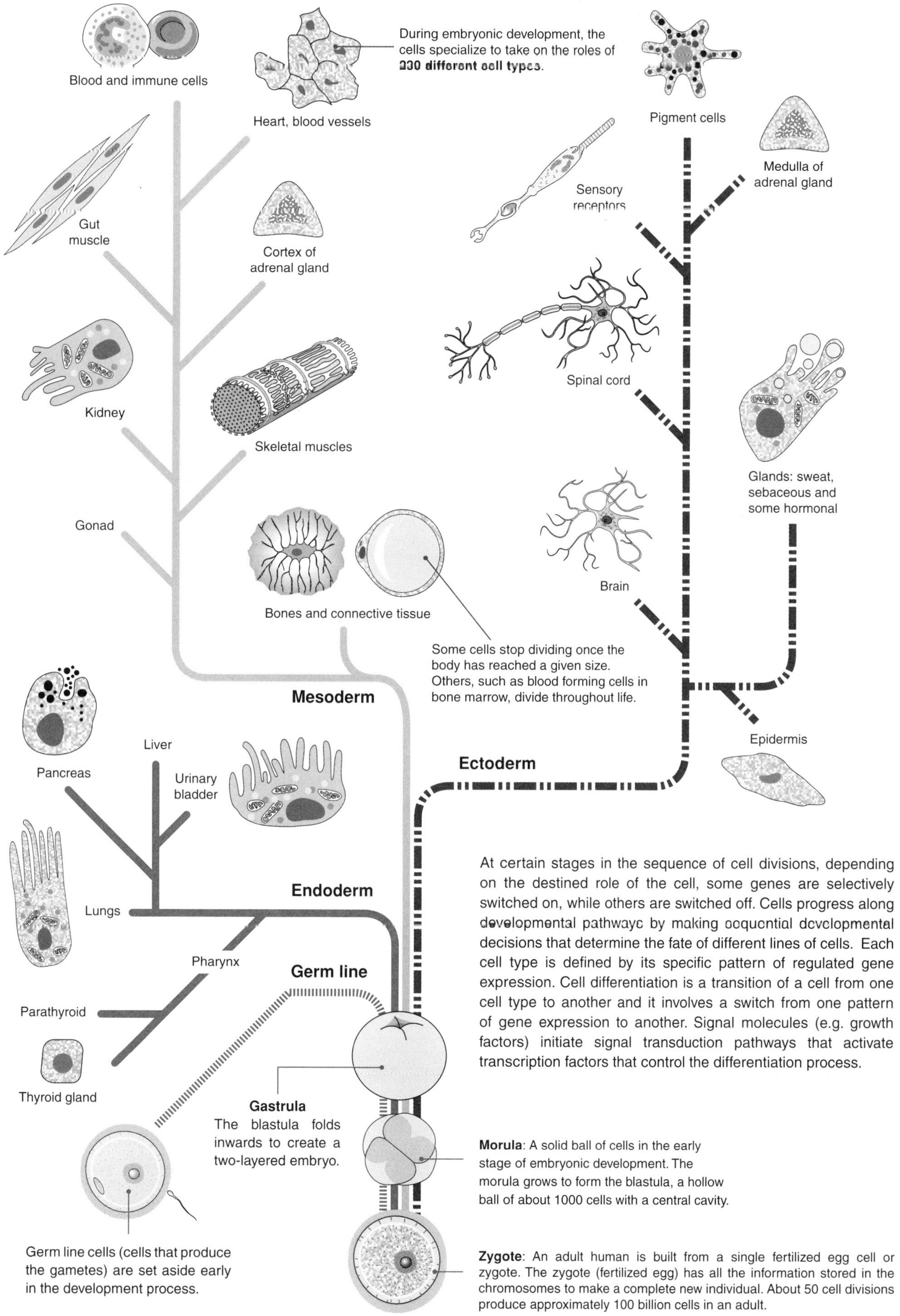

Blood and immune cells
Heart, blood vessels
During embryonic development, the cells specialize to take on the roles of **230 different cell types**.
Pigment cells
Medulla of adrenal gland
Sensory receptors
Gut muscle
Cortex of adrenal gland
Spinal cord
Kidney
Skeletal muscles
Glands: sweat, sebaceous and some hormonal
Brain
Gonad
Bones and connective tissue
Some cells stop dividing once the body has reached a given size. Others, such as blood forming cells in bone marrow, divide throughout life.
Mesoderm
Epidermis
Ectoderm
Pancreas
Liver
Urinary bladder
Endoderm
Lungs
Pharynx
Germ line
Parathyroid
Thyroid gland
Gastrula
The blastula folds inwards to create a two-layered embryo.
Morula: A solid ball of cells in the early stage of embryonic development. The morula grows to form the blastula, a hollow ball of about 1000 cells with a central cavity.
Germ line cells (cells that produce the gametes) are set aside early in the development process.
Zygote: An adult human is built from a single fertilized egg cell or zygote. The zygote (fertilized egg) has all the information stored in the chromosomes to make a complete new individual. About 50 cell divisions produce approximately 100 billion cells in an adult.

At certain stages in the sequence of cell divisions, depending on the destined role of the cell, some genes are selectively switched on, while others are switched off. Cells progress along developmental pathways by making sequential developmental decisions that determine the fate of different lines of cells. Each cell type is defined by its specific pattern of regulated gene expression. Cell differentiation is a transition of a cell from one cell type to another and it involves a switch from one pattern of gene expression to another. Signal molecules (e.g. growth factors) initiate signal transduction pathways that activate transcription factors that control the differentiation process.

ISBN: 978-1-927173-73-2

Related activities: *Human Cell Specialization, Plant Cell Specialization*

Development is the process of progressive change through the lifetime of an organism. Part of this process involves growth (increase in size) and cell division (to generate the multicellular body). Cellular **differentiation** (the generation of specialized cells) and **morphogenesis** (the creation of the shape and form of the body) are also part of development. Differentiation defines the specific structure and function of a cell. As development proceeds, the possibilities available to individual cells become fewer, until each cell's **fate** is determined. The tissues and organs making up the body form from the aggregation and organization of these differentiated cells. In animals, the final body form is the result of cell migration and the programed death of certain cells (**apoptosis**) during embryonic development. The diagram on the previous page shows how a single fertilized egg (zygote) gives rise to the large number of specialized cell types that make up the adult human body. The morula, blastula, and gastrula stages mentioned at the bottom of the diagram show the early development of the embryo from the zygote. The gastrula gives rise to the three layers of cells (ectoderm, mesoderm, and endoderm), from which specific cell types develop.

1. State how many different types of cell are found in the human body: ____________________

2. State approximately how many cell divisions take place from fertilized egg (zygote) to produce an adult: __________

3. State approximately how many cells make up an adult human body: ____________________

4. Name one cell type that continues to divide throughout a person's lifetime: ____________________

5. Name one cell type that does not continue to divide throughout a person's lifetime: ____________________

6. Germ line cells diverge (become isolated) from other cells at a very early stage in embryonic development.

   (a) Explain what the **germ line** is: ____________________

   (b) Explain why it is necessary for the germ line to become separated at such an early stage of development:

7. Cloning whole new organisms is possible by taking a nucleus from a cell during the blastula stage of embryonic development and placing it into an egg cell that has had its own nucleus removed.

   (a) Explain what a **clone** is: ____________________

   (b) Explain why the cell required for cloning needs to be taken at such an early stage of embryonic development:

8. Cancer cells are particularly damaging to organisms. Explain what has happened to a cell that has become cancerous:

9. Explain the genetic events that enable so many different cell types to arise from one unspecialized cell (the zygote):

ISBN: 978-1-927173-73-2

Stages in Meiosis

Meiosis is a special type of cell division concerned with producing sex cells (gametes) for the purpose of sexual reproduction. It involves a single chromosomal duplication followed by two successive nuclear divisions, and results in a halving of the diploid chromosome number. Meiosis occurs in the sex organs of plants and animals. If genetic mistakes (**gene** and **chromosome mutations**) occur here, they will be passed on to the offspring (they will be inherited).

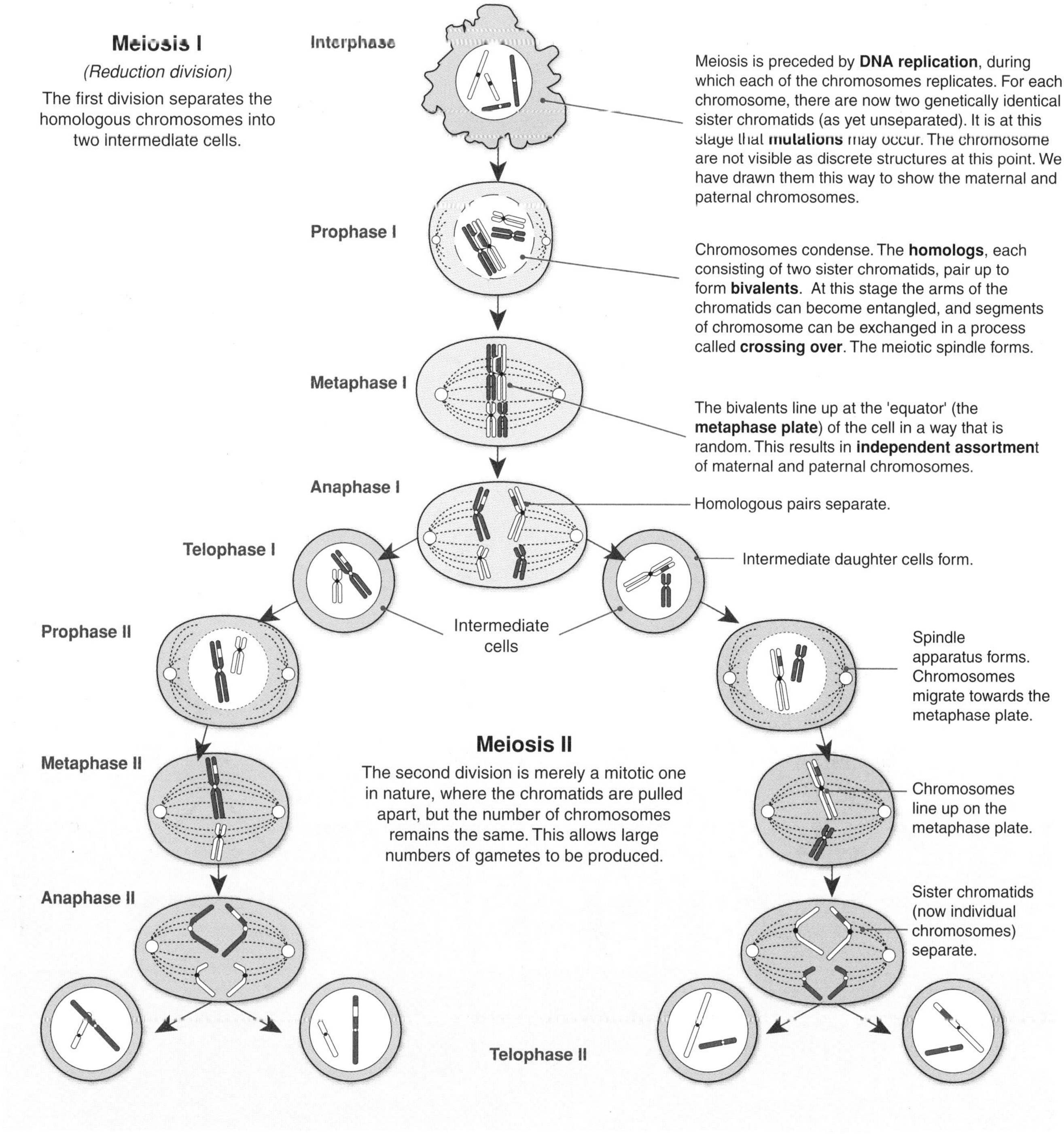

Meiosis I
(Reduction division)
The first division separates the homologous chromosomes into two intermediate cells.
Interphase
Meiosis is preceded by **DNA replication**, during which each of the chromosomes replicates. For each chromosome, there are now two genetically identical sister chromatids (as yet unseparated). It is at this stage that **mutations** may occur. The chromosome are not visible as discrete structures at this point. We have drawn them this way to show the maternal and paternal chromosomes.
Prophase I
Chromosomes condense. The **homologs**, each consisting of two sister chromatids, pair up to form **bivalents**. At this stage the arms of the chromatids can become entangled, and segments of chromosome can be exchanged in a process called **crossing over**. The meiotic spindle forms.
Metaphase I
The bivalents line up at the 'equator' (the **metaphase plate**) of the cell in a way that is random. This results in **independent assortment** of maternal and paternal chromosomes.
Anaphase I
Homologous pairs separate.
Telophase I
Intermediate daughter cells form.
Intermediate cells
Prophase II
Spindle apparatus forms. Chromosomes migrate towards the metaphase plate.
Metaphase II
Chromosomes line up on the metaphase plate.
Anaphase II
Sister chromatids (now individual chromosomes) separate.
Meiosis II
The second division is merely a mitotic one in nature, where the chromatids are pulled apart, but the number of chromosomes remains the same. This allows large numbers of gametes to be produced.
Telophase II

1. Describe the behavior of the chromosomes in the first division of meiosis: ______________________

____

____

____

2. Describe the behavior of the chromosomes in the second division of meiosis: ______________________

____

____

ISBN: 978-1-927173-73-2

Related activities: *Mitosis vs Meiosis*
Weblinks: *Meiosis, Independent Assortment of Alleles*

KNOW

Mitosis vs Meiosis

Cell division is fundamental to all life, as cells arise only by the division of existing cells. All types of cell division begin with replication of the cell's DNA. In eukaryotes, this is followed by division of the nucleus. There are two forms of nuclear division: **mitosis** and **meiosis**, and they have quite different purposes and outcomes. Mitosis is the simpler of the two and produces two identical daughter cells from a parent cell. Mitosis is responsible for growth and repair processes in multicellular organisms and reproduction in single-celled and asexual eukaryotes. Meiosis involves a **reduction division** in which haploid gametes are produced for the purposes of sexual reproduction. Fusion of haploid gametes in fertilization restores the diploid cell number in the **zygote**. These two fundamentally different types of cell division are compared below.

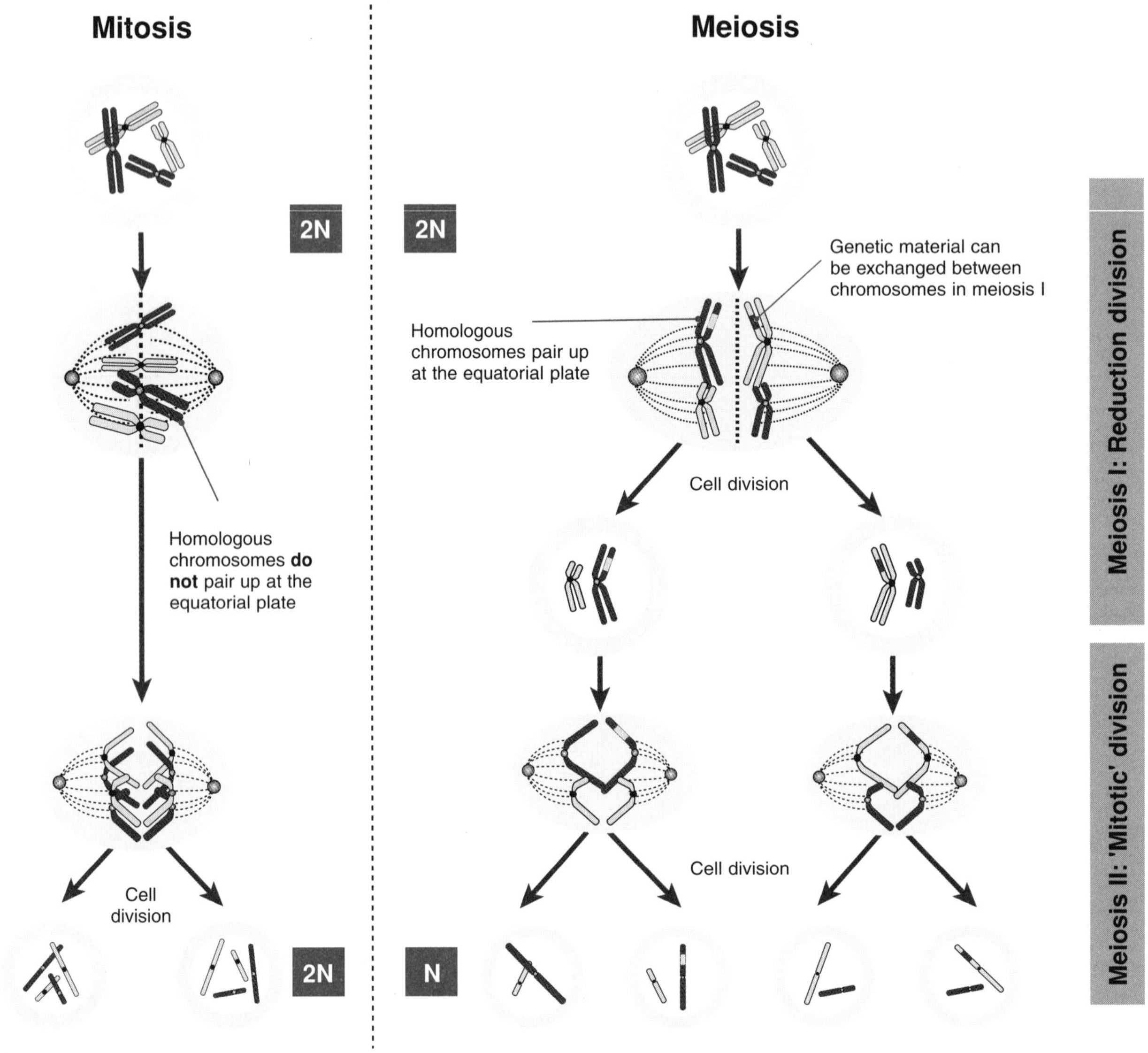
Mitosis
Meiosis
2N
2N
Genetic material can be exchanged between chromosomes in meiosis I
Homologous chromosomes pair up at the equatorial plate
Cell division
Homologous chromosomes do not pair up at the equatorial plate
Meiosis I: Reduction division
Meiosis II: 'Mitotic' division
Cell division
Cell division
2N
N

1. Explain how mitosis conserves chromosome number while meiosis reduces the number from diploid to haploid:

2. Describe a fundamental difference between the first and second divisions of meiosis:

3. Explain how meiosis introduces genetic variability into gametes and offspring (following gamete fusion in fertilization):

ISBN: 978-1-927173-73-2

KEY TERMS: Mix and Match

INSTRUCTIONS: Test your vocabulary by matching each term to its definition, as identified by its preceding letter code.

- apoptosis
- anaphase
- cell cycle
- cellular differentiation
- cell division
- cytokinesis
- DNA
- DNA polymerase
- DNA replication
- double-helix
- helicase
- interphase
- lagging strand
- leading strand
- meiosis
- metaphase
- mitosis
- nucleic acids
- prophase
- reduction division
- semi-conservative
- specialized cell
- stem cells
- telophase

A The phase of a cell cycle resulting in nuclear division.

B The division of the cytoplasm of parent eukaryotic cell into two daughter cells during the late stages of cell division.

C The changes that take place in a cell in the period between its formation as a product of cell division and its own subsequent division.

D The stage in mitosis or meiosis when the chromosomes have become aligned on the equator of the cell with all the centromeres lying along the spindle equator.

E The strand of the DNA double helix that is oriented in a 5' to 3' manner and is replicated in one continuous piece

F The enzyme that unwinds the DNA double helix.

G Process by which a less specialized cell becomes more specialized in order to perform specific function.

H Nuclear division in which the daughter cells have half the number of chromosomes as the parent. See meiosis.

I The stage of mitosis and meiosis in which the chromosomes are pulled to opposite ends of the cell.

J Process by which a parent cell divides into two or more daughter cells.

K Unspecialized cells that are able to differentiate into any one of many different kinds of cell.

L DNA replication is said to be this because the DNA molecule has one "old" strand and one "new" strand.

M The process by which a new copy of a DNA molecule is made.

N The three dimensional spiralling shape of a double stranded nucleic acid arising as a consequence of its secondary structure.

O The stage in the cell cycle between divisions.

P The first stage in meiosis or mitosis in which the replicated chromosomes condense and become visible as double structures.

Q A process of genetically programmed cell death is part of normal growth and development, and cellular regulation in multicellular organisms.

R Polynucleotide molecules that occur in two forms, DNA and RNA.

S Cell that has differentiated from a stem cell to carry out a particular task. It is unable to change into any other type of cell.

T The process of double nuclear division (reduction division) to produce four nuclei, each containing half the original number of chromosomes (haploid).

U The strand of the DNA double helix that is orientated in a 3' to 5' manner and which is replicated in fragments.

V The stage in mitosis or meiosis in which the daughter chromosomes reach the opposite poles of the cell and reform the nuclei.

W An enzyme that catalyzes the polymerization of nucleotides in DNA (i.e. it links nucleotides together). It is also used in PCR to amplify a length DNA.

X Macromolecule consisting of many millions of units containing a phosphate group, sugar and a base (A,T, C or G). Stores the genetic information of the cell.

ISBN: 978-1-927173-73-2

Index